Essential Maths

Book 7 Core

Elmwood Education

First published 2019 by

Elmwood Education Ltd
Unit 5, Mallow Park
Watchmead
Welwyn Garden City
Herts.
AL7 1GX
Tel. 01707 333232

ISBN 9781 906 622 732

Schools have a *Licence to Copy*
one chapter or 5% for teaching ✓

CCLA Copyright
Licensing Agency

Typeset and illustrated by Tech-Set Ltd., Gateshead, Tyne and Wear.

PREFACE

Essential Maths Book 7 Core has been written for pupils who are working in the middle ability range.

There is no set path through the book. The book has, however, been split into 6 units. Each unit of work can be used during one half-term with appropriate revision material at the end of the unit. Many topics are reviewed later in the book which is essential for consolidation.

Puzzles activities and mental arithmetic tasks can be found between the units, to be used whenever appropriate. Investigations appear regularly throughout the book. Ideas for discussing and exploring themes from the 'history of mathematics' are included between each pair of units.

No textbook will have the 'right' amount of material for every class. The authors believe that it is preferable to have too much material rather than too little. There are many opportunities for reasoning and for pupils to start to develop the skills to explain and to justify. Twelve 'Spot the mistakes' sections are included to encourage these aspects.

Very occasionally an exercise is labelled with an 'E'. This suggests that these questions may be particularly demanding. Each topic finishes with consolidation and extension questions to be used as appropriate.

Pupil self-assessment is very important. Regular 'check yourself' sections appear throughout the book. Answers to these parts only are provided at the back of the book for immediate feedback.

The authors are indebted to Sam Hartburn for her invaluable contribution to this book.

Michael White and David Rayner

CONTENTS

UNIT 1

1.1 Whole number arithmetic review

In section 1.1 you will practise:

- using the place value of digits in whole numbers
- solving problems involving addition, subtraction, multiplication and division

Exercise 1M

1　The figure 2 in the number 73296 stands for 2 hundreds or 200.
What do these figures stand for?

(a) the 3　　　　　(b) the 9　　　　　(c) the 7

2　Starting with the number 85607, write down the number you get when you

(a) add 100　　　　　(b) add 1000　　　　　(c) add 10

(d) add 10 000　　　　　(e) add 1　　　　　(f) add 100 000

3　What number is shown by each arrow?

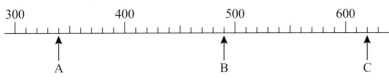

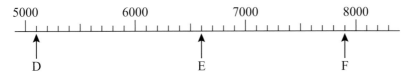

4　Here are five number cards:

(a) Use all the cards to make the largest possible number.

(b) Use all the cards to make the smallest possible number. Do not use $\boxed{0}$ as the first card.

2

5   Show how you can use the numbers **547**, **1000** and **100** to make the number 1447 by adding and subtracting.

6   Write these numbers in words.
   (a) 6200   (b) 90 000   (c) 25 010
   (d) 610 400   (e) 7 010 000

7   Here are five number cards:

   (a) Use all the cards to make the largest possible *odd* number.

   (b) Use all the cards to make the smallest possible *even* number.

8   (a) Lisa puts a 2 digit whole number into her calculator.
        She multiplies the number by 10.

        Fill in *one* other digit which you know must now be
        on the calculator.

   (b) Lisa starts again with the same 2 digit number and
        this time she multiplies it by 1000.

        Fill in all five digits on the calculator this time.

9   Find a number n so that $5 \times n + 7 = 507$.

10 Find a number p so that $6 \times p + 8 = 68$.

11 Find a pair of numbers a and b for which $8 \times a + b = 807$.

12 Find a pair of numbers p and q for which $7 \times p + 5 \times q = 7050$.

13 Write the number 'half a million' in figures.

14 On a cheque you have to write the
    amount of money in both words and
    figures.
    Write the words for the number on
    this cheque.

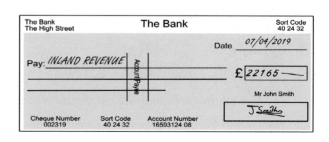

And finally…

A taxi driver who spent six years writing out every number from one to a million in an attempt to win a place in the Guinness Book of Records has been told he may have to start again.

The compilers have a rule that the numbers should be in words rather than digits!

Addition and subtraction

Exercise 2M

Copy the following cross number puzzle onto squared paper.
Complete the puzzles.

Clues across

1. $19 + 38$
3. $1104 - 128$
5. $168 - 77$
6. $261 + 548$
7. $356 + 55$
8. $850 - 286$
9. $17 + 26$
12. $288 + 471$
14. $143 + 274$
16. $1246 - 529$
17. $977 - 658$
18. $62 + 27$

Clues down

1. $849 - 267$
2. $36 + 34$
4. $257 + 387$
5. $1342 - 428$
8. $934 - 349$
10. $746 + 201$
11. $354 + 579$
12. $953 - 184$
13. $1232 - 254$
15. $1545 - 816$

Challenge – find the sum of the first 100 whole numbers (ie. 1 up to 100).

Exercise 3M

Work out

1. 153 increased by 61

2. 165 greater than 180

3. 41 less than 796

4. 1759 take away 466

5. 428 plus 535

6. decrease 640 by 280

7. 538 and 617 added together

8. take 666 from 700

9. the difference between 65 and 450

10. 249 more than 826

Find the missing numbers.

11.
```
    7  8  4
  - 6  2  7
  ☐  ☐  ☐
```

12.
```
    6  3  5
  - ☐  2  9
    2  ☐  ☐
```

13.
```
    6  8  7  4
  -       5  9  ☐
    ☐  ☐  ☐  2
```

14. In April a company made 4367 masks.
In May production increased by 1292.
How many masks were made in May?

15. 45 660 copies of a magazine were printed
but only 38 880 were sold.
How many copies were not sold?

16. In one week 2569 children used a swimming pool.
The total number of tickets sold was 4185. How many adults used the pool?

17. Copy and complete this addition square.

+	18			
		100		65
			114	
17	35			49
		81	67	

Copy and complete.
Work out

18. ☐ take away 17 is 89

19. ☐ is 240 less than 655

20. 3684 + ☐ = 4816

21. 367 − ☐ = 248

22. 4155 plus ☐ is 5230

23. ☐ subtract 17 is 815

24. ☐ decreased by 213 is 48

25. 1234 − ☐ = 416

26 Draw a copy of the grid shown. The sum of the numbers in each column ↕ is the same as the sum of the numbers in each diagonal ↗ or ↘.

What number goes in the centre?

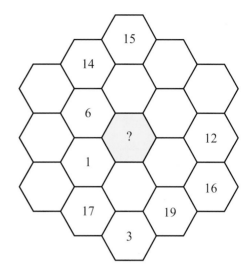

27 One subtraction, using the digits 2, 3, 4, 5, 6, is 642 − 35.

Which subtraction using all the digits 2, 3, 4, 5, 6 has the smallest positive answer?

Game

This is a game for 2 or 3 players.
You need cards numbered 0 to 9 which are placed face down on the table.

Each player draws a grid like this …

Now turn over one of the cards and then each person writes that number somewhere on their own grid.

For example,

Sue put the 5 here

and Sami put the 5 here

Now turn over four more cards, one at a time, and write each new number somewhere on the grid.

Finally add together the two numbers.

The winner is the person with the highest total.

In the game between Sue and Sami

Sue got

and Sami got

So Sami was the winner.

Magic squares

In a magic square the sum of the numbers in each column, row and main diagonal are equal. Here is an example of a magic square. The sum of each column, row and diagonal is 18.

9	5	4
1	6	11
8	7	3

Copy and complete the following magic squares

1

4	3	
	5	
		6

2

		3
	6	
9		4

3

	10	8
	7	
	4	

4

		11
5	12	7

5

6		2
	5	
8		

6

6	7	
13	8	
	9	

7

	6	10	15
16		5	4
	12	8	
		11	

8

9	14		
		16	7
12	3	15	8
6			

9

11			10
2	13	16	
		4	
7	12		6

Multiplying

Exercise 4M

1 Copy and complete the multiplication squares. The numbers outside the square are always 2, 3, 4, 5, 6, 7, 8, 9.

(a)

×	8	2	7
5			35
		32	
3	27		
6			

(b)

×	4	7	3	8
5				
		42		
2				

(c)

×	5	8	2
	28		56
6			
9			

(d)

×	4		3
		45	72
		30	
7		35	

(e)

×	7		9
24		32	
			18
	42		

(f)

×	5	7	
	40		32
3			
6	12		

(g)

×			
35	40	15	
		18	
18		27	

(h)

×	8		
			27
	56		
	40	30	
			36

(i)

	3		
7	42		
	24		
45		72	

(j)

18	14		
45		20	
54			48

(k)

		10	16
	24		48
63		72	

(l)

		40	
	18		
18		30	42

2 In the next three squares you may have the same number at the top and along the side of the square.

(a)

		4		
	56			
			15	
		36		
14	49			
30			25	

(b)

			18	48
		49		
		9		
45			40	
16	28			

(c)

		42	28		
		48		64	
15			40		
				81	
			24		

Multiplying larger numbers

```
    5 2
  ×   7
  3 6 4
    1
    ↑
  carry
```

```
    3 0 4
  ×     9
  2 7 3 6
      3
      ↑
    carry
```

```
    7 4 3
  ×     6
  4 4 5 8
      2 1
      ↖ ↗
      carry
```

Exercise 5M

Copy and complete.

1
```
    5 2 9
  ×     7
```

2
```
    6 4 4
  ×     8
```

3
```
    6 0 7
  ×     9
```

4
```
    3 7 0
  ×     6
```

5
```
  4 2 1 6
  ×     7
```

6
```
  3 6 1 4
  ×     8
```

7
```
    2 0 1 6
  ×       4
  □ □ 6 □
```

8
```
    8 7 5
  ×     7
  □ 1 □ □
```

8

9 There are 52 playing cards in a 'deck'.
How many cards are there altogether in
nine decks?

10 In one week the average daily audience at a cinema was 627 people.
How many people watched films at the cinema during that week?

11 Each month an office worker earns £2150.
How much does she earn in 6 months?

12 How many hours are there in 5 days?

13 Find the missing digits.

(a)
```
    □ 7
  ×   5
  ─────
  2 3 □
```

(b)
```
  □□ 6
  ×   7
  ─────
  2 2 8 □
```

(c)
```
  □□ 3
  ×   8
  ─────
  5 6 2 □
```

14 Wyatt eats a banana each day for 52 weeks.
Eva eats a banana six times each week
for 60 weeks. How many more bananas
does Wyatt eat than Eva?

15 Answer true or false:
(a) $3 + 4 + 5 + 6 + 7 = 5 \times 5$
(b) $77 + 78 + 79 = 3 \times 78$

16 Mike knows that $221 \times 31 = 6851$.
Explain how he can use this information to work out 222×31.

17 Given that $357 \times 101 = 36\,057$, work out 358×101 without multiplying.

18 How many spots are there on nine ordinary dice?

Dividing

Exercise 6M

1 Copy and complete.

(a) $77 \div \square = 7$

(b) $\square \div 8 = 6$

(c) $42 \div \square = 7$

(d) $54 \div \square = 6$

(e) $24 \div \square = 12$

(f) $500 \div \square = 50$

(g) $\boxed{} \div 9 = 9$ (h) $\boxed{} \div 7 = 7$ (i) $\boxed{} \div 7 = 8$

(j) $40 \div \boxed{} = 5$ (k) $\boxed{} \div 8 = 9$ (l) $30 \div \boxed{} = 15$

(m) $\boxed{} \div 7 = 6$ (n) $200 \div \boxed{} = 5$ (o) $80 \div \boxed{} = 10$

2 Write down each statement and write 'true' or 'false'.

(a) $45 \div 5 = 9$ (b) $60 \div 6 = 9$ (c) $7 \div 1 = 1 \div 7$

(d) $20 \div 2 = 10$ (e) $84 \div 4 = 12$ (f) $9 \div 9 = 0$

Copy and complete these multiplication squares.

3
×			9		
		54		36	
	35			15	
					48
		36		27	
7	49				

4
×					
		40		64	
		35		42	
			12		14
			12		
			27		63

5
×					
			49		
		30			40
					36
			21		24
		36		54		24

Work out

6   $8\overline{)2056}$ 7 $5\overline{)1025}$ 8 $6\overline{)7776}$ 9 $7\overline{)5082}$

10   $3050 \div 10$ 11 $1387 \div 1$ 12 $38\,199 \div 7$ 13 $14\,032 \div 8$

14   $31\,386 \div 6$ 15 $3490 \div 5$ 16 $28\,926 \div 9$ 17 $15\,638 \div 7$

18   Books are sold in boxes of 8.
How many boxes are needed for
184 books?

19   336 children are divided into four equal teams.
How many children are in each team?

20   Cinema tickets cost £6.
How many tickets can be bought for £162?

Rounding remainders up or down

(a) How many teams of 5 can you make from 113 people?

Work out $113 \div 5$.

$$5\overline{)11^13} \quad \begin{array}{c} 2\,2 \end{array} \quad remainder\ 3$$

Here we round *down*. You can make 22 teams and there will be 3 people left over.

(b) An egg box holds 6 eggs. How many boxes do you need for 231 eggs?

Work out $231 \div 6$.

$$6\overline{)23^51} \quad \begin{array}{c} 3\,8 \end{array} \quad remainder\ 3$$

Here we round *up* because you must use complete boxes. You need 39 boxes altogether.

Exercise 7M

Write the answer with a remainder.

1   $4079 \div 7$
2   $2132 \div 5$
3   $4013 \div 8$
4   $235 \div 6$

5   $657 \div 10$
6   $8327 \div 10$
7   $85\,714 \div 6$
8   $4826 \div 9$

In these questions you will get a remainder. Decide whether it is more sensible to round *up* or to round *down*.

9   Train tickets cost £5.
How many tickets can be bought for £88?

10   A car can carry 3 children as passengers.
How many cars are needed to carry 40 children?

11   There are 23 children in a class.
How many teams of 4 can be made?

12   Eggs are packed six in a box. How many boxes do I need for 200 eggs?

13   Tickets cost £6 each and I have £80. How many tickets can I buy?

14   I have 204 plants and one tray takes 8 plants. How many trays do I need?

15   There are 51 children in the dining room and a table seats 6.
How many tables are needed to seat all the children?

16   I have 100 cans of drink. One box holds 8 cans. How many boxes can I fill?

17 Five people can travel in one car and altogether there are 93 people to transport.
    How many cars are needed?

18 A prize consists of 10 000 one pound coins.
    The prize is shared betwen 7 people.
    How many pound coins will each person receive?

19 How many 9p stamps can I buy with a £5 note?

20 Henby School has 7 classes each of
    28 pupils in Year 7. In Year 8 there are
    6 classes each of 29 pupils.
    All the pupils are put together then split
    into sports teams. Each team has 9 pupils.
    How many teams can be formed?

Long multiplication

- Traditional method

$$
\begin{array}{r}
35 \\
\times\ \ 41 \\
\hline
35 \quad (35 \times 1) \\
1400 \quad (35 \times 40) \\
\hline
1435 \\
\end{array}
$$

- Using grids

35×41

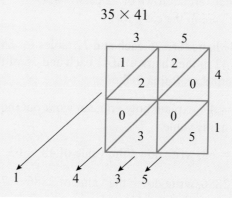

Exercise 8M

Use any method of your choice to work out the following questions.

1   36×27
2   49×24
3   36×25
4   38×44

5   326×15
6   208×24
7   141×27
8   324×14

9   27×281
10 472×23
11 897×36
12 456×213

13 Each week a shop assistant earns £84.
    How much does he earn in 15 weeks?

14 Gold-plated trees cost €69 each.
How much would 81 of these trees cost?

15 A film company hires 94 extras to film
crowd scenes. They are paid £75 each.
What is the total wage bill?

16 Fill in the boxes with the digits 2, 3, 4, 5
to make the answer correct.

$$\begin{array}{r} \square\square \\ \times\ \square\square \\ \hline 8\ 4\ 0 \end{array}$$

17 A delivery van uses an average of 43 litres of
petrol per day. How much does the van use in 14 days?

18 An aircraft holds 174 people. The aircraft was full on every
trip for three days. How many people did it carry in total
over the three days?

Day	Number of trips
Fri	16
Sat	22
Sun	18

19 In a car park there are 25 rows of 42 cars.
How many cars are in the car park?

20 Raina buys 48 chairs for £26 each and 22 tables for £89 each.
She then sells 42 of the chairs for £41 each and 16 of the tables for £136 each.
How much profit does Raina make?

21 If $1222 \div 26 = 47$, explain how you can work out the value of 47×26
and write down this value.

22 If $3024 \div 48 = 63$, write down the value of 48×63.

23 If $74 \times 39 = 2886$, write down the value of $2886 \div 74$.

Long division

With ordinary short division, you divide and find remainders. The method for 'long' division is
really the same but you set it out so that the remainders are easier to find.

Work out $864 \div 36$

$$\begin{array}{r} 2\ 4 \\ 36\overline{)8\ 6\ 4} \\ -\underline{7\ 2}\downarrow \\ 1\ 4\ 4 \\ -\underline{1\ 4\ 4} \\ 0 \end{array}$$

36 into 86 goes 2 times
$2 \times 36 = 72$
$86 - 72 = 14$
bring down 4
36 into 144 goes 4 times

Exercise 9M

1 Work out.

   (a) $7\overline{)3374}$ (b) $13\overline{)702}$

Work out. There are no remainders in these questions.

2 $286 \div 13$ 3 $360 \div 15$ 4 $672 \div 21$ 5 $621 \div 23$

6 $888 \div 24$ 7 $992 \div 32$ 8 $810 \div 18$ 9 $644 \div 46$

10 $1224 \div 51$ 11 $1035 \div 45$ 12 $612 \div 36$ 13 $1769 \div 29$

14 Copy and complete

   (a) $23 \times \boxed{} = 391$ (b) $\boxed{} \times 35 = 840$ (c) $1512 \div 42 = \boxed{}$

15 A box of 15 golf balls costs 975 pence. How much does each ball cost?

Exercise 10M

There are remainders in some of the divisions.

1 $450 \div 14$ 2 $515 \div 15$ 3 $851 \div 23$ 4 $580 \div 13$

5 $775 \div 31$ 6 $1128 \div 24$ 7 $830 \div 36$ 8 $945 \div 41$

9 A hammer costs £14. How many hammers can be bought with £355?

10 A rugby team has 15 players. How many teams can be made from 187 players?

11 How many 32 cm lengths of string can be cut from 60 metres?

12 A school hall can fit 28 chairs into one row. How many rows are needed to seat 1000 people?

13 Each box contains 25 pills. How many boxes can be filled from 6040 pills?

14 Each pack of wooden cubes contains 64 cubes. How many packs can be filled from 7845 cubes?

15 There are 35 offices in a building and each office has 14 phones.
    The phones are delivered in boxes of 15.
    How many boxes are needed?

16

	?	11	25
?	?	187	?
?	208	?	400
?	286	?	?

Copy and complete this multiplication square

Need more practice with whole number arithmetic?

Work out

1
$$523$$
$$-\ 118$$

2
$$376$$
$$-\ \ 95$$

3
$$571$$
$$-\ 363$$

4
$$850$$
$$-\ 264$$

5
$$965$$
$$-\ 575$$

6 $167 - 78$

7 $319 - 234$

8 $2644 + 55\,685$

9 $45\,609 + 20\,047$

10 $2001 - 416$

11 $67\,508 + 95\,607 + 436$

12 What is the true value of the figure 4 in the number 74186?

13 Copy and complete the grids below. Time yourself on grid 1. Try to improve your time on grid 2.

Grid 1

×	7	2	12	8	6	3	11	9	4	5
7	49									
2										
12										
8										
6				48						
3						9				
11										
9										
4										
5										

Grid 2

×	2	9	6	3	5	11	12	8	7	4
2										
9										
6										
3										
5										
11										
12										
8										
7										
4										

Copy and complete.

14
$$\begin{array}{r} 2\ 3 \\ \times\ \ \ \ 4 \\ \hline \Box\ 2 \\ \hline \end{array}$$
1

15
$$\begin{array}{r} 2\ 7 \\ \times\ \ \ \ 3 \\ \hline \Box\ 1 \\ \hline \end{array}$$
2

16
$$\begin{array}{r} 1\ 6 \\ \times\ \ \ \ \ 7 \\ \hline 1\ \Box\ 2 \\ \hline \end{array}$$
4

17
$$\begin{array}{r} 2\ 5 \\ \times\ \ \ \ \Box \\ \hline 1\ 0\ 0 \\ \hline \end{array}$$

18
$$\begin{array}{r} 1\ 9 \\ \times\quad 4 \\ \hline \square\square \\ \end{array}$$

19
$$\begin{array}{r} 4\ 5 \\ \times\quad 4 \\ \hline \square\square\square \\ \end{array}$$
2

20
$$\begin{array}{r} 3\ 4\ 2 \\ \times\qquad 3 \\ \hline \end{array}$$

21
$$\begin{array}{r} 4\ 6\ 5 \\ \times\qquad 6 \\ \hline \end{array}$$

22 Here are four number cards:

3 8 6 4

(a) Use all the cards to make the largest possible number.

(b) Use all the cards to make the smallest possible number.

23 What number, when multiplied by 3 and then divided by 4, gives an answer of 6?

24 Copy and complete: $(3 + \square) \div 5 = 4$

25 Work out

(a) $4\overline{)252}$ (b) $7\overline{)588}$ (c) $6\overline{)1638}$ (d) $8\overline{)4736}$

Extension questions with whole number arithmetic

Work out

1   68×34

2   37×46

3   218×59

4   327×74

5   $648 \div 18$

6   $1128 \div 24$

7   $858 \div 26$

8   $2176 \div 32$

9   On average a shop sells 32 chess sets a week.
How many sets are sold in a year?

10 Jars of peaches are packed 18 to a box.
How many boxes do you need for 625 jars?

11 The stairs on an escalator move up at a rate of 14 cm per second.
How far will the stairs go up in three quarters of a minute?

12 Tins of spaghetti are packed 8 to a box.
How many boxes are needed for 913 tins?

13 Find the missing numbers

(a) 714 r ☐
8)5 7 1 4

(b) 5 6 r 4
7)3 9 ☐

(c) 8 1 2 r 7
9)7 3 1 ☐

14 If 15 ÷ 3 = 5 then there are three related × or ÷ statements,
ie. 15 ÷ 5 = 3 and 3 × 5 = 15 and 5 × 3 = 15.
For each statement below, write three related × or ÷ statements.

(a) 12 × 8 = 96   (b) 96 ÷ 6 = 16   (c) 1204 ÷ 28 = 43

15 In the number pyramids below, each number is found by multiplying the two numbers below it. Copy and complete each number pyramid.

(a)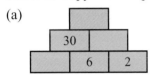

(b)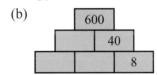

16 There are 332 children in a school. One coach holds 50 children.
How many coaches are needed for a whole school trip?

17 What is the true value of the difference between the figures underlined in the numbers 1546 and 2193?

18 If 1512 ÷ 27 = 56, write down the values of:

(a) 27 × 56   (b) 1512 ÷ 56   (c) 15 120 ÷ 27

19 Fill in the boxes with the digits 1, 2, 3, 4, 5 to make the answer correct. This is not easy but it can be done!

☐ ☐ ☐
×   ☐ ☐
———————
5 5 2 5

20 A balloon company makes £55 profit from each balloon ride in the Summer and £22 profit for each balloon ride in the Winter. The company does 98 balloon rides in the Summer and makes a profit of £6776 for all the Summer and Winter rides.
How many balloon rides take place during the Winter?

1.2 Decimals

In section 1.2 you will:

- review decimal place value and adding/subtracting decimals
- order decimals
- multiply decimals
- divide decimals by whole numbers

The number 427.35 is $427\frac{35}{100}$.

We can write it like this.

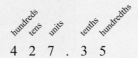

Exercise 1M

1　Write these numbers as decimals.

　(a) $7\frac{9}{10}$　　　(b) $11\frac{3}{10}$　　　(c) $5\frac{17}{100}$　　　(d) $18\frac{39}{100}$　　　(e) $126\frac{43}{100}$

2　Give the value of the underlined figure.

　(a) 5.<u>7</u>　　　　(b) <u>1</u>7.4　　　　(c) 1<u>5</u>.23　　　(d) 8.4<u>6</u>

　(e) 0.7<u>1</u>　　　(f) 3.2<u>4</u>　　　(g) 0.3<u>2</u>　　　(h) 1<u>4</u>.2

　(i) <u>3</u>6.04　　　(j) 3.0<u>7</u>　　　(k) <u>4</u>11.5　　　(l) 8.3<u>6</u>

3　Write the numbers shown by each of the arrows.

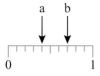 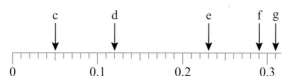

In questions ④ to ⑲ answer True (T) or False (F).

④　0.7 is less than 0.71

⑤　0.61 is more than 0.16

⑥　0.08 is more than 0.008

⑦　0.5 is equal to 0.500

⑧　0.613 is less than 0.631

⑨　7.0 is equal to 0.7

⑩　6.2 is less than 6.02

⑪　0.09 is more than 0.1

12   2.42 is equal to 2.420

13   0.63 is less than 0.36

14   0.01 is more than 0.001

15   0.78 is less than 0.793

16   8 is equal to 8.00

17   0.4 is more than 0.35

18   0.07 is less than 0.1

19   0.1 is equal to $\frac{1}{10}$

20   Here is a pattern of numbers based on 3. ⟶

Write a similar pattern based on 7 and extend it from 70 000 000 down to 0.0007. Write the numbers in figures and in words.

three thousand	3000
three hundred	300
thirty	30
three	3
nought point three	0.3
nought point nought three	0.03

21   The number 3.745 is 'three point seven four five', *not* 'three point seven hundred and forty-five'. £1.67 is spoken as 'one pound sixty-seven'. £2.05 is spoken as 'two pounds and five pence'.

Write the following in words.
(a) 7.52   (b) 6.237   (c) 11.04   (d) 60.65
(e) £5.65   (f) £3.05   (g) 6.324   (h) £0.50

22   What does the digit 3 in 5.386 represent? And the 6? And the 8?

23   Write the decimal number equivalent to:
(a) three tenths   (b) seven hundredths
(c) eleven hundredths   (d) four thousandths
(e) sixteen hundredths   (f) sixteen thousandths.

24   To change 0.24 to 0.28, you *add 0.04.*
Write down the single operation needed [+, −] when you change:
(a) 5.32 to 5.72   (b) 11.042 to 11.047
(c) 0.592 to 0.392   (d) 0.683 to 0.623.

25   Draw a line from 0.9 to 1.1 with 20 equal divisions

$\left[\begin{array}{l} ^{0.9} \sqcup_{\sqcup \sqcup \sqcup} \dots \text{etc} \end{array} \right]$

Show these numbers on your line
(a) 0.93   (b) 1.04   (c) 1.0   (d) 0.99   (e) 1.09

Ordering decimals

Consider these three decimals ...

0.09, 0.101, 0.1.

Which is the correct order from lowest to highest?

When ordering decimals it is always helpful to write them with the same number of figures after the decimal point.

0.09 ⟶ 0.090   Empty spaces can be filled with zeros.
0.101 ⟶ 0.101
0.1 ⟶ 0.100

Now we can clearly see the correct order of these decimals from lowest to highest ... 0.090, 0.1, 0.101.

Exercise 2M

In questions ① to ② , arrange the numbers in order of size, smallest first.

① 0.21, 0.31, 0.12.

② 0.04, 0.4, 0.35.

③ 0.67, 0.672, 0.7.

④ 0.05, 0.045, 0.07.

⑤ 0.1, 0.09, 0.089.

⑥ 0.75, 0.57, 0.705.

⑦ 0.41, 0.041, 0.14.

⑧ 0.809, 0.81, 0.8.

⑨ 0.006, 0.6, 0.059.

⑩ 0.15, 0.143, 0.2.

⑪ 0.04, 0.14, 0.2, 0.53.

⑫ 1.2, 0.12, 0.21, 1.12.

⑬ 2.3, 2.03, 0.75, 0.08.

⑭ 0.62, 0.26, 0.602, 0.3.

⑮ 0.5, 1.3, 1.03, 1.003.

⑯ 0.79, 0.792, 0.709, 0.97.

⑰ 5.2 m, 52 cm, 152 cm.

⑱ £1.20, 75p, £0.8.

⑲ 200 m, 0.55 km, $\frac{1}{2}$ km.

⑳ 1.2 mm, 0.1 cm, 2 mm.

㉑ Here are numbers with letters.

(a) Put the numbers in order, smallest first. Write down just the letters.

(b) Finish the sentence using letters and numbers of your own. The numbers must increase from left to right.

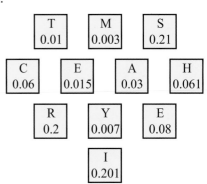

20

22 Increase the following numbers by $\frac{1}{1000}$:

(a) 3.142   (b) 2.718   (c) 1.414

24 The weights of some butterflies are given below:

0.21 g   0.18 g   0.2 g
0.206 g   0.109 g   0.24 g

Write down these weights in descending order
(ie. start with the largest weight).

Find the number which the arrow is pointing to on each of the scales.

(a)
4   6

The middle number is 5.
Each division is 0.2.
The arrow points to 4.4

(4.4)

4   5   6

(b)
8.1   8.2

Each division is 0.02.
The arrow points to 8.16

(8.16)

8.1   8.12   8.14   8.18   8.2

Exercise 3M

Work out the value indicated by the arrow.

1   40   50

2   2   3

3   14   16

4   15   15.5

5   0   1

6   0   6

7   0   10

8   5   6

9   3.1   3.2

10   0   0.1

11   1   1.04

12   0   1.5

In each of questions ⑬ to ㉔ , the arrows point to two numbers, A and B.

For each question find the difference between A and B.

13

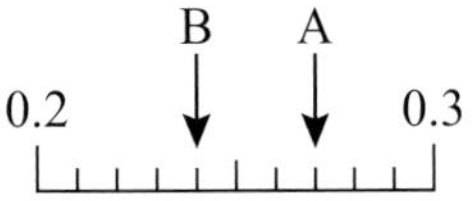

14

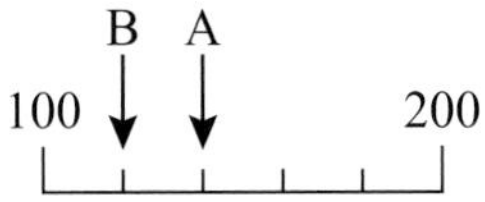

15

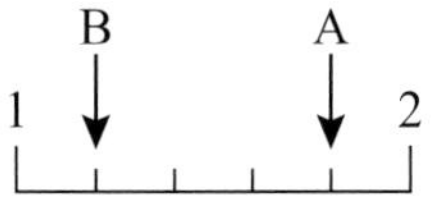

16

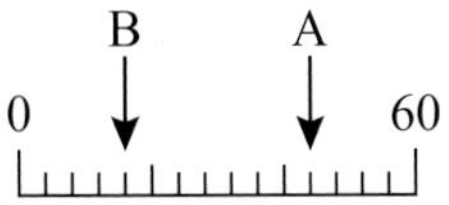

17

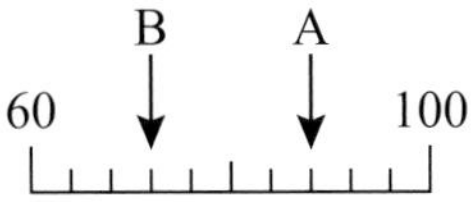

18

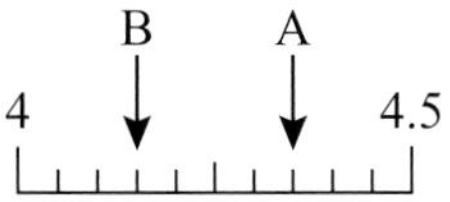

19

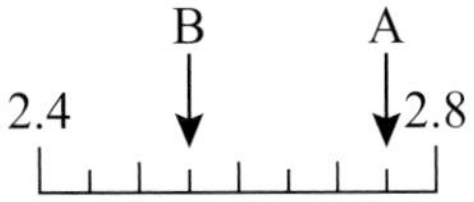

20

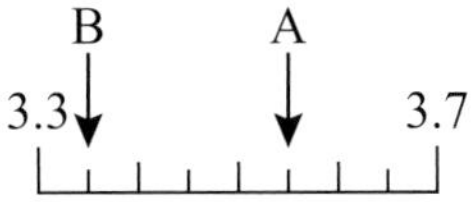

21

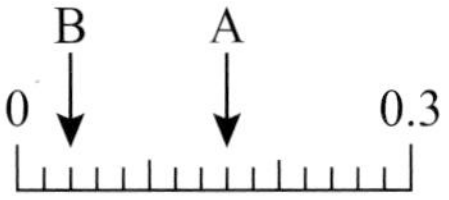

22

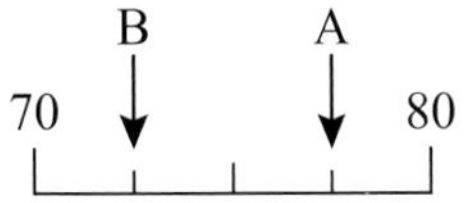

23

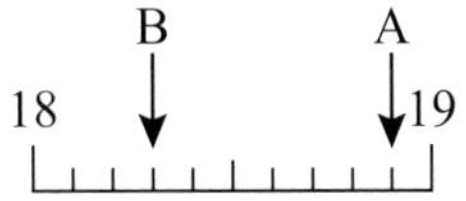

24

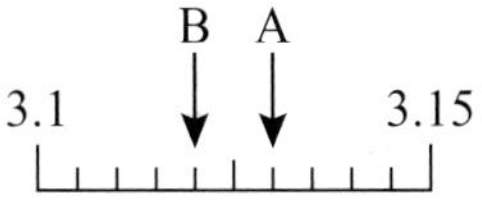

Adding and subtracting decimals

Remember: Line up the decimal points

(a) $2.4 + 3.23$

put a zero

$$
\begin{array}{r}
2.40 \\
+\ 3.23 \\
\hline
5.63
\end{array}
$$

(line up the points)

(b) $7 - 2.3$

$$
\begin{array}{r}
{}^{6}\!\!\not{7}.{}^{1}0 \\
-\ 2.3 \\
\hline
4.7
\end{array}
$$

(write 7 as 7.0)

(c) $0.31 + 4 + 11.6$

$$
\begin{array}{r}
0.31 \\
4.00 \\
+\ 11.60 \\
\hline
15.91
\end{array}
$$

(write 4 as 4.00)

Exercise 4M

Work out.

1 $6.4 - 2.7$

2 $15.6 - 10.9$

3 $8 - 2.7$

4 $5 + 0.26$

5 $2.9 + 4.37$

6 $8.6 + 7.99$

7 $16.374 + 0.947 + 27$

8 $3.142 + 2.71 + 8$

9 $0.03 + 11 + 8.74$

10 94.63 − 5.9

11 2.97 − 1.414

12 25.52 − 1.436

13 3.142 − 1.414

14 2.718 − 1.732

15 12 − 3.74

16 Jack spent £5.15 in the supermarket and £10.99 in the music shop.
How much change did he get from £20.

17 Olive has £322.15 in her bank account.
On Monday she goes shopping and buys the items
shown in the box opposite. She is also paid £135 which
her friend, Alice, owes her.
How much money does she have in her bank account at
the end of Monday?

skirt	£42.59
blouse	£23.60
socks	£14.35
food	£32.47

In questions **18** to **23** find the missing digits

18
$$\begin{array}{r} \square\,.\,5\,\square \\ -\ 4\,.\,\square\ 3 \\ \hline 3\,.\,7\ 3 \end{array}$$

19
$$\begin{array}{r} 4\,.\,\square\ 7 \\ +\ \square\,.\,9\ \square \\ \hline 9\,.\,0\ 3 \end{array}$$

20
$$\begin{array}{r} 3\,.\,1\ 7\ \square \\ -\ \square\,.\,4\ \square\ 8 \\ \hline 0\,.\,\square\ 4\ 8 \end{array}$$

21
$$\begin{array}{r} 8\,.\,\square\ 8 \\ +\ \square\,.\,8\ \square \\ \hline 9\,.\,6\ 6 \end{array}$$

22
$$\begin{array}{r} \square\,.\,9\ \square \\ -\ 2\,.\,\square\ 6 \\ \hline 3\,.\,6\ 6 \end{array}$$

23
$$\begin{array}{r} 2\,.\,\square\ 5\ 7 \\ +\ \square\,.\,3\ 4\ \square \\ \hline 6\,.\,8\ \square\ 5 \end{array}$$

24 I started with 6.658 and then subtracted a number. The answer was 6.648.
What number did I subtract?

25 Pieces of timber are used for building houses.
The table opposite shows how much timber is used
each week during February.
The total length of timber used in February is
782.5 m.
How much timber was used in week 3?

Week 1	212.65 m
Week 2	169.83 m
Week 3	?
Week 4	275.19 m

26 Explain clearly why 1.2 added to 7 is not 1.9

Top Banana! The Banana man of Tesco

The following article is a true story. Read the article (which deliberately contains blanks) and then answer the questions.

He is called the Banana man of Tesco. In a special offer Phil Calcott bought almost half a ton of bananas. He then gave it all away and still made a profit on the deal. In a way Mr Calcott made his local store pay him to take away its own fruit.

The offer said that if you bought a 3 lb bunch of bananas for £1.17, you would gain 25 Tesco 'Club Card' points. These points could be used to buy goods worth £1.25.

Mr Calcott asked the store to load up his Peugeot 205 with bananas.

'I took a car load at a time because even with the back seat down and the boot full I could only fit in 460 lbs of bananas', he said.

He returned for another load the next day and altogether spent £— buying 942 lbs of the fruit. This earned him almost —,000 Tesco 'Club Card' points.

1 How much would it cost to buy ten 3 lb bunches of bananas?

2 How many Tesco Club Card points would you get?

3 How much would the points be worth?

4 How much profit would you make on this deal?

5 Do you like bananas?

6 Write down the paragraph that starts 'He returned …' and fill in the missing numbers.

Multiplying decimals by whole numbers

Method 1

- $7.93 \times 4 \approx 8 \times 4 = 32$
  (Estimate first)

  7.93×4 $7.00 \times 4 = 28.00$
  $0.90 \times 4 = 3.60$
  $0.03 \times 4 = \underline{0.12} +$
  31.72

- $3.16 \times 6 \approx 3 \times 6 = 18$
  (Estimate first)

  3.16×6 $3.00 \times 6 = 18.00$
  $0.10 \times 6 = 0.60$
  $0.06 \times 6 = \underline{0.36} +$
  18.96

Method 2

- $7.24 \times 4 \approx 7 \times 4 = 28$
  (Estimate first)

  $\ 7.24$
  $\underline{\times 4}$
  28.96
  ${}_1$

- $0.096 \times 9 \approx 0.1 \times 9 = 0.9$
  (Estimate first)

  $\ 0.096$
  $\underline{\times 9}$
  0.864
  ${}_{85}$

> The answer has the same number of figures after the point as there are in the numbers being multiplied

Exercise 5M

Work out the following. Find an estimate first.

1. $\quad 5.1$
   $\times \quad 2$

2. $\quad 2.3$
   $\times \quad 3$

3. $\quad 3.7$
   $\times \quad 4$

4. $\quad 5.6$
   $\times \quad 5$

5. $\quad 6.13$
   $\times \quad 6$

6. $\quad 10.22$
   $\times \quad 7$

7. $\quad 5.34$
   $\times \quad 8$

8. $\quad 1.29$
   $\times \quad 9$

9. 7×0.63

10. 1.452×6

11. 9×0.074

12. 11.3×5

13. 13.6×5

14. 0.074×5

15. 6×2.22

16. 8.4×11

17. Copy and complete with the missing numbers.

    (a) $0.3 \times 4 = \boxed{}$

    (b) $0.6 \times \boxed{} = 4.2$

    (c) $\boxed{} \times 5 = 2.0$

    (d) $1.5 = 6 \times \boxed{} + 0.3$

    (e) $\boxed{} \times 7 - 2 = 1.5$

    (f) $8 \times \boxed{} = 0.16$

18. Find the cost of 6 golf balls at £1.95 each.

19. A new car tyre costs £29.99.
    What is the total cost of 4 new tyres?

20. Find the total cost of 8 batteries at £1.19 each.

21. If 1 kg of cheese costs £4.59, find the cost of 3 kg.

Exercise 6M

Copy and complete

1. $7.5 \times \boxed{} = 7500$

2. $280 \div \boxed{} = 2.8$

3. $\boxed{} \times 1000 = 32$

4. $17 \div 100 = \boxed{}$

5. $36 \times \boxed{} = 36$

6. $56 \div \boxed{} = 0.56$

7. $0.42 \times \boxed{} = 420$

8. $\boxed{} \times 1000 = 6540$

9. $0.07 \times \boxed{} = 0.7$

10. $0.8 \div \boxed{} = 0.8$

11. $0.03 \times \boxed{} = 30$

12. $110 \div \boxed{} = 1.1$

13. Work out

    (a) 6.35×4
    (b) 0.72×9
    (c) 1.45×7
    (d) $0.4 \times 3 \times 10$
    (e) $1.7 \times 3 \times 100$

14. Find the cost of 3 tins of beans at £0.64 each, 5 packets of bread sauce at £1.12 each
    and 2 litres of milk at £1.24 per litre.

15   Find the answer to the calculation in each box.

Arrange the answers in order of size, smallest first. What word do you get?

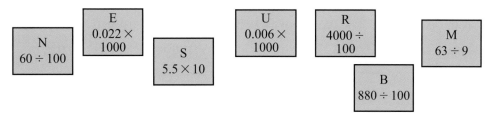

N
60 ÷ 100

E
0.022 ×
1000

S
5.5 × 10

U
0.006 ×
1000

R
4000 ÷
100

B
880 ÷ 100

M
63 ÷ 9

16   Tony can stitch 0.32 m of cloth in one minute.
How much can he stitch in 7 minutes?

17   If 1 litre equals 1.76 pints, how many pints is 8 litres?

18   Max says that 4.2 × 3.1 is equal to 1.302.
Explain clearly how Max can check his answer to see if he is likely to be correct.

19   Copy and complete

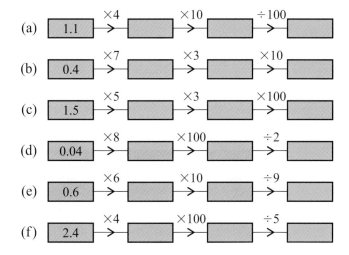

(a)   1.1   ×4 →   ×10 →   ÷100 →

(b)   0.4   ×7 →   ×3 →   ×10 →

(c)   1.5   ×5 →   ×3 →   ×100 →

(d)   0.04 ×8 →   ×100 →   ÷2 →

(e)   0.6   ×6 →   ×10 →   ÷9 →

(f)   2.4   ×4 →   ×100 →   ÷5 →

20

A pair of sandals costs £14.50.
A parcel contains 8 pairs of sandals.
A van contains 1000 parcels full of sandals.

(a) What is the cost of one parcel?

(b) What is the cost of the sandals on the van?

Multiplying decimal numbers

- 5×0.3 is the same as $5 \times \frac{3}{10}$. Work out $(5 \times 3) \div 10 = 15 \div 10 = 1.5$

  4.2×0.2 is the same as $4.2 \times \frac{2}{10}$. Work out $(4.2 \times 2) \div 10 = 8.4 \div 10 = 0.84$

  0.7×0.04 is the same as $0.7 \times \frac{4}{100}$. Work out $(0.7 \times 4) \div 100 = 2.8 \div 100 = 0.028$

- Quick method:

> When we multiply two decimal numbers together, the answer has the same number of figures to the right of the decimal point as the total number of figures to the right of the decimal point in the question.

(a) 0.3×0.4
$(3 \times 4 = 12)$

So $0.3 \times 0.4 = 0.12$

(b) 0.7×0.05
$(7 \times 5 = 35)$

So $0.7 \times 0.05 = 0.035$

Exercise 7M

1. 0.4×0.2
2. 0.6×0.3
3. 0.8×0.2
4. 0.4×0.03

5. 0.7×3
6. 0.7×0.02
7. 0.9×0.5
8. 6×0.04

9. 0.04×0.05
10. 0.7×0.7
11. 8×0.1
12. 14×0.3

13. 15×0.03
14. 0.4×0.04
15. 0.001×0.6
16. 33×0.02

17. If £1 = €1.14, how many euros do Ava and Jack get for £80 when on holiday?

18. Phone cable costs £0.55 per metre. Calculate the cost of 2.6 m of cable.

19. Copy and complete

    (a) $6 \times 0.2 = \square$

    (b) $0.4 \times \square = 0.04$

    (c) $1.5 \times \square = 150$

    (d) $0.3 \times \square = 0.06$

    (e) $0.1 \times \square = 0.08$

    (f) $\square \times 0.013 = 1.3$

20. If $0.26 \times 0.3 = 0.078$, what is the value of $0.078 \div 0.3$?

21 If $0.0486 \div 0.27 = 0.18$, what is the value of 0.18×0.27?

22 Work out
   (a) 160×0.1 (b) 1800×0.1 (c) 238×0.1
   (d) Explain the quickest way to multiply by 0.1

23 Work out the area of each shape.

(a)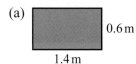
0.6 m
1.4 m

(b)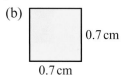
0.7 cm
0.7 cm

(c)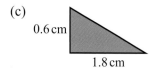
0.6 cm
1.8 cm

24
1.5 m

The length of a rectangle is 1.5 m and its perimeter is 4.2 m.
Find the area of the rectangle.

Division of decimals by whole numbers

(a) $9.6 \div 3$

$$\begin{array}{r} 3.2 \\ 3\overline{)9.6} \end{array}$$

(b) $22.48 \div 4$

$$\begin{array}{r} 5.\ 62 \\ 4\overline{)22.^248} \end{array}$$

(c) $7.3 \div 4$

$$\begin{array}{r} 1.\ 8\ 2\ 5 \\ 4\overline{)7.^33^10^20} \end{array}$$

↑ ↑
Note the extra zeros.

(d) $21.28 \div 7$

$$\begin{array}{r} 3.0\ 4 \\ 7\overline{)21.2^28} \end{array}$$

(e) $3.12 \div 4$

$$\begin{array}{r} 0.\ 7\ 8 \\ 4\overline{)3.^31^32} \end{array}$$

Exercise 8M

1 $8.42 \div 2$ 2 $205.2 \div 6$ 3 $18.52 \div 4$

4 $4.984 \div 7$ 5 $236.0 \div 5$ 6 $18.93 \div 3$

7 $49.92 \div 8$ 8 $487.26 \div 9$ 9 $6.7 \div 5$

10 A father shares £4.56 between his three children.
    How much does each receive?

11 If 5 bricks weigh 4.64 kg, find the weight of one brick.

12 Barbecued sausages cost £5.94 for six. How much does each one cost?

13 The total bill for a meal for four people is £33.88. How much does each person pay if they each paid the same?

14 Five people share the fuel cost of a car journey which amounts to £18.65. How much does each person pay?

15 Copy and complete the cross number puzzle. There are decimal points on some lines.

1	2		3	4	5
6		7		8	
	9		10		
11			12	13	
14	15			16	17
18			19		

Clues across
1. 4×1.9
3. $6.2 \div 5$
6. $83.2 \div 4$
8. $0.42 \times 2 \times 50$
9. $348 \div 3$
12. 0.95×40
14. $928 + 45$
16. $31.8 \div 6$
18. $2004 - 1989$
19. $5.1 \div 5$

Clues down
1. $36.4 + 35.6$
2. $542 + 5 + 54$
4. $7.2 \div 3$
5. $(85 \times 5) \div 10$
7. 0.081×1000
10. $31.5 \div 5$
11. $200 - (0.9 \times 10)$
13. 0.85×1000
15. $60 \div 8$
17. $0.0032 \times 100 \times 100$

Need more practice with decimals?

1 I started with 0.954 and then added a number. The answer was 0.956. What number did I add?

2 Write down the answers.
(a) $1.242 + 0.03$
(b) $9.042 - 0.03$
(c) $11.817 + 0.002$
(d) $8.679 - 0.001$
(e) $6.53 + 0.002$
(f) $41.44 - 0.4$
(g) $0.473 - 0.2$
(h) $0.046 + 0.004$
(i) $11.617 - 0.005$

3 Write the numbers in order, smallest first, to make a word.

A	Q	N	I	U	E	O	T
0.104	0.031	3	0.231	0.04	0.028	0.4	0.21

Copy and complete.

4 $0.8 \times \boxed{} = 80$

5 $\boxed{} \times 1000 = 5500$

6 $\boxed{} \times 10 = 0.52$

7 $1.8 \times 100 = \boxed{}$

8 $0.81 \times \boxed{} = 810$

9 $0.4 \times 1000 = \boxed{}$

10   $7.2 \times \boxed{} = 7.2$ 11 $\boxed{} \times 100 = 11.7$ 12 $\boxed{} \times 100 = 0.2$

13   Answer true or false: $0.3 \times 10 = 0.03 \times 1000$

14   A book costs £6.90. Find the total cost of 9 books.

15   If one brick weighs 1.35 kg, how much do 7 weigh?

16   A bag of popcorn costs £5.24.
How much do 8 bags of popcorn cost?

17   A length of wood measuring 39.41 cm has to be cut into seven equal lengths.
How long is each piece?

18   Work out
     (a) $11.2 \div 5$ (b) $9.01 \div 4$ (c) $12.1 \div 8$
     (d) $0.82 \div 4$ (e) $17 \div 5$ (f) $22 \div 8$

19   Use estimation to decide if 2.2×5.7 might equal 12.54.
Explain your answer fully.

20   Work out
     (a) 0.6×0.08 (b) 2.6×0.4 (c) 0.03×0.09
     (d) 0.08×1.2 (e) 6.4×0.003 (f) 0.004×0.06

Extension questions with decimals

1   Answer true or false
     (a) $0.1 \times 0.1 = 0.1$ (b) $0.1 - 0.01 = 0.09$ (c) $0.1 \div 100 = 0.01$
     (d) $0.1 > 0.02$ (e) $3.3 - 0.6 = 0.6 - 3.3$ (f) $0.71 = 710 \div 1000$

2   A steel rod of length 2.86 m is divided into 11 equal pieces.
How long is each piece?

Each empty square contains either a number or an operation ($+$, $-$, $\times$, $\div$). Copy each square and fill in the missing details. The arrows are equals signs.

3

32	÷	4	→	
+		×		
		7	→	280
↓		↓		
72	−		→	

4

18	×		→	90
−		+		
7		6	→	42
↓		↓		
	−		→	

5

25	+		→	89
×		+		
	×		→	
↓		↓		
150	−		→	69

6

35	×		→	350
−		÷		
	×		→	
↓		↓		
34.8	+	0.1	→	

7

38	×	8	→	
÷		×		
2	×		→	
↓		↓		
	+	112	→	

8

		574	→	1532
÷		+		
9	×	25	→	
↓		↓		
234	+		→	

9

10	×		→	1
÷		×		
	÷		→	
↓		↓		
2.5	+	1.6	→	

10

19.6	÷	7	→	
×		+		
0.1	×		→	1
↓		↓		
	+		→	

11

8.42	−	0.2	→	
×		×		
100	×		→	1200
↓		↓		
	+		→	

12

20	÷	100	→	
×		÷		
	×	200	→	
↓		↓		
440	×		→	

13

1.22	×	3	→	
+		−		
	+		→	
↓		↓		
5	+		→	7.8

14

	+		→	902
÷		−		
9	×	52	→	
↓		↓		
	+	526	→	

CHECK YOURSELF ON SECTIONS 1.1 AND 1.2

1 Using the place value of digits in whole numbers

Here are four number cards:

(a) Use all the cards to make the smallest possible number.

(b) Use all the cards to make the largest possible *odd* number.

2 Solving problems involving addition, subtraction, multiplication and division

Work out

(a) 234 + 51 + 618   (b) 422 − 53   (c) 73 × 49

(d) 252 ÷ 7   (e) (3617 − 1422) ÷ 5   (f) 1035 ÷ 23

(g) A calculator costs £7. How many can I buy with £90?

(h) Tins of blackcurrants are packed 6 to a box. How many boxes are needed for 70 tins?

(i) On average a shop sells 48 copies of a newspaper each day.
How many copies of the newspaper are sold during the month of March?

3 Reviewing decimal place value and adding/subtracting decimals

Write the decimal number equivalent to:

(a) seven tenths   (b) three hundredths   (c) fifteen hundredths

(d) Copy and complete the addition square.

	3.2	0.54		
			3.6	4.5
11.8				10.4
		0.58		
8				

4 Ordering decimals

Write the numbers in order, smallest first, to make a word.

5   Multiplying decimals

Work out

(a) 0.64×6 (b) 3.8×7 (c) 0.03×0.4

(d) Find the total cost of 2 tins at £1.65 each and 7 bottles at £0.40 each.

6   Dividing decimals by whole numbers

Work out

(a) $9.42 \div 2$ (b) $31.8 \div 6$ (c) $22 \div 4$

(d) A cake weighing 2.24 kg is shared equally between seven people. How much does each person get?

1.3 Using a calculator

In section 1.3 you will:

- review the order of operations (BIDMAS)
- use a calculator for fractions
- use brackets on a calculator

Order of operations

Consider the possible answers to this question:
'Work out $5 + 7 \times 3$'

On some calculators, we get: $5 + 7 \times 3$
$$= 12 \times 3 \quad \text{(adding first)}$$
$$= 36$$

On other calculators, we get: $5 + 7 \times 3$
$$= 5 + 21 \quad \text{(multiplying first)}$$
$$= 26$$

Both answers seem sensible but if we could get different answers to the same question people around the world would argue over who is correct. Another question comes when there are brackets in a calculation, for example $6 \times (8 - 3)$.

The rule we use is

'work out the brackets first and then multiply or divide before you add or subtract'

The correct answers to the calculations above are

$$5 + 7 \times 3 = 26$$
$$6 \times (8 - 3) = 30$$

Later we will work with indices like 5^2 or 4^3 and when they are involved the complete rule is shown in the table below.

B rackets	( )	do first	'B'
I ndices	x^y	do next	'I'
D ivision M ultiplication	$\div$ $\times$	do this pair next	'D' 'M'
A ddition S ubtraction	$+$ $-$	do this pair next	'A' 'S'

Remember the word 'B I D M A S'.

(a) $40 \div 5 \times 2$
$= 8 \times 2$
$= 16$

(b) $9 + 8 - 7$
$= 17 - 7$
$= 10$

(c) $5 + 2 \times 3$
$= 5 + 6$
$= 11$

$\times$ before $+$

(d) $10 - 8 \div 2$
$= 10 - 4$
$= 6$

$\div$ before $-$

Exercise 1M

Work out the following. Show every step in your working.

1   $5 + 3 \times 2$ 2 $4 - 1 \times 3$ 3 $7 - 4 \times 3$

4   $2 + 2 \times 5$ 5 $9 + 2 \times 6$ 6 $13 - 11 \times 1$

7   $7 \times 2 + 3$ 8 $9 \times 4 - 12$ 9 $2 \times 8 - 7$

10   $4 \times 7 + 2$ 11 $13 \times 2 + 4$ 12 $8 \times 5 - 15$

13   $6 + 10 \div 5$ 14 $7 - 16 \div 8$ 15 $8 - 14 \div 7$

16   $5 + 18 \div 6$ 17 $5 + 8 \times 6$ 18 $6 - 12 \div 4$

19   $20 \div 4 + 2$ 20 $15 \div 3 - 7$ 21 $24 \div 6 - 8$

22   $30 \div 6 + 9$ 23 $8 \div 2 + 9$ 24 $28 \div 7 - 4$

25   $13 + 3 \times 13$ 26 $9 + 26 \div 13$ 27 $10 \times 8 - 70$

28   $96 \div 4 - 4$ 29 $36 \div 9 + 1$ 30 $1 \times 2 + 3$

31   Copy each calculation and write in the missing number.

(a) $4 \times \boxed{} - 7 = 9$ (b) $20 - 3 \times \boxed{} = 5$ (c) $24 \div \boxed{} - 4 = 4$

(d) $(10 - \boxed{}) \times 4 = 36$ (e) $26 - (10 - \boxed{}) = 19$ (f) $36 \div (7 - \boxed{}) = 6$

(g) $(\boxed{} + 7) \times 5 = 65$ (h) $11 - \boxed{} \div 2 = 5$ (i) $\boxed{} + 7 \times 3 = 30$

(j) $44 + (24 \div \boxed{}) = 56$ (k) $(\boxed{} \times 7) - 21 = 0$ (l) $48 \div \boxed{} + 11 = 17$

(a) $8 + 3 \times 4 - 6$
$= 8 + (3 \times 4) - 6$
$= 8 + 12 - 6$
$= 14$

$\times$ and $\div$ before $+$ and $-$

(b) $3 \times 2 - 8 \div 4$
$= (3 \times 2) - (8 \div 4)$
$= 6 - 2$
$= 4$

Notice that we have put brackets in to make the working easier.

Exercise 2M

Evaluate the following. Show every step in your working.

1 $2 + 3 \times 4 + 1$ 2 $4 + 8 \times 2 - 10$ 3 $7 + 2 \times 2 - 6$

4 $25 - 7 \times 3 + 5$ 5 $17 - 3 \times 5 + 9$ 6 $11 - 9 \times 1 - 1$

7 $1 + 6 \div 2 + 3$ 8 $6 - 28 \div 7 - 2$ 9 $8 + 15 \div 3 - 5$

10 $5 - 36 \div 9 + 3$ 11 $6 - 24 \div 4 + 0$ 12 $8 - 30 \div 6 - 2$

13 $3 \times 4 + 1 \times 6$ 14 $4 \times 4 + 14 \div 7$ 15 $2 \times 5 + 8 \div 4$

16 $21 \div 3 + 5 \times 4$ 17 $10 \div 2 + 1 \times 3$ 18 $15 \div 5 + 18 \div 6$

19 $5 \times 5 - 6 \times 4$ 20 $2 \times 12 - 4 \div 2$ 21 $7 \times 2 - 10 \div 2$

22 $35 \div 7 - 5 \times 1$ 23 $36 \div 3 - 1 \times 7$ 24 $42 \div 6 - 56 \div 8$

25 $72 \div 9 + 132 \div 11$ 26 $19 + 35 \div 5 - 16$ 27 $50 - 6 \times 7 + 8$

28 $30 - 9 \times 2 + 40$ 29 $4 \times 11 - 28 \div 7$ 30 $13 \times 11 - 4 \times 8$

In questions 31 to 48 remember to perform the operation in the brackets first.

31 $3 + (6 \times 8)$ 32 $(3 \times 8) + 6$ 33 $(8 \div 4) + 9$

34 $3 \times (9 \div 3)$ 35 $(5 \times 9) - 17$ 36 $10 + (12 \times 8)$

37 $(16 - 7) \times 6$ 38 $48 \div (14 - 2)$ 39 $64 \div (4 \times 4)$

40 $81 + (9 \times 8)$ 41 $67 - (24 \div 3)$ 42 $(12 \times 8) + 69$

43	$(6 \times 6) + (7 \times 7)$	44	$(12 \div 3) \times (18 \div 6)$	45	$(5 \times 12) - (3 \times 9)$
46	$(20 - 12) \times (17 - 9)$	47	$100 - (99 \div 3)$	48	$1001 + (57 \times 3)$

Exercise 3M

1   Theo puts some brackets into a
    calculation as shown below:

$$36 - (9 \div 3)$$

He wants the answer to be 9.

Explain clearly what mistake he has made.

Copy each question and write brackets so that each calculation gives the correct answer.

2	$3 + 4 \times 5 = 35$	3	$6 + 9 \times 7 = 69$	4	$7 \times 2 + 3 = 17$
5	$9 + 12 \times 5 = 105$	6	$6 \times 8 - 2 = 36$	7	$3 \times 8 - 6 = 18$
8	$19 - 6 \times 3 = 39$	9	$27 - 9 \div 3 = 24$	10	$51 \div 3 + 4 = 21$
11	$7 \times 24 - 5 = 133$	12	$6 + 14 \div 2 = 10$	13	$11 + 6 \times 4 = 68$
14	$12 \times 8 - 9 \times 7 = 33$	15	$8 \times 9 - 4 \times 7 = 44$		

16   Which calculations below have the brackets in the correct place? For those that do not, write
     out the sum with the brackets in the correct position.

    (a) $5 \times (6 - 4 \div 2) = 13$ (b) $(81 \div 9) \times (12 - 4) = 72$

    (c) $(3 + 5) \times (9 - 7) = 16$ (d) $(16 - 10) \div (18 \div 6) = 2$

    (e) $6 + (7 - 1) \div 2 = 6$ (f) $(5 + 7) \div 3 \times 0 = 0$

Jumble the numbers

Exercise 3E

Using each number once, find the calculation which gives
the correct answer.

For example:

Numbers	Answer	Calculation
5, 3, 6	3	$(6 - 5) \times 3 = 3$

	Numbers			Answer	Calculation		Numbers			Answer	Calculation
1.	2	4	8	6		**2.**	2	3	5	21	
3.	7	2	3	3		**4.**	9	2	4	7	
5.	8	4	5	20		**6.**	20	2	3	6	
7.	7	2	4	30		**8.**	7	22	6	20	
9.	6	4	3	8		**10.**	8	40	3	8	
11.	8	36	4	5		**12.**	7	49	2	14	
13.	21	14	11	24		**14.**	16	3	9	57	
15.	12	4	16	7		**16.**	24	42	6	24	
17.	18	5	13	25		**18.**	40	6	16	4	
19.	7	8	6	50		**20.**	13	8	4	44	
21.	4	3	9	12		**22.**	7	9	3	21	
23.	45	4	3	11		**24.**	121	11	7	77	

25 Make up your own question to try on a friend.
You may use as many numbers as you like.

Using a calculator for fractions

Division can be written with a horizontal line

$$8 \div 2 = \frac{8}{2} \qquad\qquad (4 + 6) \div 2 = \frac{4 + 6}{2} \qquad\qquad 4 + 6 \div 2 = 4 + \frac{6}{2}$$

$$12 \div (4 + 2) = \frac{12}{4 + 2} \qquad\qquad (8 - 3) \div (11 + 2) = \frac{8 - 3}{11 + 2}$$

The fraction button on a calculator is

Use the arrow keys to move between the numerator and denominator.

Exercise 4M

1 Write the following expressions with a horizontal line
   (a) $8 + 6 \div 2$ (b) $10 \div 2 + 4$ (c) $12 - (8 \div 2)$
   (d) $10 \div (3 + 1)$ (e) $(12 - 7) \div 2$ (f) $10 \div 5 - 1$

In questions 2 to 13 use a calculator to find the answer.

2 $\dfrac{8 - 2}{3}$ 3 $12 - \dfrac{8}{2}$ 4 $\dfrac{14 - 8}{2}$

5 $\dfrac{8}{4} + 1$ 6 $\dfrac{8}{3 + 1}$ 7 $\dfrac{12 - 8}{2}$

8 $\dfrac{16}{1 + 3}$ 9 $15 + \dfrac{12}{3}$ 10 $\dfrac{15.48}{1.72}$

11 $\dfrac{8.448}{1.32}$ **12** $2.9 + \dfrac{6.039}{1.83}$ **13** $\dfrac{1.5 \times 1.5}{25}$

14 Emma types $\dfrac{8+4}{4}$ into her calculator which gives 3 as the answer. The correct answer to the sum is 9. Describe what mistake Emma might have made when typing in this sum?

15 Use a calculator to work out

(a) $\dfrac{9.408}{6.72} - 0.28$ (b) $\dfrac{1.9 + 2.953}{2.3}$ (c) $\dfrac{8.7 - 5.622}{1.14} + 2.3$

16 Explain which fraction buttons could be used on a calculator for the sum $(6.6 + 3.4) \div 2.5 + 15 \div 1.5$

Using brackets

For the calculation $14 - (8 \div 2)$ you press

[1] [4] [−] [(] [8] [÷] [2] [)] [=]

The calculation inside the brackets will be done first by the calculator.

Exercise 5M

1 Work out what answer you would get when the buttons are pressed.

(a) [(] [8] [+] [7] [)] [÷] [3] [=] (b) [1] [8] [−] [(] [5] [×] [2] [)] [=]

(c) [1] [2] [÷] [(] [6] [−] [3] [)] [=] (d) [9] [÷] [(] [6] [÷] [2] [)] [=]

2 Write down the sequence of buttons you would press to work out the following calculations.

(a) $17 - (4.2 \times 3)$ (b) $\dfrac{28}{2.41 + 4.59}$

Work out

3 $18.41 - (7.2 \times 1.3)$ **4** $11.01 + (2.45 \div 7)$ **5** $(2.38 + 5.6) \div 1.4$

6 $9.6 + (11.2 \div 4)$ **7** $(8.73 \div 3) - 1.4$ **8** $11.7 - (2.6 \times 2.7)$

9 $7.41 - \left(\dfrac{6.44}{1.4}\right)$ **10** $\left(\dfrac{11.39}{1.7}\right) - 2.63$ **11** $\dfrac{28.65}{(1.7 + 0.21)}$

12 $(1.56 + 4.32) \div 2.45$ **13** $3.2 \times (1.9 - 0.74)$ **14** $4.956 \div (1.3 - 0.71)$

15 $(7.77 \div 1.4) \times 1.49$ **16** $(2.67 + 1.2 + 5) \times 1.1$ **17** $23 - (9.2 \times 1.85)$

18 $\dfrac{(8.41 + 0.704)}{1.47}$ **19** $\dfrac{132.43}{8.2 \times 0.95}$ **20** $\dfrac{43.87 - 8.17}{17}$

21 Find three pairs of equivalent expressions

A $\dfrac{24}{3} - 2$ B $\dfrac{24 - 2}{3}$ C $24 - 2 \div 3$ D $(24 - 2) \div 3$

E $24 - \dfrac{2}{3}$ F $\dfrac{24}{3 - 2}$ G $24 \div (3 - 2)$

22 Write down the sequence of buttons you would press to evaluate the following.

(a) $\dfrac{9 - 3}{4 + 8}$ (b) $\dfrac{30}{8 - 3} + 4 \times 7$

Need more practice with using a calculator?

Work out and write down all the numbers in your calculator display.

1. $0.13 + 8.9 - 3.71$
2. $5.3 \times 1.7 + 3.7$
3. $2.4 \times 2.4 - 3.45$

4. $8.17 - 1.56 + 7.4$
5. $7.81 + 0.7 \times 1.82$
6. $8.73 + 3.45 \div 0.5$

7. $4.48 \div 0.32 + 1.15$
8. $1.6 \times 1.7 + 2.62$
9. $5.2 + \dfrac{4.995}{1.85}$

10. $9.64 + \dfrac{10.92}{0.42}$
11. $\dfrac{14.24}{8.17 - 3.72}$
12. $\dfrac{17.5 + 3.62}{0.62 + 4.18}$

13. $\dfrac{6.16 \times 4}{11.5 - 7.65}$
14. $\dfrac{17}{8} + \dfrac{13}{4}$
15. $(1.75 + 0.6) \times (8.93 - 4.03)$

16. $\dfrac{17.6}{2.2} + \dfrac{13.5}{1.5}$
17. $\dfrac{13.86}{3.15} - \dfrac{5.94}{2.7}$
18. $\dfrac{24.65 + 6.55}{6.5 \times 3}$

19. $\left(\dfrac{17.2}{9.8} - 1.2\right)^2$
20. $14.5 - \dfrac{1.9}{0.7}$
21. $\dfrac{9.84 \times 0.751}{6.3 \times 0.95}$

22 The calculation $0.6 + 0.2 \times 0.3 - 0.1$ needs brackets to give the answer 0.14. Write out the calculation with the brackets in the correct position.

23 Carly says the answer to $0.73 + \dfrac{1.4}{0.02}$ is 106.5.

Explain clearly why Carly is not correct.

24 A man's heart beats at 70 beats/min. How many times will his heart beat between 03.30 and 23.30 on the same day?

Extension questions with using a calculator

Indices

Remember BIDMAS: **B** rackets
                    I ndex
                    D ivide
                    M ultiply
                    A dd
                    S ubtract

$$2 \times (8 - 3)^3$$
$$= 2 \times 5^3$$
$$= 2 \times 125$$
$$= 250$$

bracket then index then multiply

Evaluate the following, showing all your working.

1 2^4

2 3^3

3 0^5

4 $10 + 3^3$

5 $4^2 - 8$

6 $32 - 5^2$

7 $3 + 3^2$

8 8^2

9 5×4^2

10 $3^2 \times 2$

11 62×2^3

12 $5^3 \times 1$

13 $1^4 \times 3^4$

14 $(1 + 1)^3$

15 $(1 + 2)^3$

16 $(5 - 4)^3$

17 $4 \times (3 + 1)^2$

18 $(9 - 5)^4 \div 4$

19 $2 \times (3^2 - 1)$

20 $(5^2 + 5^2) \div 5$

21 $2 \times (6 - 3)^2$

22 $5 \times (2 \times 1)^3$

23 3×2^3

24 $20 - 4^2$

Work out and write down all the numbers in your calculator display.

25 $25.1 - 4.2^2$

26 $(9.8 - 4.43)^2$

27 $9.23^2 - 7.42^2$

28 $\dfrac{16.1}{4.7} - 1.8^2$

29 $1.21 - \dfrac{9}{14^2}$

30 $\dfrac{11.7 - 3.73}{2.45^2}$

Spot the mistakes 1

Number calculations

Work through each question and *explain clearly* what mistakes have been made.
Beware – some questions are correctly done.

1
$$\begin{array}{r} 52 \\ \times\ 69 \\ \hline 468 \\ 312 \\ \hline 780 \end{array}$$
so 52×69 $= 780$

2 $0.6 \times 0.2 = 1.2$

3 A box contains 28 packets when full. What is the least number of boxes needed to hold 1000 packets?

$$\begin{array}{r} 3\ \ 5\ \text{r. }20 \\ 28\overline{)100^{16}0} \end{array}$$ so 35 boxes are needed.

4
$$\begin{array}{r} 148 \\ \times\ \ 39 \\ \hline 1332 \\ 4440 \\ \hline 5772 \end{array}$$
so 148×39 $= 5772$

5
$$\begin{array}{r} 2\ 5.\ 8 \\ 7\overline{)18^47.^56} \end{array}$$
so $187.6 \div 7 = 25.8$

6 Ruhi buys 2 kg of grapes at £4.60 per kg and 3 peppers at £0.67 each. What is the total cost?

$$\begin{array}{r} 460 \\ \times\ \ \ 2 \\ \hline 820 \end{array}$$
so 4.60×2 $= £8.20$

0.67×3 $= £2.01$

total cost $= 8.20 + 2.01 = £10.21$

7 $0.12 + 16 + 0.14 = 0.42$

8 $3 + \dfrac{17}{5} = \dfrac{20}{5} = 4$

9 Mr Avis arranges a trip to the theatre by coach for 83 people. One coach can carry up to 50 people. Each person pays £29 for the coach and theatre ticket. The leftover money is given to charity. How much money is given to charity?

	cost
theatre ticket	£19
1 coach	£322

Each person pays £10 for the coach
total $= 83 \times 10 = £830$
2 coaches $= 2 \times 322 = £644$
So charity money $= 830 - 644 = £186$

10 $8 + 12 \div (2 \times 3) = 30$
Are the brackets in the correct place?

1.4 Rules of algebra

In section 1.4 you will learn how to:

- use letters for numbers
- simplify algebraic expressions
- substitute numbers into a formula
- tackle balance puzzles

Using letters for numbers

Many problems can be solved by using letters instead of numbers. This is called using *algebra*.

> Remember: the *letters stand for numbers*

- Suppose there are N cows in a field. If the farmer puts 3 more cows in the field, there will be $N + 3$ cows in the field.
- $N + 3$ is an expression. An expression is usually a mixture of letters, numbers and signs. An expression has no '=' sign.
- A term is a single number or letter (or a product of numbers or letters), eg. 3 or N or $3N$.
- Suppose there are y people on a bus. At a bus stop n people get off the bus. There are now $y - n$ people on the bus.
- $y - n$ is an expression.
- If I start with a number N and treble it, I will have $N \times 3$. In algebra the '$\times$' sign is left out and the number is written before the letter so I will have $3N$.
- If I start with a number x then double it and add 4, I will have $2x + 4$.
- $2x + 4$ is an expression.

Exercise 1M

In questions 1 to 10 write down the expression.

1   I start with a number N then add 3.

2   I start with a number d then take away 9.

3   I start with a number x then double it.

4   I start with a number y then add 25.

5   I start with a number k, double it then subtract 8.

6   I start with a number M, treble it then take away 4.

7   I start with a number p and multiply it by 25.

8   I start with a number w, double it then add 15.

9   I start with a number q, multiply it by 10 then subtract 8.

10   I start with a number b, multiply it by 3 then add 8.

11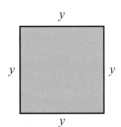

The perimeter p of the triangle is
$$p = x + x + x$$
This is written as $p = 3x$

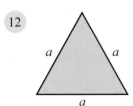

Complete the statement below for the perimeter p of this square
$$p = \ldots\ldots$$

Use algebra to find the perimeter p of each shape in questions 12 to 14 .

12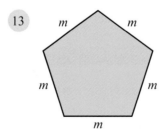

13

14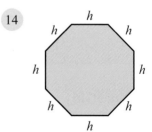

15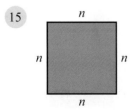

Louise says that the perimeter of this square is $n + n + n + n$.

Greg says she is not correct and the perimeter is $4n$.

Explain clearly who is correct.

16 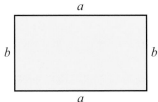 The perimeter p of this rectangle is
$$p = a + b + a + b$$
This is written as $p = 2a + 2b$

Write down the perimeter p for this triangle.

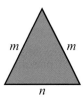

Use algebra to find the perimeter p of each shape in questions 17 to 19

17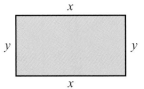

18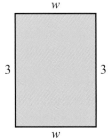

19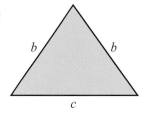

20 Harry says the perimeter of this shape
is $2m + 18$.
He then says that this equals $20m$.
Do you think that Harry is correct?
Give a reason for your answer.

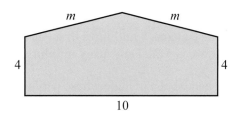

21 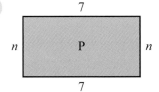 Which rectangle has the
larger perimeter?
Give a reason for your
answer.

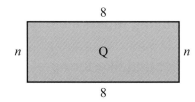

Exercise 1E

In questions 1 to 10 write down the expression.

1 I start with b, add c and then take away m.   2 I start with x, double it and then add y.

3   I start with Q, add 8 and then take away p.

4   I start with s, treble it and then take away w.

5   I add together a, b and c then subtract 8.

6   I start with $4x$, take away y and then add 5.

7   I subtract f from g and then add n.

8   I start with $2y$, add $3w$ and then take away x.

9   I start with m, multiply by 6 and then add $3n$.

10   I subtract $3p$ from $5q$ and then add $4m$.

11   A sweet weighs x grams. How many grams do five sweets weigh?

12   A piece of rope is 20 m long. A prisoner ties on an extra piece of rope of length y metres. How long is the entire piece of rope now?

13   A piece of wood is w cm long. I cut off a piece 9 cm long. What is the length of the remaining piece of wood?

14   Carl has m books. Shalina has 3 times as many books. How many books does Shalina have?

15   On Tuesday there are x people in a cinema. On Saturday there are four times as many people plus another 45. How many people were in the cinema on Saturday?

16   Tania spends £n on magazines. Chris spends £4 more than Tania. Tania says that Chris spends £$4n$ in total. Is Tania correct? Give a reason for your answer.

17   A bottle contains n millilitres of medicine. 8 doses of medicine are given from the bottle. Each dose is 5 ml. How many millilitres of medicine remain in the bottle?

18   Draw and label a triangle whose perimeter p is given by the formula $p = 2x + 5$.

19   Draw and label a rectangle whose perimeter p is given by the formula $p = 2a + 2b$.

Simplifying algebraic expressions

Collecting like terms

The expression $4a + 3a$ can be simplified to $7a$.

a means $1a$ so $6a - a = 6a - 1a = 5a$

$5x$ and $3x$ are called *like* terms

$5x$ and $3y$ are called *unlike* terms

The sum or difference of two terms can only be simplified if the terms are *like* terms.

We can collect like terms.

(a) $5 + n + 2 + 4n = 5n + 7$

(b) $y + 3 + y + 4 + w = w + 2y + 7$

> collect in alphabetical order, with letter terms written before any numbers on their own

(c) $4x - 4$ cannot be simplified (no like terms)

(d) $5y + x - 5y = x$

> do not write $0y$
> do not write $1x$

(e) Simplify $6x + 4y + 2x - 2y$

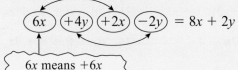

$= 8x + 2y$

> $6x$ means $+6x$

(f) Simplify $6m + 3x - m + 6 - 3x$

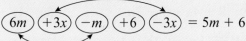

$= 5m + 6$

Exercise 2M

Simplify the following expressions where possible. If you cannot simplify write down the expression given.

1. $3a + 5a$
2. $6x - 2x$
3. $4a + 3b$
4. $6c - 4d$

5. $3d + d$
6. $3x + 2$
7. $7y + 2y$
8. $5h - 3h$

9. $8w - 5w$
10. $6y - 5y$
11. $7x + y$
12. $8m + m$

13. $16y - 9y$
14. $6m + 5n$
15. $4x + 6$
16. $5b + 8b$

17. $20t - 8t$
18. $7p - 6p$
19. $10n + 15n$
20. $6a - 5$

21. $8x + 2$
22. $14h + 16h$
23. $9 - 7x$
24. $8b - 4$

25. $7a + 6$
26. $5c + c$
27. $12y - 12$
28. $12y - y$

29. Ollie says that $4n + 4$ is equal to $8n$.
Explain clearly what mistake Ollie has made.

30. Amy says that $9m - m$ is the same as $6m + 2m$.
Is she correct? Give a reason for your answer.

Exercise 3M

Simplify the following expressions as far as possible by collecting like terms.

1. $3a + 5b + 3a + 2b$
2. $2x + 4y + 7x + 3y$
3. $8x + 4y - 5x - 2y$
4. $7m + 5n - 4m + 3n$
5. $6a + 5 + a + 4$
6. $8a + 3b - 6a + 4b$
7. $5x + 9 - 2x - 7$
8. $7p + 9q + 2p - 4q$
9. $7x + 8 + x - 6$
10. $a + 14b + 5a - 4b$
11. $6m + 8 + 6m - 7$
12. $3h + 20 - h + 5$
13. $5m + 2n + 4n + 7m$
14. $8p + 6q - 3q - 2p$
15. $6x + 10 - 6 + 3x$
16. $7x + 3y + x + 6$
17. $8a + 3b - 4a + 4c$
18. $5w + 8 - 3w + w$
19. $8 + 4a + 7 - 2a$
20. $4y + 8 - 5 - 3y$
21. $5c - c + 6a + 8c$
22. $5p + 6q + 4p - 4q$
23. $7m + 9n - 7n + 4$
24. $6x + 8 - x + 9x$

25. Kosh says that $8n + 3 - n + 6$ simplifies to $8n + 9$.
Explain clearly the mistake that Kosh has made.

26. Write down an expression for the perimeter of each shape below.
Collect like terms where possible.

(a)

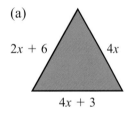

$2x + 6$ $4x$
$4x + 3$

(b)

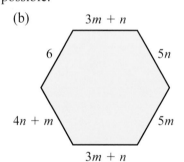

$3m + n$
6 $5n$
$4n + m$ $5m$
$3m + n$

(c) $2a + 3$

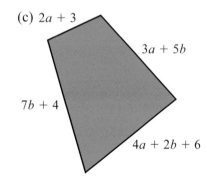

$3a + 5b$
$7b + 4$
$4a + 2b + 6$

27. Which expressions below are equivalent to $5m + 3n - n - 2 - 3m$?

    A $\boxed{2m + 2n - 2}$ B $\boxed{8m + 2n - 2}$ C $\boxed{2m + 3n - 2}$

28. Mark has £$(5n + 4)$ and Lauren has £$(7n + 9)$. They give their money to their mother who already has £$(3n + 1)$ in her purse. How much money does their mother now have?

29.

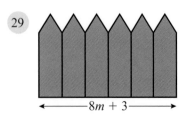

$8m + 3$

Mr and Mrs Ryall have a fence which is $(8m + 3)$ metres long.
They extend the fence by $(2n + 4m)$ metres.
How long is the fence now?

30 Which two expressions below are *equivalent* (this means they give the same answer when the like terms are collected).

    (a) $5x + 3 - 2x + 6y + x$ (b) $3y + 4x + 3y + 6 - 2$ (c) $7 + 4y + 4x + 2y - 3$

More rules

$a + b = b + a$

$a \times b = b \times a$ ($a \times b$ is written as ab so $ab = ba$)

$a \times a = a^2$

$\dfrac{a}{b} = a \div b$

Exercise 4M

1   Think of a pair of values for a and b to show that $a + b = b + a$

2   Think of a pair of values for m and n to show that $mn = nm$

3   Which expression below is the odd one out?

     $n + n$ $n \times n$ $2n$ $4n - n - n$

4   m and n are whole numbers where m does not equal n.

     Can you find any values for m and n so that $\dfrac{m}{n} = \dfrac{n}{m}$?

5   (a) Write down any pairs of expressions from below that are equal to each other.

      xy $\dfrac{y}{x}$ $x - y$

     $\dfrac{x}{y}$ $y - x$ $x + y$

      yx $y + x$

     (b) For each chosen pair from part (a), write down a pair of values for x and y which show that you are correct.

6   Does $(4 - n)$ equal $(n - 4)$ for all values of n?
     If so, show a value of n that works.

7 (a) Choose values for m, n and p to show that $mnp = mpn = pmn$.

   (b) Repeat part (a) with a different set of values for m, n and p.

8 An expression for the area of the shape opposite is $a^2 + bc$.
   Explain clearly why this is the correct expression.

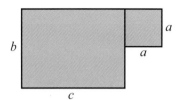

9 Write down an expression for the area of the shape opposite.

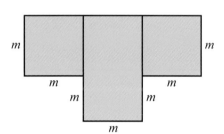

10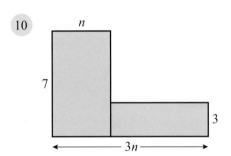

Lin says that an expression for the area of the shape opposite is

$$7n + 3 \times 2n$$
$$= 7n + 6n = 13n$$

Is Lin correct?
Give clear reasons for your answer.

Multiplying terms

(a) Simplify $3b \times 6a$

$3b \times 6a = 3 \times b \times 6 \times a$
$\qquad = 3 \times 6 \times b \times a$
$\qquad = 18ba$
write in alphabetical order
$\qquad = 18ab$

(b) Simplify $8n \times 4n$

$8n \times 4n = 8 \times n \times 4 \times n$
$\qquad = 8 \times 4 \times n \times n$
$\qquad = 32n^2$

Exercise 5M

Simplify

1 $4a \times 2b$

2 $5c \times 3d$

3 $6m \times 7n$

4 $3p \times 8q$

5 $9b \times 2a$

6 $3p \times 3p$

7 $8m \times 5m$

8 $4m \times 3n$

9 $7a \times 4b$

10   $9b \times 5a$

11   $7n \times 9m$

12   $12a \times 12a$

13   Use algebra to write down an expression for the area of each rectangle below.

(a)

(b)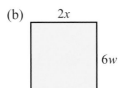

(c)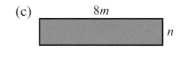

14   Charlie says that $5n \times 7m = 35mn$. Faith says that Charlie is not correct and the answer is $35nm$. Who is correct? Give a reason for your answer.

15   What must be added to $6ba$ to give $8ab$?

16   Neil multiplies two algebraic terms together and gets the answer $12ab$. Write down all the different pairs of terms that Neil may have used (numbers used must be whole numbers).

17   Write down an expression for the perimeter of the rectangle opposite. Make the answer as simple as possible.

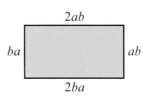

Investigation – Number walls

Here we have three bricks with a number written inside each one.

A wall is built by putting more bricks on top to form a sort of pyramid.

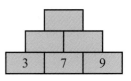

The number in each of the new bricks is found by adding together the numbers in the two bricks below like this:

Part A

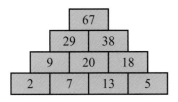

Here is another wall.

1   If you rearrange the numbers at the bottom, does it affect the total at the top?

2   What is the largest total at the top that you can get using the same numbers?

3   What is the smallest total?

4   *How* do you get the largest total?

Part B

1 What happens to the total at the top if the bottom numbers are
   (a) the same? (eg. 5, 5, 5, 5)
   (b) consecutive? (eg. 2, 3, 4, 5)

2 Write down any patterns or rules that you notice.

Part C

1 What happens if you use different numbers at random (eg. 7, 3, 5, 11)

2 Given 4 numbers at the bottom, can you find a way to predict the top number without finding all the bricks in between?

Part D
Can you find a rule with 3 bricks at the bottom, or 4 bricks?
Can algebra help? (Hint: see diagram)

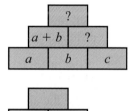

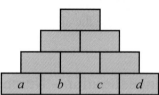

Substituting into a formula

(a) The perimeter p of this shape is given by the formula

$$p = 3a + 2b$$

Find p when $a = 5$ and $b = 4$.

$p = 3a + 2b$

$p = (3 \times 5) + (2 \times 4)$

$p = 15 + 8$

$p = 23$

(b) $h = 4(x + 3)$ Find h when $x = 7$.

(Remember: always work out brackets first)

$h = 4(x + 3)$

$h = 4(7 + 3)$ do brackets first

$h = 4 \times 10$

$h = 40$

Exercise 6M

1 The perimeter p of this triangle is given by the formula $p = 3x$
   Find p when $x = 6$.

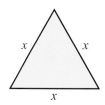

2 The perimeter p of a pentagon is given by the formula $p = 5y$
   Find p when $y = 8$.

3 The perimeter p of a four-sided shape (quadrilateral) is given by the formula
   $p = a + b + c + d$.
   Find p when $a = 9$, $b = 6$, $c = 14$ and $d = 17$

4 The cost in pounds, C, for hiring a bike is
   given by the formula $C = 8d + 12$
   where d is the number of days of hire.
   Find C when $d = 6$.

5 The voltage V is given by the formula $V = IR$
   Find V when $I = 9$ and $R = 15$.

6 A cinema ticket costs £9 for an adult. When A adults go to the cinema, Dave says the total
   money M taken by the cinema is given by the formula $M = 9A$.
   (a) Is Dave correct? Give a reason for your answer.
   (b) If $M = 9A$, what is the value of A when $M = 180$?

7 The perimeter p of a rectangle with sides x and y is given by the formula $p = 2(x + y)$.
   Find p when $x = 8$ and $y = 6$.

8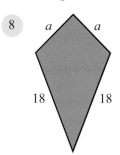
   A formula for the perimeter p of this kite is
   $$p = 2a + 36$$
   Find p when   (a) $a = 7$ (b) $a = 43$ (c) $a = 3.5$

9 A formula to work out the speed v of an object is $v = u + at$.
   Find v when $u = 5$, $a = 10$ and $t = 7$.

10 Perimeter $p = 5m + 7n$. Diya and Jordan are asked to work out the value of p when
   $m = 6$ and $n = 3$.

> Diya's answer
> $p = 5m + 7n$
> $\quad = 5 \times 6 + 7 \times 3$
> $\quad = 30 + 21 = 51$

> Jordan's answer
> $p = 5m + 7n$
> $\quad = 56 + 73$
> $\quad = 129$

Who is correct and what mistake did the other person make?

Exercise 6E

A formula is given in each question. Find the value of the letter required in each case.

1 $a = 3b + 5$ Find a when $b = 4$

2 $p = 4n - 9$ Find p when $n = 6$

3 $y = 5x - 3$ Find y when $x = 8$

4 $m = 16 - n$ Find m when $n = 7$

5 $h = 18 - 2g$ Find h when $g = 6$

6 $w = 4(p + 5)$ Find w when $p = 3$

7 $p = 7(q - 4)$ Find p when $q = 8$

8 $y = \dfrac{m}{4}$ Find y when $m = 36$

9 $a = \dfrac{b}{3}$ Find a when $b = 21$

10 $c = \dfrac{d}{3} + 9$ Find c when $d = 12$

11 $y = \dfrac{x}{10} - 6$ Find y when $x = 80$

12 $m = n^2$ Find m when $n = 5$

13 $p = qr$ Find p when $q = 6, r = 5$

14 $y = ab - 8$ Find y when $a = 8, b = 3$

15 $h = 6(x + y)$ Find h when $x = 7, y = 5$

16 $k = a(a + b)$ Find k when $a = 8, b = 2$

17 $x = m(9 - n)$ Find x when $m = 10, n = 4$

18 $c = 3fg$ Find c when $f = 2, g = 9$

19 $y = a^2 - b^2$ Find y when $a = 8, b = 3$

20 $n = \dfrac{x}{y} + x$ Find n when $x = 12, y = 4$

21 The cost in pounds, C, for hiring a boat from
   'Jacob's boats' is given by the formula $C = 9n + 15$
   where n is the number of hours of hire.
   The cost in pounds, C, for hiring a boat from
   'Cathy's sails' is given by the formula
   $C = 12n + 6$ where n is the number of hours
   of hire.
   Jack wants to hire a boat for 6 hours.
   Which is the cheaper option and by how much?

22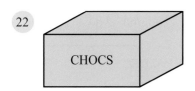

A box contains n packets of chocolates.

A van can carry m boxes. There are p vans.

The total number of packets, T, is given by the formula

$$T = mnp$$

Find the value of n if $T = 20\,000$, $m = 50$ and $p = 10$.

Balance Puzzles

On the balance ◯ and △ represent weights

Find ◯ if △ = 5 for this balance puzzle

Clearly for these scales to balance exactly, then ◯ = 10

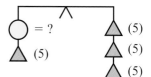

Exercise 7M

Copy each diagram and find the value of the required symbol.

1 Find ☐ if △ = 4.

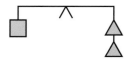

2 Find ◯ if △ = 10.

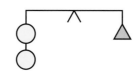

3 Find ◯ if ☐ = 4.

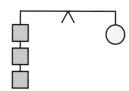

4 Find ☐ if △ = 12.

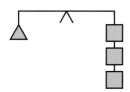

5 Find △ if ☐ = 2.

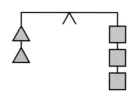

6 Find △ if ◯ = 6.

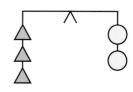

7 Find ☐ if ◯ = 8.

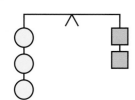

8 Find △ if ☐ = 15.

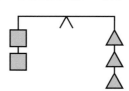

9 Find △ if ◯ = 14.

54

10 Find ☐ if ◯ = 8.

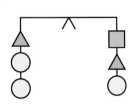

11 Find ◯ if △ = 6.

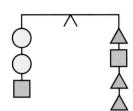

12 Find ◯ if ☐ = 5.

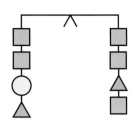

Exercise 7E

Copy each diagram and find the value of the unknown symbols.

1 ◯ = 10, find △ and ☐.

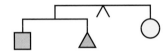

2 △ = 8, find ◯ and ☐.

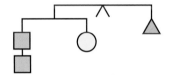

3 ☐ = 14, find ◯ and △.

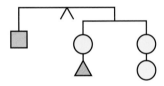

4 ☐ = 6, find ◯ and △.

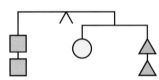

5 ◯ = 8, find ☐ and △.

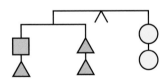

6 ☐ = 4, find ◯ and △.

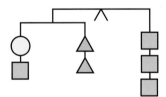

7 △ = 4, find ◯ and ☐.

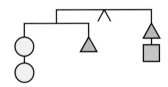

8 ◯ = 10, find △ and ☐.

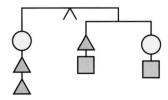

9   △ = 5, find ○ and □.

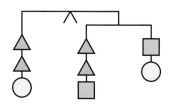

10   □ = 3, find ○ and △.

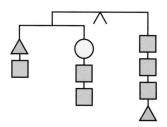

11   □ = 6, find △ and ○.

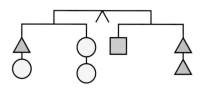

12   ○ = 5, find □ and △.

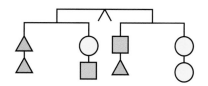

13   △ = 4, find ○ and □.

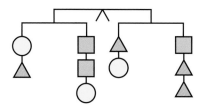

14   ○ = 8, find □ and △.

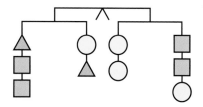

Need more practice with the rules of algebra?

1   Simplify

(a) $7m \times 4n$ (b) $4x \times 3y$ (c) $6n \times 4n$

(d) $5a \times 7b$ (e) $m \times n \times p$ (f) $9a \times 3a$

2   Pair off expressions below which are equivalent:

A $m + 3m + 4$ B $1 + 7m - 2m + 4$ C $5m + 9 - m - 5$

D $m + 4 + m - 2$ E $7 + 2m - 2 + 3m$ F $4m + 2 - 2m$

3   Gilbert says that the perimeter p of this shape is given by the formula

$$p = 6n + 6$$

Is Gilbert correct? Explain your answer fully.

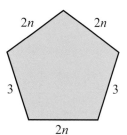

4    $m = 9p + 2$

     Find m when $p = 5$.

5    $y = 4n - 3m$

     Find y when $n = 6$ and $m = 2$.

6   Simplify by collecting like terms.

     (a) $6x + 3y + 2x + 5y$ (b) $7x + 4y - 3x - 2y$ (c) $8m + 4n - 3n + 2m$

     (d) $7m + 3n - 4m + n$ (e) $6m + 8 - 4m - 3$ (f) $4x + 7 + 2 - 3x$

7   A pair of glasses weighs m grams.
Write down an expression for
how much 7 pairs of glasses
will weigh.

8   There are x people on a bus. At the next bus stop, y people get off the bus
and 5 people get on the bus.
Write down an expression for how many people are now on the bus.

9   $p = 6(2a + 5)$ Harriet works out that $p = 15$ when $a = 2$.
                      Is Harriet correct? Explain your answer fully.

Extension questions with the rules of algebra

In questions 1 to 12 write down each statement and say whether it is 'true' or 'false' for all
values of the symbols used.

> If you are not sure, try different values for the letter

1   $x + x + x = 3x$

2   $xw = wx$

3   $m \times m = 2m$

4   $m + n = n + m$

5   $y \times y = y^2$

6   $a - b = b - a$

7   $a \times 5 = 5a$

8   $\dfrac{x}{2} = \dfrac{2}{x}$

9   $a \times a \times a = 3a$

10   $a \div 3 = 3 \div a$

11   $\dfrac{1}{2}$ of $b = \dfrac{b}{2}$

12   $a^2 = 2a$

13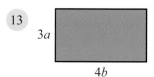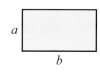

$3a$ a

$4b$ b

Write down an expression for the sum of the areas of the two rectangles opposite.

14 Robin says that $5mn - 2nm + 6nm$ is equal to $9mn$.
Is he correct? Explain your answer fully.

15 Draw and label a triangle whose perimeter p is given by the formula $p = 5x + 6$.

16 Which expression below is the odd one out?

P $5ab + 4ba - 3ab$ Q $4ab + 2ba$

R $3ab - 2ab + ba$ S $ba + 4ba + ab$

17 $y = m(m - c)$
Find y when $m = 7$ and $c = 3$.

18 $x = \dfrac{n + 6}{n}$
Find x when $n = 3$.

19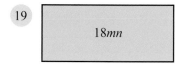

$18mn$

The area of this rectangle is $18mn$.
Sophie says the length of the rectangle is $6m$ and the width is $3n$. Is Sophie *definitely* correct?
Explain your answer fully.

20 Simplify

(a) $5mn + 7 - 2nm$ (b) $3ab + 4a - ba + 2a$ (c) $4m \times n \times 3m$

(d) $5ab + 3b + ba - 2b$ (e) $2n \times 4 \times 4n$ (f) $2n + 4mn + n - 3nm$

21 The front of a house has a wooden framework as shown.

(a) Write down an expression for the total length of wood used.

(b) What is the total length of wood used when $n = 2$ metres?

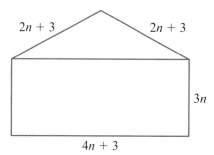

$2n + 3$ $2n + 3$

$3n$

$4n + 3$

CHECK YOURSELF ON SECTIONS 1.3 AND 1.4

1   Order of operations

Work out, without a calculator.

(a) $17 - 3 \times 4$ (b) $82 + 10 \div 2$ (c) $32 \div (12 - 8)$

(d) $(3 + 8) \times (9 - 4)$ (e) $25 \div (15 \div 3)$ (f) $5 + 5 \times 5$

2   Using a calculator for fractions

Use a calculator to work out

(a) $6.31 + \dfrac{3.68}{1.6}$ (b) $\dfrac{9.28 - 1.84}{0.02}$

3   Using brackets on a calculator

(a) $61.65 \div (8.27 - 1.42)$ (b) $31.8 \times (7.19 - 2.3) \times 4$

4   Using letters for numbers

(a) I start with a number x then multiply it by 4.
   Write down an expression for what I now have.

(b) Joe has n mints. He gives six mints to his sister.
   Write down an expression for how many mints Joe now has.

(c) 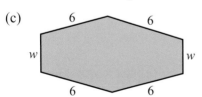   Write down an expression for the
   perimeter of this shape.

5   Simplifying algebraic expressions

Simplify the following expressions as far as possible

(a) $4m + 3n - 2m + 6n$ (b) $8y - y$

(c) $8p + 6 + 3p - 7p$ (d) $6a + 4b - 2b - 4a$

(e) $4m \times 7n$ (f) $6a \times 4b$

(g) $8p \times q \times r$ (h) $9n \times 9n$

(i) Which two rectangles below have the same area?

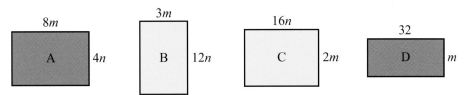

---

6   Substituting numbers into a formula

(a) The cost in pounds, C, for hiring a van is given by the formula $C = 3n + 45$, where n is the number of miles travelled. Find C when $n = 200$.

(b) $w = 6m - 3$ Find w when $m = 6$.

(c) $y = 3(7 - x)$ Find y when $x = 5$.

---

7   Tackling balance puzzles

(a) Find ▢ if ◯ = 12.

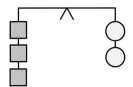

(b) Find ▢ and ◯ if △ = 6.

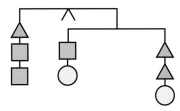

1.5 Negative numbers

In section 1.5 you will learn how to:

- compare negative numbers
- add and subtract negative numbers
- multiply and divide negative numbers.

Comparing negative numbers

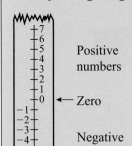

Positive numbers

← Zero

Negative numbers

- All numbers above zero are positive numbers.
- Zero is not positive or negative.
- All numbers below zero are negative numbers.

- Temperatures are given in degrees Celsius (°C)
- Water freezes at 0°C.

Exercise 1M

1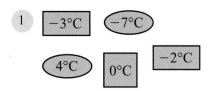

(a) Which of these temperatures is the hottest?

(b) Which of these temperatures is the coldest?

(c) Which temperatures are below freezing?

2 Copy and complete the table below.

Temperature °C	Change °C	New temperature °C
7	falls by 9	
−3	rises by 6	
−8	rises by 2	
−10	falls by 2	
12	falls by 15	

3 The graph shows the temperatures for one day in Greenland.

(a) What was the temperature at 6 pm?

(b) What was the temperature at 9 am?

(c) What was the lowest temperature recorded?

(d) At what times was it −12°C?

(e) By how many degrees did the temperature go up between 6 am and 6 pm?

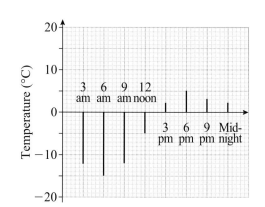

4   Write down each statement with either $>$ or $<$ in place of the box.

(a) $-5\ \square\ -4$ (b) $0\ \square\ -2$ (c) $-3\ \square\ -6$

5   $-10\ -9\ -8\ -7\ -6\ -5\ -4\ -3\ -2\ -1\ 0\ 1\ 2\ 3\ 4\ 5\ 6\ 7\ 8\ 9\ 10$

Find the difference between

(a) -4 and 2 (b) -8 and -3 (c) 5 and -2

(d) -7 and 0 (e) -6 and 6 (f) -9 and -1

6   Find the difference between the two lowest numbers in the list below.

| -4 | -7 | 1 | -3 | 2 | -5 | 6 | -9 | 8 | -1 |

7   What number is exactly half way between -22 and 8?

8   The temperature is $-6°C$. It rises by $5°C$. Toni counts up on her fingers and says the answer is $-2°C$. This is not correct. Explain what mistake you think she has made.

9   The temperature in London is $-3°C$. It rises by $9°C$ then drops by $7°C$. What is the new temperature?

10   A diver is below the surface of the water at $-25\,m$. She dives a further $9\,m$ then rises $4\,m$. At what depth is she now?

11   The temperature drops $3°C$ every hour. At $4\,am$ the temperature is $-7°C$. What was the temperature at $2\,am$?

12   Write down these temperatures in order, coldest first.

$-3°C$ $0°C$ $-2°C$ $5°C$ $-5°C$ $-1°C$

13   Which statement is true, A or B?

A $-4.5 > -4$ B $-4.5 < -4$

Use the number line 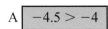 to explain your answer.

$-6\quad -5\quad -4\quad -3\quad -2$

14   The heights of places on a map are always measured in relation to sea level. For example a hill marked $510\,m$ is $510\,m$ above sea level.

(a) Think of something which could be at a height of $-20\,m$

(b) Some places in Holland are at a height of $-3\,m$.
    What problems does this cause and what do the people do about it?

Adding and subtracting negative numbers

For adding and subtracting with negative numbers a number line is very useful.

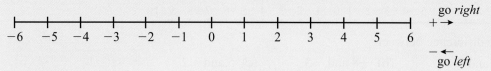

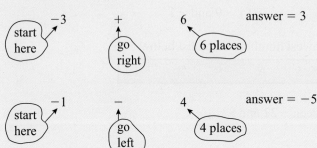

Exercise 2M

1   Use a number line to work out

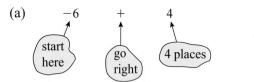

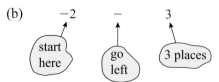

2   Use a number line to work out

(a) $4 - 7$ (b) $-3 + 5$ (c) $-1 - 3$ (d) $-5 + 8$

(e) $6 - 9$ (f) $-9 + 3$ (g) $6 - 12$ (h) $-7 + 6$

(i) $-2 - 6$ (j) $-2 + 8$ (k) $-8 + 8$ (l) $10 - 14$

3   Work out

(a) $-9 + 3$ (b) $5 - 11$ (c) $-4 - 4$ (d) $7 - 20$

(e) $-6 + 8$ (f) $7 - 3$ (g) $-6 - 5$ (h) $-10 + 6$

(i) $-3 + 3$ (j) $1 - 10$ (k) $-8 + 1$ (l) $-8 - 4$

4   Faith says that $-7 + 3$ is equal to -10.
Her teacher says that she is not correct.
Use a number line to explain why the teacher
says this.

5   If $-4 - 4 = -8$,
    what does $-4 - 4 - 4$ equal?

6   Copy and complete each empty box.

    (a) $-3 + \boxed{} = 9$ (b) $-7 + \boxed{} = 0$ (c) $-6 - \boxed{} = -7$

    (d) $-5 - \boxed{} = -9$ (e) $-10 + \boxed{} = 0$ (f) $3 - \boxed{} = -12$

    (g) $-7 + \boxed{} = 1$ (h) $-4 - 1 + \boxed{} = -2$ (i) $30 - \boxed{} = -30$

    (j) $-6 - \boxed{} = -20$ (k) $-60 + \boxed{} = -40$ (l) $5 - 7 - \boxed{} = -4$

7   Work out
    $$-4 + 1 - 6 - 3 + 2 + 5 - 3$$

8   Which calculation below gives the largest answer?

    A $\boxed{-5 + 2}$ B $\boxed{-3 - 2}$ C $\boxed{-4 + 2}$

9   Work out
    $$-7 + 3 + 1 - 4 - 2 + 3$$

10 The sum of the numbers on the cards below is -5.
    What is the missing number on the cards?

    $\boxed{-5}$ $\boxed{4}$ $\boxed{?}$ $\boxed{1}$ $\boxed{-3}$ $\boxed{2}$

In the sequence of subtractions on the right the numbers in column A go down by one each time. The numbers in column B increase by one each time.

Continue the sequence downwards:

We see that $8 - (-3)$ becomes $8 + 3$.

This always applies when subtracting negative numbers. It is possible to replace *two* signs next to each other by *one* sign as follows:

$+$	$+$	$=$	$+$
$-$	$-$	$=$	$+$
$-$	$+$	$=$	$-$
$+$	$-$	$=$	$-$

$$\begin{array}{c} \quad A \quad B \\ \quad \downarrow \quad \downarrow \\ 8 - (+3) = \ 5 \\ 8 - (+2) = \ 6 \\ 8 - (+1) = \ 7 \\ 8 - \ (0) \ = \ 8 \\ 8 - (-1) = \ 9 \\ 8 - (-2) = 10 \\ 8 - (-3) = 11 \end{array}$$

Remember: 'same signs: $+$'
          'different signs: $-$'

When two signs next to each other have been replaced by one sign in this way, the calculation is completed using the number line as before.

(a) $-3 + (-5)$
    $= -3 - 5$
    $= -8$

(b) $6 + (-12)$
    $= 6 - 12$
    $= -6$

(c) $4 - (-3)$
    $= 4 + 3$
    $= 7$

(d) $5 - (-2) + (-6)$
    $= 5 + 2 - 6$
    $= 1$

Exercise 3M

1   Work out
    (a) $7 + (-3)$ (b) $9 - (-2)$ (c) $4 - 9$ (d) $-5 + 2$
    (e) $-4 + (-5)$ (f) $-8 + (-3)$ (g) $10 - 12$ (h) $6 - (-4)$
    (i) $12 - (-4)$ (j) $-6 + (-6)$ (k) $-4 - (-4)$ (l) $-5 + (-6)$

2   Work out
    (a) $8 + (-7)$ (b) $-5 + (-1)$ (c) $-2 - (-3)$ (d) $-9 - (-9)$
    (e) $8 - 12$ (f) $6 + (-9)$ (g) $-4 - (-3)$ (h) $3 + (-3)$
    (i) $-7 - 5$ (j) $6 + (-13)$ (k) $-5 - (-6)$ (l) $3 + (-10)$

3   What is the missing number for each box below?
    (a) $\square - (-3) = 7$ (b) $\square + (-4) = 6$ (c) $3 + \square = 1$
    (d) $4 - \square = 8$ (e) $\square - 6 = -8$ (f) $8 + \square = -1$

4   Copy and complete each number wall below. The number in each box is found by adding the two numbers below it.

    (a)   (b)

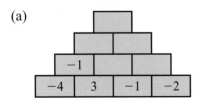
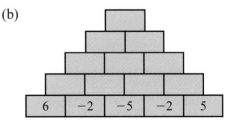

5   Julia says that $-8 - (-2) = -8 + 2 = -10$
    Aidan says that $-8 - (-2) = -8 - 2 = -6$
    Who has a completely correct method and answer ?
    Explain clearly how you decided.

6   Write down whether each statement below is true or false
    (a) $4 + (-6) = -2$ (b) $8 - (-2) = 6$ (c) $-7 - 2 = -9$
    (d) $8 - (-4) = 12$ (e) $5 + (-5) = -10$ (f) $2 - (-2) = 0$
    (g) $16 + (-3) = 13$ (h) $10 + (-3) = 13$ (i) $-6 - (-8) = -14$

7 Work out

$$-9 - (-5) - 2 + (-3) - (-1)$$

Multiplying and dividing negative numbers

A	B
↓	↓

$5 \times 3 = 15$
$5 \times 2 = 10$
$5 \times 1 = 5$
$5 \times 0 = 0$

$5 \times -1 = -5$
$5 \times -2 = -10$
$5 \times -3 = -15$

In the sequence of multiplications shown, the numbers in column A go down by one each time. The numbers in column B go down by five each time.

C	D
↓	↓

$-3 \times 3 = -9$
$-3 \times 2 = -6$
$-3 \times 1 = -3$
$-3 \times 0 = 0$

$-3 \times -1 = 3$
$-3 \times -2 = 6$
$-3 \times -3 = 9$

In this sequence the numbers in column C go down by one each time.

The numbers in column D *increase* by 3 each time.

We see that:

> When a positive number is multiplied by the negative number the answer is negative.

We see that:

> When two negative numbers are multiplied together the answer is positive.

> For division, the rules are the same as for multiplication.

$-4 \times (-6) = 24$
$40 \div (-4) = -10$
$(-3) \times 15 = -45$

$7 \times (-3) = -21$
$-60 \div (-20) = 3$
$(-12) \div (-1) \times (5) = 60$

$-15 \div 3 = -5$
$(-2) \times (-3) \times (-2) = -12$
$(-7) \times (-8) = 56$

Exercise 4M

Work out

1 (a) $4 \times (-2)$ (b) $5 \times (-4)$ (c) -3×4 (d) $-2 \times (-3)$
(e) -6×3 (f) $8 \times (-2)$ (g) $-5 \times (-6)$ (h) -1×7
(i) -9×4 (j) $5 \times (-7)$ (k) $-7 \times (-7)$ (l) -6×-9

2 (a) $12 \div (-3)$ (b) $20 \div (-4)$ (c) $-8 \div 2$ (d) $-12 \div (-4)$
(e) $-18 \div (-6)$ (f) $25 \div (-5)$ (g) $-15 \div 3$ (h) $-30 \div (-10)$

3
(a) $-40 \div 20$ (b) $8 \times (-6)$ (c) $-4 \times (-7)$ (d) $4 \times (-8)$

(e) $-50 \div (-25)$ (f) $24 \div (-8)$ (g) $10 \times (-9)$ (h) $-63 \div (-7)$

4 Write down two negative numbers which multiply together to make 8.
Are there any other pairs of negative numbers which will multiply together to make 8?
Write them down.

5 Copy and complete the squares below:

(a)

$\times$	-3	6	-1	4
5	-15			
-2				
7				
-5				

(b)

$\times$	-4	-7	2	0	-8	5
3	-12					
-9						
6						
-4						
-6						
-1						

6 Rosa multiplies -6 by -9 and Jade divides 108 by -2.
They add their two answers together. What is the final answer?

7 Find two numbers that multiply to give -12 and add together to make -4.

8 Work out

(a) $(-2) \times (-4) \times (-1)$ (b) $3 \times (-5) \times (-2)$ (c) $(-3)^2$

(d) $(-6)^2$ (e) $4 \times (-2) \times 4$ (f) $(-5) \times (-2) \times (-4)$

(g) $(-10)^2$ (h) $(-1)^2$

9 What is the missing number for each box below?

(a) $-4 \times \square = -28$ (b) $-6 \times \square = 42$ (c) $32 \div \square = -16$

(d) $-45 \div \square = 5$ (e) $\square \div (-10) = 5$ (f) $\square \div (-9) = -8$

Need more practice with negative numbers?

1 Which number gives the greater answer? $-7 + 4$ or $-7 - 4$

2 For each statement below, write true or false.

(a) $-6 < -5$ (b) $-4 > -7$ (c) $-2 > -4$

3 In a test there are $+2$ marks for a correct answer and -1 mark for an incorrect answer. Find the total marks in the tests below:

Test A ✓, ✓, ✗, ✗, ✗, ✓, ✓, ✗, ✓, ✗

Test B ✗, ✗, ✓, ✓, ✗, ✓, ✗, ✗, ✗, ✗

4 Work out
   (a) $8 + (-4)$ (b) $-9 - 2$ (c) $-7 - (-3)$ (d) $5 + (-9)$
   (e) $4 - (-2)$ (f) $-6 - 3$ (g) $-1 - 7$ (h) $-4 - (-3)$

5 Write down these temperatures in order, coldest first.
   (a) $5°C$ $-4°C$ $-9°C$ $-2°C$ $6°C$ $-7°C$
   (b) $-4°C$ $5°C$ $-13°C$ $23°C$ $-5°C$ $4°C$
   (c) $-5°C$ $14°C$ $3°C$ $-2°C$ $-7°C$ $5°C$

6 Work out
   (a) $4 \div (-2)$ (b) $2 \times (-9)$ (c) $-8 \times (-3)$ (d) -6×5
   (e) $-40 \div (-8)$ (f) $-63 \div 7$ (g) -7×8 (h) $-7 \times (-3)$

7 The acceleration a of a small vehicle is given by the formula $a = 5t + 3$ where t is the time taken.
   Find the value of a when   (a) $t = -2$ (b) $t = -6$ (c) $t = -10$.

8 Ravi says the answer to $4 \times (-3)$ is greater than the answer to $-7 - 6$.
   Is he correct? Explain your answer fully.

9 Work out
      $-7 \times (-4) \div (-2)$

10 What number when subtracted from -6 gives -9?

Extension questions with negative numbers

1 What is the missing number for each box below?
   (a) $-56 \div \square = 8$ (b) $9 \times \square = -36$ (c) $-48 \div \square = -8$
   (d) $100 \div \square = -10$ (e) $\square \div 4 = -8$ (f) $\square \times (-6) = 54$

2 Work out the calculation in each box and put the answers in order of size, smallest first, to make a word.

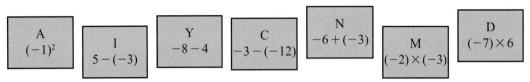

| A $(-1)^2$ | I $5-(-3)$ | Y $-8-4$ | C $-3-(-12)$ | N $-6+(-3)$ | M $(-2)\times(-3)$ | D $(-7)\times 6$ |

3 Complete the chain, filling in the empty boxes.

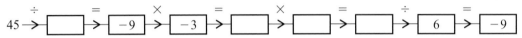

$45 \xrightarrow{\div} \boxed{} \xrightarrow{=} \boxed{-9} \xrightarrow{\times} \boxed{-3} \xrightarrow{=} \boxed{} \xrightarrow{\times} \boxed{} \xrightarrow{=} \boxed{} \xrightarrow{\div} \boxed{6} \xrightarrow{=} \boxed{-9}$

4 Work out

$$-3 + 4 \times 2 - 6 \div 3$$

5 Copy and complete the squares below:

(a)

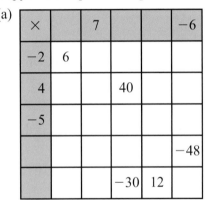

×		7			−6
−2	6				
4			40		
−5					
					−48
			−30	12	

(b)

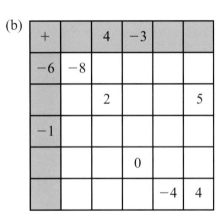

+		4	−3		
−6	−8				
		2			5
−1					
			0		
				−4	4

CHECK YOURSELF ON SECTION 1.5

1 Comparing negative numbers

(a) Write these temperatures in order, hottest first.

$$-8°C, \qquad 1°C, \qquad -4°C, \qquad -3°C, \qquad 2°C, \qquad -9°C$$

(b) Which number is larger $\boxed{-5}$ or $\boxed{-6}$?

2 Adding and subtracting negative numbers

Work out

(a) $-6 + 2$ (b) $-3 - 4$ (c) $2 + (-5)$ (d) $-8 - (-6)$

3   Multiplying and dividing negative numbers

Work out

(a) $3 \times (-5)$ (b) $-16 \div (-2)$ (c) $-30 \div 10$ (d) $-8 \times (-4)$

 Spot the mistakes 2 ✗

Algebra rules and negative numbers

Work through each question below and *explain clearly* what mistakes have been made.
Beware – some questions are correctly done.

1   $3 + 2m = 5m$

2   $4mn + 6n - 4n - 2nm = 2mn + 2n$

3   $-5 + 3 = -8$

4   $-4 \times (-4) = -16$

5   $4m \times 7m = 28m$

6   $2n + 6n + 4 - n = 7n + 4$

7   $v = u + 4t$ Louise uses $u = 6$ and $t = 3$ to
get the answer $v = 6 + 43 = 49$.

8   The formula $S = 180(n - 2)$ gives the sum
of the angles in a polygon with n sides.
George finds the value of S when $n = 6$.
He writes $S = 180(6 - 2) = 180 \times 4 = 720$.

9   Arjun works out $-3 \times 4 - 5$ and gets the answer -7.

10   Tamsin completes a number wall where
the number in each box is found by
adding the two numbers below it.

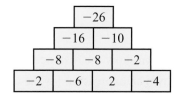

1.6 Applying mathematics 1

In section 1.6 you will apply maths in a variety
of situations.

1   Write down these calculations and find the missing digits.

(a)   5 ☐ 5
    + 3 2 ☐
    ─────────
      9 0 1

(b)   3 ☐ 9
    + 5 8 ☐
    ─────────
    ☐ 5 3

(c)   ☐ 1 ☐
    + 5 ☐ 4
    ─────────
      7 5 0

2 How many minutes are there from 06.40 to 08.05?

3 Write down an expression for the
   perimeter of each rectangle shown
   opposite then work out the difference
   between the two perimeters.

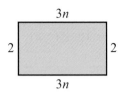

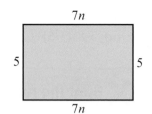

4 Carlton thinks of a number and subtracts -4 from it.
   The answer is 6. What number did Carlton think of?

5

   An artist won the Turner prize by 'carefully' walking
   across his canvas with bare feet. Unfortunately his prize
   winning piece was thrown in the bin by the cleaner at
   his studio.

   The painting was on sale for £620 000. The cleaner
   offered to make up for his mistake by paying the artist
   £20 per week. How many years would it take to pay the
   full amount?

6 $\dfrac{7}{10} \times \dfrac{4}{10} = \dfrac{28}{100}$ so $0.7 \times 0.4 = 0.28$

   Use fractions to explain why $0.7 \times 0.04 = 0.028$

7

   The letters above show the distances (in metres) between the places indicated.
   (a) Write down an expression for the total distance from Home to the Friend's house.
   (b) Rowena cycles from Home to the Shop then to the Cinema then towards the Friend's
       house. Write down an expression for the total distance she has cycled when she is still
       300 m short of the Friend's house.

8 A book has 658 pages. Gina has read 42 pages
   in 3 days. At that rate how long will it take her
   to read the whole book?

9 Ronnie has the same number of 10p and 20p coins.
   The total value of the coins is £6.
   How many of each coin does he have?

10 A shopkeeper bought 30 pens at £3 each and a number of books costing £8 each.
    In all the shopkeeper spent £450. How many books did the shopkeeper buy?

UNIT 1   MIXED REVIEW

Part one

Copy and complete by writing the missing digits in the boxes.

1 (a) $\square$0 − 4$\square$ = 7

   (b) 4$\square$ − $\square$8 = 8

   (c) $\square$6 + 5$\square$ = 138

   (d)
   ```
        □ 1 □
     −  2 □ 3
     ─────────
        6   3
   ```

   (e)
   ```
        6 □ 1
     −  □ 7 □
     ─────────
        4 1 3
   ```

   (f)
   ```
        4 □ 4
     −  □ 2 □
     ─────────
        3 4 5
   ```

2 (a)
   ```
          □ 7
     ×      2
     ─────────
        1 3 □
   ```

   (b)
   ```
          □ 6
     ×      4
     ─────────
        3 4 □
   ```

   (c)
   ```
          □ 7
     ×      6
     ─────────
        3 4 □
   ```

   (d)
   ```
          □ 9
     ×      3
     ─────────
        1 1 □
   ```

   (e)
   ```
        □ □ 9
     ×      6
     ─────────
      1 4 3 □
   ```

   (f)
   ```
        □ □ 3
     ×      4
     ─────────
      2 1 3 □
   ```

3 (a)
   ```
          5 3
     3) 1 □ 9
   ```

   (b)
   ```
          5 7
     4) 2 □ 8
   ```

   (c)
   ```
          9 4
     6) 5 □ 4
   ```

   (d)
   ```
          6 5
     7) 4 5 □
   ```

   (e)
   ```
          6 3
     7) □ 4 1
   ```

   (f)
   ```
          5 4
     9) 4 □ 6
   ```

4 Write down an expression for the perimeter of each shape.

   (a)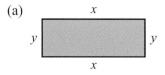

   (b)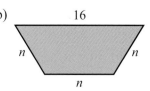

5   Draw a shape with a perimeter of $m + 2n$.

6   Solve the following balance puzzle, writing your answer $x = \ldots$

7   The temperature in Manchester one day is 1°C.
During the night it drops by 5°C. What is the new temperature?

8   Look at the following numbers …

$$-8, \quad 3, \quad 0, \quad -3, \quad 6$$

(a) Write down the positive numbers.

(b) Write down the negative numbers.

(c) Write the numbers in order, lowest to highest.

(d) Write down the difference between the highest and lowest numbers.

9   Charlie uses his calculator to work out the answer to $\dfrac{n - 1.6}{0.5}$. The answer is 14.

Find the value of n.

10   Copy and complete the cross number

Clues across	Clues down
1. $57 \div 3$	**1.** $203 - 86$
3. $2 \times 3 \times 4$	**2.** $7 \times 2 \times 7$
5. $(17 - 8) \times 2$	**3.** $(1000 \div 4) + 4$
6. $448 \div 8$	**4.** $7 \times 7 - 3$
7. $49 + 35$	**7.** $445 \div 5$
8. $87 - 18$	**8.** $3 \times 4 \times 5$
10. $(10 \times 10) - 10$	**9.** 11×4
11. $47 + 47$	

1	2		3	4
5			6	
		7		
	8			9
10			11	

Part two

1   There are 32 biscuits in a packet and there are 7 packets. How many biscuits are there?

2   Copy and complete by finding the missing number.

(a) $5 \times \square - 6 = 24$ (b) $30 - 4 \times \square = 2$ (c) $36 \div \square + 7 = 11$

(d) $(12 - \square) \times 4 = 20$ (e) $32 - (12 - \square) = 28$ (f) $13 - \square \div 2 = 7$

3 Write the numbers below in order of size, smallest first.

     0.71, 0.605, 0.65, 0.7

4 Evaluate, using a calculator

  (a) $\dfrac{11.39}{1.7} - 2.63$ (b) $3.2 + \dfrac{4.704}{3.36}$ (c) $\dfrac{28.1 + 0.55}{1.6 + 0.31}$

  (d) $25 - (8.2 \times 1.75)$ (e) $4.956 \div (1.5 - 0.91)$ (f) $\dfrac{14.24}{9.17 - 4.72}$

5 Copy and complete the multiplication squares

	8		
5	35		40
	8	18	
		54	48
63			

	9			
	15		18	
7		63		28
	10			
		40		20
		72	48	

6 Here are six algebra cards.

  (a) Add the expressions on card B and card E.

  (b) Which two cards always have the same value?

  (c) Which card has the largest value when $n = 3$.

  (d) Add the expressions on all six cards.

A $2n + 1$ B $4n$ C $3n$

D $n + 2n$ E $2n + 3$

F $4 - n$

7

London	$-5°C$
Paris	$-3°C$
Rome	$+1°C$
Melbourne	$+11°C$
New York	$-8°C$

  (a) From the table above, what is the difference in temperature between Rome and London?

  (b) At 12:00 the temperature in New York has risen by 5°C. What is the temperature in New York at 12:00?

8 Simplify:

  (a) $5w + w + 3y + 2w$ (b) $6p + 2q - p + 4q$ (c) $3m + 5 - m - 3$

9 Write down an expression for each of the following:

    (a) I start with n, double it and then subtract 8.

    (b) I start with p, treble it and then add r.

10 Find the missing digits.

(a)
$$\begin{array}{r} 3\,.\,2\,\square \\ +\ 1\,.\,\square\,4 \\ \hline \square\,.\,0\ \ 1 \end{array}$$

(b)
$$\begin{array}{r} \square\,.\,5\ \ 5 \\ +\ 0\,.\,\square\,3 \\ \hline 5\,.\,1\ \ \square \end{array}$$

(c)
$$\begin{array}{r} 3\,.\,6\ \ \square \\ -\ \square\,.\,\square\,7 \\ \hline 2\,.\,0\ \ 7 \end{array}$$

11 You are looking for a mystery number.
Use the clues to find it.

- the sum of the digits is 10
- the number reads the same forwards as backwards
- the number is less than 2000
- the number has no zeros
- the number has four digits

12 In number walls each brick is made by adding the two bricks underneath it.

Fill in the missing expressions on these walls.

(a)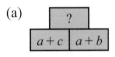

(b)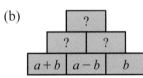

(c)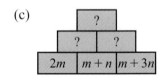

13 The cost in pounds C, of hiring a cement mixer is given by the formula $C = 18n + 53$, where n is the number of days the cement mixer is hired for.

Find C when the cement mixer is hired for 3 days.

14 Copy and complete each chain.

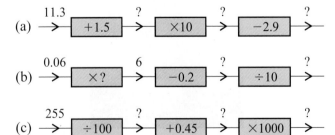

15 If $y = 3x - c$, find the value of y when $x = 3$ and $c = -8$.

Puzzles and Problems 1

1. Arrange the digits 1, 2, 3 and 4, one into each box,
so that the answer is as large as possible. You may use a calculator.

□□
×□□
───────

or

□□□
× □
───────

2. Arrange the digits 1, 2, 3, 4 and 5, one into each box, so that the answer
is as large as possible.

□□□
× □□
───────

or

□□□□
×   □
───────

3. What is the largest number which can be found with a single
multiplication using each of the digits 1, 2, 3, 4, 5 and 6 once only?

4. Here are some black and white beads in a pattern

(a) What colour is the 20th bead?
(b) What colour is the 71st bead?
(c) What position in the line is the 12th black bead?
(d) What position in the line is the 12th white bead?

5. What is the largest possible number of people in a room if
no two people have a birthday in the same month?

6. Two different numbers on this section of a till receipt are
obscured by food stains. What are the two numbers?

tapes at £ ⬭.99 : £87.89

7. The letters A, B, C, D, E appear once in every row, every
column and each main diagonal of the square. Copy the
square and fill in the missing letters.

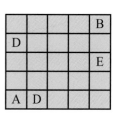

8 King Henry has 9 coins which look identical but in fact one of them is an underweight fake. Describe how he could discover the fake using just *two* weighings on an ordinary balance.

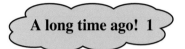
A long time ago! 1

The Four Colour Theorem

If you need to colour the areas on a map (in geography, history, etc), it should be possible to use no more than 4 colours. At no boundary between the two areas must the same colour be used for both areas.

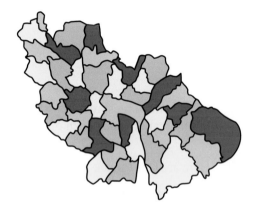

You may have two areas of the same colour meeting at a single point if necessary. A gentleman called August Ferdinand Möbius first wrote about this problem in the nineteenth century.

Exercise

Make a rough copy of each map below and try to colour each section using 4 colours only. The colour in one section must not be the same as that in any section next to it.

1

2
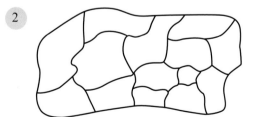

3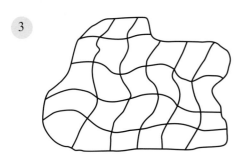

4 Have you managed with 4 colours only so far? Now draw your own map and see if no more than 4 colours are needed to fill it in.

At last! This theorem was finally proved to be correct late in the twentieth century by using a computer programme.

Mental Arithmetic Practice 1

There are two sets of mental arithmetic questions in this section. Ideally a teacher will read out each question twice, with pupils' books closed. Each test of 20 questions should take about 20 minutes.

Test 1

1 What is thirty multiplied by ten?

2 What is forty-two divided by seven?

3 Write the number eight thousand and forty-three in figures.

4 Write 0.25 as a fraction.

5 Add together seven, nine and fifteen.

6 What number should you subtract from seventy-three to get the answer nineteen?

7 How many thirds make up three whole ones?

8 How many centimetres are equal to eighty millimetres?

9 What is four point eight multiplied by ten?

10 What is four squared?

11 If seventy per cent of the children in a class are girls, what percentage of the class are boys?

12 Write a factor of 16 which is greater than 5.

13 The side of a square is six metres. What is the area of the square?

14 Write down any multiple of seven.

15 At midnight the temperature is minus four degrees celsius. By midday the temperature rises eighteen degrees. What is the temperature at midday?

16 Write down the number that is halfway between twelve and eighteen.

17 A train leaves Derby at eight ten. It arrives at Birmingham fifty-five minutes later. At what time does it arrive at Birmingham?

18 Ten per cent of a number is twenty-eight. What is the number?

19 What is the obtuse angle between clock hands showing four o'clock?

20 How much change from five pounds would you get after spending three pounds and forty-two pence?

Test 2

1   What is eight multiplied by seven?

2   Write the number five thousand and twenty-seven in figures.

3   Write the number that is sixteen less than two hundred.

4   What is double sixteen?

5   Add together eight, fifteen and seven.

6   Write three-quarters as a decimal.

7   How many twenty pence coins make two pounds and eighty pence?

8   Change fifteen centimetres into millimetres.

9   Round three hundred and sixty-six to the nearest ten.

10   What is three hundred and forty divided by one hundred?

11   One quarter of a number is seven. What is the number?

12   What number is nine squared?

13   If twenty-three per cent of the people in a cinema wear glasses, what percentage of the people do not wear glasses?

14   What number is halfway between four and eleven?

15   What is three-fifths of one hundred?

16   The temperature in Newcastle was minus three degrees. The temperature in Madrid was nineteen degrees warmer. What was the temperature in Madrid?

17   Write three tenths as a decimal number.

18   Ali buys a pen for £1.25 and a drink for 53p. How much change will Ali receive from a five pound note?

19   Two angles in a triangle are seventy-four degrees and sixty degrees. How large is the third angle?

20   A television programme starts at twenty minutes to six and lasts forty-five minutes. At what time does the programme finish?

UNIT 2

2.1 Fractions

In section 2.1 you will:
- find equivalent fractions
- find a fraction of a number
- multiply fractions
- add and subtract fractions

Equivalent fractions

When the numerator and denominator are changed into smaller numbers, we say the fraction is *cancelled down* by dividing the numerator and denominator by the same number.

(a) Cancel $\dfrac{9}{21}$

$$\frac{9}{21} = \frac{3}{7}$$

(b) Cancel $\dfrac{10}{15}$

$$\frac{10}{15} = \frac{2}{3}$$

(c) Find the missing number to make these fractions equivalent

$$\frac{3}{8} = \frac{\square}{32}$$

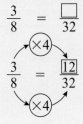

$$\frac{3}{8} = \frac{\boxed{12}}{32}$$

Exercise 1M

1. Copy each diagram below then shade them in to show that the given fractions are equivalent.

(a)

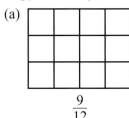

$$\frac{9}{12}$$

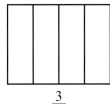

$$\frac{3}{4}$$

(b)

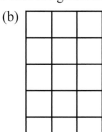

$$\frac{5}{15}$$

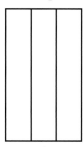

$$\frac{1}{3}$$

2 Cancel down each fraction to its simplest terms.

(a) $\dfrac{6}{10}$ (b) $\dfrac{10}{30}$ (c) $\dfrac{9}{15}$ (d) $\dfrac{7}{35}$ (e) $\dfrac{24}{30}$

(f) $\dfrac{28}{36}$ (g) $\dfrac{20}{30}$ (h) $\dfrac{14}{21}$ (i) $\dfrac{12}{18}$ (j) $\dfrac{27}{45}$

(k) $\dfrac{35}{45}$ (l) $\dfrac{20}{24}$ (m) $\dfrac{40}{50}$ (n) $\dfrac{18}{63}$ (o) $\dfrac{33}{77}$

(p) $\dfrac{45}{60}$ (q) $\dfrac{54}{81}$ (r) $\dfrac{18}{72}$ (s) $\dfrac{56}{72}$ (t) $\dfrac{32}{48}$

(u) $\dfrac{75}{100}$ (v) $\dfrac{36}{63}$ (w) $\dfrac{36}{96}$ (x) $\dfrac{72}{108}$ (y) $\dfrac{75}{135}$

3 Jo says that the fraction $\dfrac{63}{81}$ is equivalent to $\dfrac{7}{9}$. Is this correct? Explain your answer clearly.

4 Find the missing number to make these fractions equivalent.

(a) $\dfrac{3}{4} = \dfrac{\square}{16}$ (b) $\dfrac{1}{5} = \dfrac{\square}{20}$ (c) $\dfrac{5}{6} = \dfrac{\square}{12}$ (d) $\dfrac{8}{10} = \dfrac{\square}{5}$

(e) $\dfrac{5}{9} = \dfrac{\square}{27}$ (f) $\dfrac{4}{7} = \dfrac{\square}{35}$ (g) $\dfrac{3}{8} = \dfrac{\square}{24}$ (h) $\dfrac{12}{20} = \dfrac{\square}{60}$

(i) $\dfrac{7}{10} = \dfrac{\square}{30}$ (j) $\dfrac{5}{8} = \dfrac{25}{\square}$ (k) $\dfrac{4}{11} = \dfrac{20}{\square}$ (l) $\dfrac{16}{20} = \dfrac{48}{\square}$

(m) $\dfrac{20}{25} = \dfrac{4}{\square}$ (n) $\dfrac{18}{30} = \dfrac{\square}{5}$ (o) $\dfrac{8}{18} = \dfrac{4}{\square}$ (p) $\dfrac{28}{40} = \dfrac{7}{\square}$

5 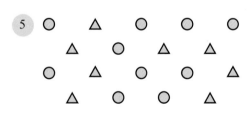 Cameron says that $\frac{5}{9}$ of the shapes opposite are circles. Anna says that $\frac{10}{18}$ of the shapes are circles. Who is correct?

6 Change each fraction below so that the denominator is 24 and the fraction is equivalent.

   $\dfrac{5}{6}$ Write down which fraction is the largest.

7   In each part of this question, one fraction is not equivalent to the others.
Write down the fraction which is the odd one out.

(a) $\dfrac{4}{6}$ $\dfrac{6}{10}$ $\dfrac{12}{18}$ $\dfrac{2}{3}$ $\dfrac{10}{15}$

(b) $\dfrac{15}{18}$ $\dfrac{35}{42}$ $\dfrac{50}{60}$ $\dfrac{40}{48}$ $\dfrac{32}{40}$

8   Write down four fractions that are equivalent to $\frac{2}{3}$.

Exercise 2M

Example: In the table given below, pick out all the letters above the fractions which are equivalent to one half $\left(\frac{1}{2}\right)$.

C	Q	E	A	Y	P	R	N	H	F	letters
$\frac{5}{10}$	$\frac{3}{4}$	$\frac{2}{4}$	$\frac{21}{42}$	$\frac{1}{3}$	$\frac{3}{5}$	$\frac{6}{12}$	$\frac{3}{6}$	$\frac{4}{7}$	$\frac{5}{10}$	fractions

The letters are   C,   E,   A,   R,   N,   F

because ... $\frac{5}{10}, \frac{2}{4}, \frac{21}{42}, \frac{6}{12}, \frac{3}{6}, \frac{5}{10}$ are all the same as $\frac{1}{2}$.

Now rearrange the letters to make the name of a country,

       C,   E,   A,   R,   N,   F $\longrightarrow$ FRANCE

In the questions below, find the fractions in the table which are equivalent to the given fraction.
Rearrange the letters to make a word using the clue.

1   $\left(\frac{1}{10}, \text{drink}\right)$

R	E	F	E	F	T	O	W	C	A
$\frac{2}{20}$	$\frac{5}{60}$	$\frac{9}{108}$	$\frac{5}{50}$	$\frac{12}{96}$	$\frac{3}{30}$	$\frac{4}{20}$	$\frac{10}{100}$	$\frac{6}{50}$	$\frac{7}{70}$

2   $\left(\frac{2}{3}, \text{country}\right)$

A	N	E	R	S	B	I	Z	Q	L
$\frac{4}{6}$	$\frac{9}{12}$	$\frac{14}{22}$	$\frac{60}{90}$	$\frac{16}{25}$	$\frac{8}{12}$	$\frac{22}{33}$	$\frac{20}{30}$	$\frac{32}{49}$	$\frac{12}{18}$

3   $\left(\frac{3}{5}, \text{sport}\right)$

T	G	U	F	O	Y	R	A	B	L
$\frac{18}{36}$	$\frac{36}{60}$	$\frac{27}{45}$	$\frac{30}{40}$	$\frac{20}{25}$	$\frac{12}{20}$	$\frac{9}{15}$	$\frac{12}{18}$	$\frac{6}{10}$	$\frac{18}{21}$

4   $\left(\frac{1}{3}, \text{city}\right)$

L	P	A	U	R	I	D	N	S	B
$\frac{3}{9}$	$\frac{2}{8}$	$\frac{5}{7}$	$\frac{4}{12}$	$\frac{7}{20}$	$\frac{6}{18}$	$\frac{8}{24}$	$\frac{10}{30}$	$\frac{3}{5}$	$\frac{5}{15}$

5   $\left(\frac{5}{9}, \text{clothing}\right)$

T	M	S	R	K	C	E	H	O	I
$\frac{100}{180}$	$\frac{21}{70}$	$\frac{20}{36}$	$\frac{35}{63}$	$\frac{18}{21}$	$\frac{40}{70}$	$\frac{24}{45}$	$\frac{45}{81}$	$\frac{140}{160}$	$\frac{15}{27}$

6   $\left(\frac{3}{4}, \text{fruit}\right)$

B	O	P	A	E	I	H	C	R	T
$\frac{6}{7}$	$\frac{12}{16}$	$\frac{33}{44}$	$\frac{6}{8}$	$\frac{6}{9}$	$\frac{30}{40}$	$\frac{18}{25}$	$\frac{15}{20}$	$\frac{36}{48}$	$\frac{9}{12}$

7 Now make up your own question like question ⑥ and test it on a friend.

8 Ask your teacher for card. Cut out 24 cards as shown. On each pair of cards write down two equivalent fractions.

Now play a game with 2, 3 or 4 players using these equivalent fraction cards.

How to play:

- Shuffle the cards, place them face down in a pattern of 6 rows by 4 columns.

- Decide who will go first.

- Each turn requires a player to turn over a pair of cards.

- If the pair of cards are equivalent, such as $\frac{1}{5}$ and $\frac{2}{10}$, the player keeps the pair. If the cards are not equivalent, turn the cards face down again.

- Try to remember which cards are where!

- If you find a pair you get another go. The player with the most pairs when no cards are left is the winner.

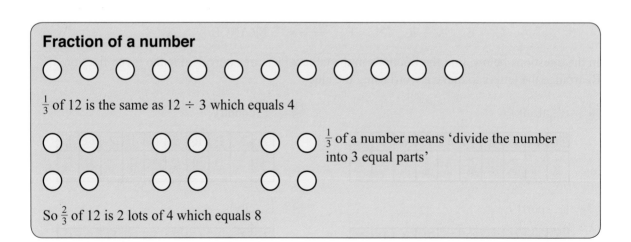

Fraction of a number

$\frac{1}{3}$ of 12 is the same as $12 \div 3$ which equals 4

$\frac{1}{3}$ of a number means 'divide the number into 3 equal parts'

So $\frac{2}{3}$ of 12 is 2 lots of 4 which equals 8

Exercise 3M

1 Work out   (a) $\frac{1}{5}$ of 35   (b) $\frac{4}{5}$ of 35

2 Work out   (a) $\frac{1}{8}$ of 72   (b) $\frac{3}{8}$ of 72

3 Work out

(a) $\frac{3}{4}$ of 20

(b) $\frac{5}{8}$ of 24

(c) $\frac{7}{10}$ of 90

(d) $\frac{2}{5}$ of 55

(e) $\frac{5}{6}$ of 42

(f) $\frac{4}{9}$ of 18

(g) $\frac{2}{3}$ of 48

(h) $\frac{5}{7}$ of 56

4 Mario has an order for 60 pizzas. If $\frac{5}{12}$ of his pizzas must be vegetarian, how many will be non-vegetarian?

5 A petrol tank in a car holds 56 litres when full. How much is in the tank when it is $\frac{3}{8}$ full?

6 Full marks in a science test were 80. How many marks did Hannah get if she got $\frac{9}{10}$ of full marks?

7 Is $\frac{2}{5}$ of £30 the same as $\frac{1}{5}$ of £60? Explain your answer fully.

8 Jocelyn has £42. She spends $\frac{1}{6}$ of the money on lunch and then buys a jacket with $\frac{4}{5}$ of the remaining money.

(a) How much does the jacket cost?

(b) How much money is left over for Jocelyn?

9 Here are calculations with letters. Put the answers in order of size, smallest first. Write down the letters to make a word.

R	A	P
$\frac{2}{7}$ of 49	$\frac{1}{11}$ of 165	$\frac{1}{3}$ of 27

M	Y	D	I
$\frac{4}{9}$ of 45	$\frac{3}{4}$ of 16	$\frac{5}{6}$ of 300	$\frac{5}{8}$ of 96

10 Felipe has 50 sweets. He gives $\frac{3}{10}$ of his sweets to his brother and $\frac{2}{5}$ of his sweets to his sister. How many more sweets does his sister have than his brother?

11 Explain clearly why $\frac{7}{8}$ of 40 is greater than $\frac{8}{9}$ of 36.

Exercise 3E

1 Work out

(a) $\frac{2}{3}$ of 45 kg

(b) $\frac{4}{5}$ of 90 cm

(c) $\frac{5}{9}$ of £108

(d) $\frac{4}{7}$ of £63

(e) $\frac{5}{8}$ of 240 kg

(f) $\frac{3}{20}$ of 160 m

(g) $\frac{5}{12}$ of 48 cm

(h) $\frac{8}{9}$ of 54 m

(i) $\frac{37}{100}$ of £400

2 A table is bought for £217 and sold at a car boot sale for $\frac{3}{7}$ of the original price.
   How much was the table sold for?

3 Jack has saved £125. He spends
   $\frac{2}{5}$ of this money. He then saves
   another £15. He now spends $\frac{5}{6}$
   of his money on a computer game.
   How much money does he have left?

4 Find each missing number below.

   (a) $\frac{3}{\square}$ of 30 = 18   (b) $\frac{\square}{3}$ of 15 = 10   (c) $\frac{3}{\square}$ of 40 = 12

   (d) $\frac{3}{\square}$ of 28 = 21   (e) $\frac{4}{5}$ of $\square$ = 16   (f) $\frac{7}{10}$ of $\square$ = 28

5 Tatiana eats half a pizza. Her mother then eats a quarter of what is left.
   What fraction of the whole pizza did her mother eat?

6 Work out each question below then put the questions in order of answer size, starting
   with the smallest.

$\frac{8}{15}$ of 105	$\frac{7}{12}$ of 156	$\frac{3}{25}$ of 225	$\frac{5}{9}$ of 153	$\frac{3}{7}$ of 84
A	B	C	D	E

7 $\frac{2}{5}$ of a number is 10. What is the number?

Multiplying fractions

The red shaded strip
is $\frac{1}{4}$ of the rectangle.

The black section is $\frac{1}{3}$ of $\frac{1}{4}$
of the rectangle.

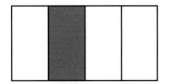
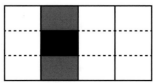

$\frac{1}{3}$ of $\frac{1}{4}$ = $\frac{1}{12}$

$\frac{1}{3}$ × $\frac{1}{4}$ = $\frac{1}{12}$

(a) $\dfrac{3}{7} \times \dfrac{4}{5} = \dfrac{12}{35}$ Multiply the numerators and multiply the denominators.

(b) $\dfrac{3}{4} \times \dfrac{1}{9} = \dfrac{\cancel{3}^{1}}{36_{12}} = \dfrac{1}{12}$ or $\dfrac{\cancel{3}^{1}}{4} \times \dfrac{1}{\cancel{9}_{3}} = \dfrac{1}{12}$

Multiply then cancel or cancel then multiply.

Exercise 4M

1. Copy the two diagrams opposite.

   Shade $\dfrac{1}{4}$ of the first rectangle then

   shade in the second rectangle to

   show that $\dfrac{1}{5} \times \dfrac{1}{4} = \dfrac{1}{20}$

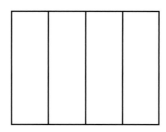 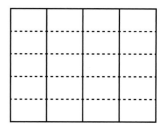

2. Work out

   (a) $\dfrac{3}{4} \times \dfrac{4}{7}$ (b) $\dfrac{5}{8} \times \dfrac{1}{9}$ (c) $\dfrac{2}{7} \times \dfrac{3}{5}$ (d) $\dfrac{7}{9} \times \dfrac{2}{3}$

   (e) $\dfrac{1}{4}$ of $\dfrac{1}{9}$ (f) $\dfrac{1}{10}$ of $\dfrac{1}{4}$ (g) $\dfrac{11}{20} \times \dfrac{3}{7}$ (h) $\dfrac{3}{4}$ of $\dfrac{1}{5}$

3. Hayley works out that $\dfrac{3}{4} \times \dfrac{2}{9} = \dfrac{6}{36} = \dfrac{1}{6}$ when cancelled.

   Ted cancels before multiplying so writes

   $\dfrac{{}^{1}\cancel{3}}{{}_{2}\cancel{4}} \times \dfrac{\cancel{2}^{1}}{\cancel{9}_{3}} = \dfrac{1}{6}$

   Both methods are correct. Use both methods to work out each question below.

   (a) $\dfrac{1}{5} \times \dfrac{10}{11}$ (b) $\dfrac{2}{3} \times \dfrac{3}{4}$ (c) $\dfrac{5}{6} \times \dfrac{4}{5}$ (d) $\dfrac{5}{9} \times \dfrac{6}{15}$

4. $\dfrac{8}{1}$ means $8 \div 1$ which equals 8 so $8 = \dfrac{8}{1}$

   This means that $7 = \dfrac{7}{1}$ and $10 = \dfrac{10}{1}$

   Work out

   (a) $\dfrac{3}{10} \times \dfrac{3}{1}$ (b) $\dfrac{2}{9} \times \dfrac{4}{1}$ (c) $\dfrac{1}{10} \times 7$ which means $\dfrac{1}{10} \times \dfrac{7}{1}$

   (d) $\dfrac{3}{20} \times 3$ (e) $\dfrac{2}{15} \times 7$ (f) $\dfrac{1}{8} \times 5$ (g) $\dfrac{7}{50} \times 3$

5 Work out the area of each
   rectangle opposite.

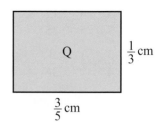

$\frac{1}{2}$ cm   P

$\frac{5}{6}$ cm

Q $\frac{1}{3}$ cm

$\frac{3}{5}$ cm

6 One day a grocer sells $\frac{4}{5}$ of the strawberries on sale. Mr. Jenkins buys $\frac{7}{8}$ of the strawberries
   sold. What fraction overall of the strawberries on sale did Mr. Jenkins buy?

7 Work out and remember to cancel answers.

(a) $\frac{3}{8} \times \frac{5}{7}$ (b) $\frac{2}{9} \times \frac{4}{5}$ (c) $\frac{6}{7} \times \frac{14}{21}$ (d) $\frac{4}{9} \times \frac{3}{8}$

(e) $\frac{2}{5} \times \frac{15}{20}$ (f) $\frac{7}{8} \times \frac{24}{28}$ (g) $\frac{9}{10} \times \frac{5}{12}$ (h) $\frac{3}{7} \times \frac{5}{9}$

8 At 8:30 am one morning $\frac{5}{8}$ of the
   cars on a bridge are heading west.
   $\frac{3}{10}$ of these cars are stuck in a traffic jam.
   What fraction of all the cars on the bridge
   are stuck in the traffic jam?

9 Work out $\frac{1}{3} \times \frac{2}{5} \times \frac{3}{4}$

Adding and subtracting fractions

Fractions can be added or subtracted when they have the same denominator.

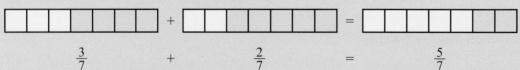

$\frac{3}{7}$ + $\frac{2}{7}$ = $\frac{5}{7}$

Only add the numerators, *not* the denominators.

If fractions do not have the same denominator, change them into *equivalent fractions* which do
have the same denominator before adding or subtracting.

(a) $\dfrac{1}{6} + \dfrac{1}{3}$

    $= \dfrac{1}{6} + \dfrac{2}{6}$

    $= \dfrac{3}{6} = \dfrac{1}{2}$

(b) $\dfrac{7}{8} - \dfrac{3}{4}$

    $= \dfrac{7}{8} - \dfrac{6}{8}$

    $= \dfrac{1}{8}$

(c) $\dfrac{2}{5} + \dfrac{3}{7}$

    $= \dfrac{14}{35} + \dfrac{15}{35}$

    $= \dfrac{29}{35}$

Cancel final answer if you can.

Exercise 5M

1 Copy and complete each box below.

(a) $\dfrac{2}{3} = \dfrac{\square}{9}$ so $\dfrac{1}{9} + \dfrac{2}{3} = \dfrac{1}{9} + \dfrac{\square}{9} = \dfrac{\square}{9}$ (b) $\dfrac{1}{2} = \dfrac{\square}{8}$ so $\dfrac{7}{8} - \dfrac{1}{2} = \dfrac{7}{8} - \dfrac{\square}{8} = \dfrac{\square}{8}$

(c) $\dfrac{7}{10} = \dfrac{\square}{20}$ so $\dfrac{7}{10} - \dfrac{9}{20} = \dfrac{\square}{20} - \dfrac{9}{20} = \dfrac{\square}{20} = \dfrac{\square}{4}$

In questions 2 to 17 , change one of the fractions to an equivalent fraction first before adding or subtracting.

2 $\dfrac{2}{5} + \dfrac{3}{10}$

3 $\dfrac{1}{4} - \dfrac{1}{8}$

4 $\dfrac{3}{4} - \dfrac{1}{2}$

5 $\dfrac{3}{8} - \dfrac{1}{4}$

6 $\dfrac{5}{8} + \dfrac{1}{4}$

7 $\dfrac{1}{4} + \dfrac{1}{2}$

8 $\dfrac{1}{16} + \dfrac{1}{2}$

9 $\dfrac{5}{8} - \dfrac{1}{2}$

10 $\dfrac{4}{5} + \dfrac{1}{10}$

11 $\dfrac{3}{8} + \dfrac{1}{2}$

12 $\dfrac{7}{20} - \dfrac{1}{10}$

13 $\dfrac{1}{6} + \dfrac{1}{3}$

14 $\dfrac{5}{9} - \dfrac{7}{18}$

15 $\dfrac{27}{50} - \dfrac{3}{10}$

16 $\dfrac{5}{12} + \dfrac{1}{3}$

17 $\dfrac{19}{40} - \dfrac{3}{8}$

18 Marie photographs $\frac{1}{9}$ of a herd of elephants and Wes photographs another $\frac{2}{3}$ of the herd. What total fraction of the herd of elephants was photographed?

19 Edmund says that $\frac{1}{6} + \frac{1}{3}$ is equal to $\frac{2}{9}$. Explain clearly why Edmund is not correct.

20 Dawn gave $\frac{3}{10}$ of her money to her son and $\frac{2}{5}$ of her money to her daughter.
    What fraction of her money does Dawn still have?

Exercise 6M

1 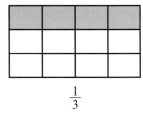   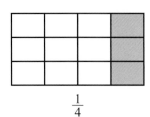 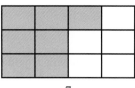

$$\frac{1}{3} \qquad + \qquad \frac{1}{4} \qquad = \qquad \frac{7}{12}$$

Draw similar diagrams to show that $\frac{2}{3} + \frac{1}{4} = \frac{11}{12}$.

2 Copy and complete each box below.

(a) $\frac{1}{2} + \frac{1}{5}$

$$= \frac{\square}{10} + \frac{\square}{10}$$

$$= \frac{\square}{10}$$

(b) $\frac{2}{3} + \frac{1}{4}$

$$= \frac{\square}{12} + \frac{\square}{12}$$

$$= \frac{\square}{12}$$

(c) $\frac{7}{8} - \frac{2}{3}$

$$= \frac{\square}{24} - \frac{\square}{24}$$

$$= \frac{\square}{24}$$

In questions ③ to ⑭ , work out the answers and cancel if necessary.

3 $\frac{3}{5} + \frac{1}{4}$

4 $\frac{1}{6} + \frac{3}{4}$

5 $\frac{3}{4} - \frac{1}{3}$

6 $\frac{2}{3} - \frac{4}{7}$

7 $\frac{3}{8} + \frac{2}{5}$

8 $\frac{5}{6} - \frac{5}{8}$

9 $\frac{9}{10} - \frac{7}{9}$

10 $\frac{3}{5} + \frac{3}{8}$

11 $\frac{11}{12} - \frac{1}{5}$

12 $\frac{5}{7} + \frac{2}{9}$

13 $\frac{4}{9} + \frac{1}{5}$

14 $\frac{7}{10} - \frac{2}{3}$

15

Ruby goes shopping. She spends $\frac{1}{3}$ of her money on shoes and $\frac{1}{5}$ of her money on shirts.

(a) What fraction of her money has she spent in total?

(b) What fraction of her money does she have left?

16 Find the perimeter of this rectangle.

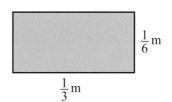

$\frac{1}{6}$ m

$\frac{1}{3}$ m

17 Find the missing fraction for each box. Cancel if necessary.

(a) $\frac{2}{5} + \boxed{} = \frac{11}{15}$

(b) $\frac{9}{10} - \boxed{} = \frac{7}{30}$

(c) $\frac{3}{4} - \boxed{} = \frac{5}{12}$

18 An ice-cream seller is able to sell $\frac{1}{6}$ of the ice-creams in the morning and $\frac{3}{5}$ of the ice-creams in the afternoon. What fraction of the ice-creams does the seller have left over?

19 Which answer is greater and by how much?

$\left(\frac{3}{4} - \frac{1}{6} \right)$ or $\left(\frac{7}{15} + \frac{1}{5} \right)$

Need more practice with fractions?

1 Which fractions below are equivalent?

$\left(\frac{6}{15} \right)$ $\left(\frac{14}{35} \right)$ $\left(\frac{10}{25} \right)$ $\left(\frac{12}{45} \right)$ $\left(\frac{22}{55} \right)$

2 $\frac{5}{8} \times \dfrac{\boxed{}}{\boxed{}} = \frac{35}{72}$ Write down this calculation with the correct value in each box.

3 In each part of this question, one fraction is not equivalent to the others.
Write down the fraction that is the odd one out.

(a) $\frac{9}{24}, \frac{15}{40}, \frac{3}{8}, \frac{5}{9}, \frac{12}{32}$

(b) $\frac{16}{28}, \frac{36}{63}, \frac{44}{77}, \frac{20}{45}, \frac{28}{49}$

4 Work out

(a) $\frac{5}{8} \times \frac{4}{9}$

(b) $\frac{2}{11} \times 5$

(c) $\frac{3}{10} \times 2$

(d) $\frac{6}{7} \times \frac{21}{24}$

5 Draw a copy of the rectangle.

(a) Shade in $\frac{1}{3}$ of the squares.

(b) Draw crosses in $\frac{1}{5}$ of the unshaded squares.

(c) How many squares are neither shaded nor have crosses in them?

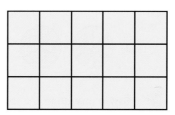

6   Mr Richards buys 80 fireworks. He uses $\frac{3}{5}$ of the fireworks on Bonfire night and then uses $\frac{5}{8}$ of the remaining fireworks on the night after Bonfire night. How many fireworks does he have left?

7   Work out

(a) $\frac{3}{8} + \frac{3}{5}$ (b) $\frac{6}{7} - \frac{2}{5}$ (c) $\frac{8}{9} - \frac{1}{4}$ (d) $\frac{1}{3} + \frac{5}{8}$

(e) $\frac{9}{10} - \frac{4}{7}$ (f) $\frac{5}{8} - \frac{2}{9}$ (g) $\frac{1}{4} + \frac{3}{7}$ (h) $\frac{7}{12} - \frac{1}{3}$

8   If ⑦ of 20 $= \frac{4}{7}$ of 28, what fraction does ⑦ equal?

Extension questions with fractions

Adding and subtracting mixed numbers

Convert mixed numbers into improper fractions before adding or subtracting.

proper fraction   *improper* fraction   *mixed number*

⬇   ⬇   ⬇

numerator is less than denominator.

examples: $\frac{3}{7}, \frac{17}{59}$

numerator is larger than denominator.

examples: $\frac{4}{3}, \frac{17}{5}$

contains both a whole number and a fraction.

examples: $4\frac{1}{2}, 7\frac{3}{4}$

(often called 'top-heavy' fractions)

$1\frac{3}{4} + 2\frac{1}{3} = \frac{7}{4} + \frac{7}{3} = \frac{21}{12} + \frac{28}{12} = \frac{49}{12}$

Convert back to a mixed number at the end

$\frac{49}{12} = 49 \div 12 = 4\frac{1}{12}$

1   Change the following improper fractions to mixed numbers or whole numbers only.

(a) $\frac{8}{3}$ (b) $\frac{13}{7}$ (c) $\frac{12}{5}$ (d) $\frac{17}{9}$ (e) $\frac{73}{10}$

2   How many quarters are there in $7\frac{3}{4}$?

③ Change the mixed numbers to improper fractions.

(a) $3\frac{1}{4}$ (b) $4\frac{3}{7}$ (c) $2\frac{4}{5}$ (d) $8\frac{1}{5}$ (e) $7\frac{4}{9}$

Work out

④ $1\frac{3}{4} + \frac{1}{3}$ ⑤ $1\frac{4}{5} + \frac{2}{3}$ ⑥ $2\frac{1}{2} - \frac{7}{8}$ ⑦ $3\frac{1}{4} - 1\frac{5}{6}$

⑧ $2\frac{3}{5} + 1\frac{3}{4}$ ⑨ $3\frac{1}{6} - 1\frac{3}{8}$ ⑩ $4\frac{1}{2} - 2\frac{4}{5}$ ⑪ $3\frac{1}{2} + 1\frac{2}{3}$

⑫ $\frac{1}{5}$ of the dogs in a full kennels leave on a Friday and $\frac{1}{6}$ leave on a Saturday.

What fraction of the dogs remain if no new dogs arrive?

⑬ Work out

(a) $\frac{1}{2} + \frac{1}{3} + \frac{1}{12}$ (b) $\frac{3}{5} + \frac{1}{4} - \frac{7}{10}$ (c) $\frac{5}{6} + \frac{1}{10} - \frac{4}{5}$

⑭ A baker sells chocolate cakes on a market stall one day. In the morning $5\frac{1}{4}$ cakes are sold and in the afternoon $7\frac{5}{6}$ cakes are sold. The baker started with 15 cakes. How many cakes are left?

⑮ The fraction sum $\frac{1}{3} + \frac{4}{6}$ is made from four different digits and the sum is 1.

Find other fraction sums using four different digits so that the sum is 1.

2.2 Fractions, decimals, percentages

In section 2.2 you will:

- convert between fractions, decimals and percentages

Changing fractions to decimals

Convert denominator to 10, 100, etc.

$\frac{1}{5} = \frac{2}{10} = 0.2$ $\frac{1}{25} = \frac{4}{100} = 0.04$ $\frac{9}{20} = \frac{45}{100} = 0.45$

Cancelling fractions can help.

$\frac{12}{16} = \frac{3}{4} = 0.75$ $\frac{60}{240} = \frac{1}{4} = 0.25$

Exercise 1M

Convert these fractions into decimals.

1. $\dfrac{7}{10}$

2. $\dfrac{39}{100}$

3. $\dfrac{1}{2}$

4. $\dfrac{7}{100}$

5. $\dfrac{9}{10}$

6. $\dfrac{13}{100}$

7. $\dfrac{1}{4}$

8. $\dfrac{1}{100}$

9. $\dfrac{41}{100}$

10. $\dfrac{3}{4}$

Copy and complete the boxes.

11. $\dfrac{7}{20} = \dfrac{35}{100} = 0.\square\square$

12. $\dfrac{3}{20} = \dfrac{\square}{100} = 0.\square\square$

13. $\dfrac{4}{5} = \dfrac{\square}{10} = 0.\square$

14. $\dfrac{3}{12} = \dfrac{\square}{4} = 0.\square\square$

15. $\dfrac{3}{5} = \dfrac{\square}{10} = 0.\square$

16. $\dfrac{4}{25} = \dfrac{\square}{100} = 0.\square\square$

17. Jed says that 0.4 is $\frac{1}{4}$. Explain clearly why Jed is not correct.

18. Make two copies of the rectangle opposite. Shade 0.7 of one rectangle and $\frac{3}{4}$ of the other rectangle. Explain clearly why $\frac{3}{4}$ is greater than 0.7.

Convert these fractions into decimals.

19. $\dfrac{11}{20}$

20. $\dfrac{2}{5}$

21. $\dfrac{7}{25}$

22. $\dfrac{27}{36}$

23. $\dfrac{17}{20}$

24. $\dfrac{23}{25}$

25. $\dfrac{19}{25}$

26. $\dfrac{150}{200}$

27. $\dfrac{120}{200}$

28. $\dfrac{18}{72}$

29. Copy and complete the table.

Fraction	$\frac{2}{5}$		$\frac{71}{100}$		$\frac{1}{50}$		$\frac{9}{20}$
Decimal		0.03		0.45		0.53	

Changing decimals into fractions

$0.6 = \dfrac{6}{10} = \dfrac{3}{5}$

$0.27 = \dfrac{27}{100}$

$0.65 = \dfrac{65}{100} = \dfrac{13}{20}$

$0.04 = \dfrac{4}{100} = \dfrac{1}{25}$

Cancel down the fractions if possible

Exercise 2M

Change these decimals into fractions.

| 1 | 0.3 | 2 | 0.7 | 3 | 0.01 | 4 | 0.09 | 5 | 0.13 |

| 6 | 0.51 | 7 | 0.69 | 8 | 0.9 | 9 | 0.23 | 10 | 0.37 |

Copy and complete.

11 $0.4 = \dfrac{\square}{10} = \dfrac{\square}{5}$

12 $0.05 = \dfrac{\square}{100} = \dfrac{\square}{\square}$

13 $0.08 = \dfrac{8}{\square} = \dfrac{\square}{25}$

14 $0.12 = \dfrac{\square}{100} = \dfrac{\square}{\square}$

15 $0.37 = \dfrac{\square}{\square}$

16 $0.017 = \dfrac{17}{\square}$

17 Carol and Oscar each have a bar of chocolate. Carol has eaten 0.85 of her bar and Oscar has eaten $\frac{17}{20}$ of his bar. Who has eaten the most chocolate?

Change these decimals into fractions (cancel down fractions when possible).

| 18 | 0.8 | 19 | 0.05 | 20 | 0.08 | 21 | 0.25 | 22 | 0.24 |

| 23 | 0.02 | 24 | 0.4 | 25 | 0.32 | 26 | 0.15 | 27 | 0.18 |

| 28 | 0.014 | 29 | 0.125 | 30 | 0.56 | 31 | 0.025 | 32 | 0.675 |

33 Which number is the odd one out below?

$\left(\dfrac{14}{50}\right)$ $\left(0.28\right)$ $\left(\dfrac{7}{20}\right)$ $\left(\dfrac{7}{25}\right)$

Changing fractions and percentages

(a) Percentage to fraction
     ('per cent' means 'out of 100')

$$60\% = \frac{60}{100} = \frac{3}{5}$$

$$24\% = \frac{24}{100} = \frac{6}{25}$$

$$2\% = \frac{2}{100} = \frac{1}{50}$$

(b) Fraction to percentage
     (make the denominator equal to 100)

$$\frac{4}{5} = \frac{80}{100} = 80\%$$

$$\frac{3}{20} = \frac{15}{100} = 15\%$$

$$3\frac{1}{2} = \frac{350}{100} = 350\%$$

- Learn the following:

$$\frac{1}{4} = 25\% \qquad \frac{1}{8} = 12\frac{1}{2}\% \qquad \frac{1}{3} = 33\frac{1}{3}\% \qquad \frac{2}{3} = 66\frac{2}{3}\%$$

Exercise 3M

1   Change these percentages into fractions. Cancel down answers where possible.

(a) 40%   (b) 7%   (c) 22%   (d) 80%   (e) 5%
(f) 89%   (g) 10%   (h) 28%   (i) 4%   (j) 35%

2   Copy and complete the following.

(a) $\dfrac{2}{5} = \dfrac{40}{100} = \square\%$ (b) $\dfrac{9}{20} = \dfrac{45}{100} = \square\%$ (c) $\dfrac{3}{25} = \dfrac{\square}{100} = \square\%$

(d) $\dfrac{11}{20} = \dfrac{\square}{100} = \square\%$ (e) $\dfrac{9}{10} = \dfrac{\square}{100} = \square\%$ (f) $\dfrac{19}{50} = \dfrac{\square}{100} = \square\%$

3   Andrei spends 36% of his money on popcorn.
    What fraction of his money does he still have?

4   Rosa was absent from school for $\frac{1}{25}$ of
    the Autumn term. What percentage of
    the term was she absent for?

5   Eden sat three tests. His marks are below.

Test 1	Test 2	Test 3
$\dfrac{17}{20}$	$\dfrac{13}{25}$	$\dfrac{46}{50}$

Change the marks into percentages then find the difference between
the highest test percentage and the lowest.

6  During one season, Lewis won 70% of his races. What *fraction* of his races did he not win?

7 Write down each fraction with its equivalent percentage.

(a) $\frac{1}{3}$ (b) $\frac{3}{4}$ (c) $\frac{2}{3}$ (d) $\frac{1}{8}$

8 Zoe and Luke sell items at a car boot sale. Zoe sells $\frac{13}{20}$ of her items and Luke sells 63% of his items. Who sells the greater percentage of items and by how much?

9 Write down which fractions are greater than the given percentage.

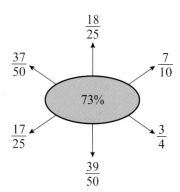

10 $\frac{1}{4}$ of the people on a bus were wearing black coats and $\frac{8}{25}$ of the people were wearing blue coats. What percentage of the people on the bus were not wearing black or blue coats?

Changing decimals, fractions and percentages

Exercise 4M

1 Copy and complete to change the following decimals into percentages.

(a) $0.37 = \dfrac{\square}{100} = \square\%$ (b) $0.17 = \dfrac{\square}{100} = \square\%$

(c) $0.03 = \dfrac{\square}{100} = \square\%$ (d) $0.4 = \dfrac{4}{10} = \dfrac{\square}{100} = \square\%$

2 Change these percentages into decimals.

(a) 29%   (b) 52%   (c) 80%   (d) 6%

(e) 3%   (f) 13%   (g) 130%   (h) 240%

3 Copy and complete the table.

	fraction	decimal	percentage
(a)		0.3	
(b)			55%
(c)			12%
(d)	$\frac{1}{20}$		
(e)		0.48	

4 Christy ate 0.4 of an extra large pizza and Rob ate $\frac{9}{20}$ of the pizza.
What percentage of the pizza was not eaten?

5 Answer true or false for each of the following statements:

(a) $\dfrac{4}{25} = 16\%$ (b) $\dfrac{1}{3} = 35\%$ (c) $\dfrac{7}{50} = 14\%$

(d) $\dfrac{19}{20} = 95\%$ (e) $\dfrac{1}{8} = 18\%$ (f) $\dfrac{2}{3} = 66\frac{2}{3}\%$

6 Each fraction, decimal or percentage has an equivalent in the list with letters.
Find the letters to make a sentence.

(a) $\boxed{50\%,\ \frac{1}{4},\ 10\%,\ 0.2,\ 0.11}$ $\boxed{17\%,\ 11\%}$ $\boxed{0.75,\ 99\%,\ \frac{1}{10}}$ $\boxed{20\%,\ \frac{1}{4},\ \frac{1}{8},\ 0.7}$

(b) $\boxed{\frac{7}{10},\ 0.8,\ 45\%,\ \frac{17}{100},\ 0.5,\ \frac{1}{4},\ \frac{10}{25},\ 0.11}$ $\boxed{\frac{3}{6},\ \frac{4}{16},\ 0.05,\ 80\%}$ $\boxed{\frac{22}{200},\ 0.8\ 75\%,\ 11\%,\ \frac{8}{10}}$

(c) $\boxed{17\%}$ $\boxed{45\%,\ 0.25,\ 75\%}$ $\boxed{0.11,\ \frac{99}{100},\ \frac{4}{10},\ \frac{41}{50},\ \frac{400}{500}}$ $\boxed{\frac{3}{20},\ \frac{2}{16},\ \frac{99}{100},\ \frac{1}{3},\ 0.4,\ 0.8,\ \frac{10}{20},\ 11\%}$

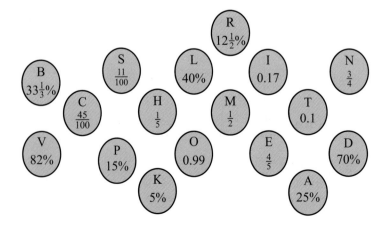

Need more practice with fractions, decimals, percentages?

1. Which fractions below are equivalent to 0.35?

    $\dfrac{7}{20}$ $\dfrac{35}{50}$ $\dfrac{21}{60}$ $\dfrac{35}{1000}$ $\dfrac{3}{25}$

2. A football team takes 5 penalties and scores 4 of them. A newspaper report the following day suggests that the football team had an 80% success rate at taking penalties. Explain clearly whether this is correct.

3. Pair off the numbers below. Beware there is one number with no pairing.

    | $66\frac{2}{3}\%$ | $\dfrac{3}{25}$ | 45% | $\dfrac{17}{20}$ | 0.6 | 0.85 | 60% | 34% |

    | 26% | 6% | $\dfrac{9}{20}$ | $\dfrac{2}{3}$ | 0.12 | $\dfrac{17}{50}$ | $\dfrac{52}{200}$ |

4. Write down true or false for each statement below.

    (a) $0.3 = 3\%$

    (b) $0.55 > \dfrac{13}{20}$

    (c) $\dfrac{17}{50} > 0.32$

    (d) $\dfrac{48}{400} < 14\%$

    (e) $0.04 < 40\%$

    (f) $\dfrac{11}{20} = 0.55$

5. One in five people in a city own a laptop computer. What percentage of people in the city do not own a laptop?

6. $\dfrac{8}{25} = \dfrac{32}{100} = 0.032$ Is this statement correct? If not, identify the mistake.

7. Which of the numbers below is the largest. You must show working out to explain your answer.

    $\left(\dfrac{8}{25}\right)$ $\left(\dfrac{7}{20}\right)$ (0.34) $\left(\dfrac{1}{3}\right)$

Extension questions with fractions, decimals, percentages

1   Change the fractions to decimals.

(a) $\dfrac{19}{1000}$ (b) $\dfrac{1}{125}$ (c) $\dfrac{17}{125}$ (d) $\dfrac{54}{72}$ (e) $\dfrac{150}{2000}$

(f) $\dfrac{7}{250}$ (g) $\dfrac{19}{76}$ (h) $\dfrac{89}{500}$ (i) $\dfrac{36}{3000}$ (j) $\dfrac{173}{10\,000}$

2   Change these decimals into fractions (cancel down fractions when possible).

(a) 3.2   (b) 7.12   (c) 3.75   (d) 2.95   (e) 4.36

3   Convert the fractions to decimals and then write the numbers in order of size, smallest first.

(a) $\dfrac{3}{4}, \dfrac{3}{5}, 0.7$ (b) $\dfrac{8}{20}, 0.3, \dfrac{9}{25}$ (c) $\dfrac{12}{16}, 0.7, \dfrac{4}{5}$

4   Write these fractions as percentages.

(a) $\dfrac{25}{125}$ (b) $\dfrac{600}{2000}$ (c) $\dfrac{120}{125}$ (d) $\dfrac{200}{5000}$ (e) $\dfrac{1}{1000}$

5

Player	Wins	Games
Alexis	12	20
Hunter	20	50
Arnav	30	40
Shun	15	25

Four people play squash. The table shows the number of wins and games for each player.

(a) Which two players won the same percentage of games?

(b) Who won the greatest percentage of games and by how much more than the next best percentage of wins?

6   Use the symbols $<, >$ or $=$ to copy and complete each statement below:

(a) $\dfrac{7}{20}$ ☐ 0.4 (b) 0.22 ☐ $\dfrac{6}{25}$ (c) 32% ☐ $\dfrac{16}{50}$

(d) 83% ☐ $\dfrac{21}{25}$ (e) 7% ☐ 0.7 (f) 0.18 ☐ $\dfrac{110}{500}$

7   300 students out of 450 in total are girls.

Explain *clearly* why $33\frac{1}{3}\%$ of the students are boys.

Investigation – Escape

In the town of Decford a prison has 10 cells. All the cells have one prisoner in them and all the cell doors are locked.

- A jailer walks from cell 1 to cell 10 and unlocks each door.

- The jailer returns to the start and locks every second door.

- The jailer returns to the start and changes the state of every third door (ie. cells 3, 6, 9). *'Changes the state of a door'* means *'lock if unlocked'* or *'unlock if locked'*.

- The jailer repeats the process for every fourth door then fifth door, sixth, seventh, eighth, ninth and finally tenth.

(a) How many prisoners can now escape through an unlocked door? Write down the cell numbers of those prisoners who can escape.

(b) The prison in the city of Centford has 100 cells. A jailer repeats the above process from changing the state of every door then every second door, etc to changing the state of every 100th door. How many prisoners can now escape through an unlocked door? Write down the cell numbers of those prisoners who can escape. Can you explain *why* these cell doors are unlocked at the end?

CHECK YOURSELF ON SECTIONS 2.1 AND 2.2

1   Finding equivalent fractions

Find the missing number to make these fractions equivalent.

(a) $\dfrac{1}{6} = \dfrac{\square}{42}$ (b) $\dfrac{7}{9} = \dfrac{28}{\square}$ (c) $\dfrac{32}{48} = \dfrac{2}{\square}$ (d) $\dfrac{5}{7} = \dfrac{30}{\square}$

(e) Write down which fractions are equivalent to $\dfrac{7}{8}$.

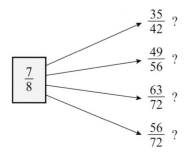

$\dfrac{35}{42}$?

$\dfrac{49}{56}$?

$\dfrac{7}{8}$

$\dfrac{63}{72}$?

$\dfrac{56}{72}$?

2   Finding a fraction of a number

Work out

(a) $\frac{1}{6}$ of 24

(b) $\frac{5}{6}$ of 24

(c) $\frac{3}{5}$ of 70

(d) $\frac{2}{7}$ of 56

3   Multiplying fractions

Work out

(a) $\frac{9}{10} \times \frac{3}{7}$

(b) $\frac{3}{4} \times \frac{7}{10}$

(c) $\frac{4}{5} \times \frac{1}{8}$

(d) $\frac{2}{9} \times 4$

(e) Work out the area of this rectangle.

$\frac{2}{3}$ cm

$\frac{7}{10}$ cm

4   Adding and subtracting fractions

Work out

(a) $\frac{8}{9} - \frac{1}{9}$

(b) $\frac{2}{5} + \frac{3}{7}$

(c) $\frac{3}{4} - \frac{2}{3}$

(d) $\frac{3}{4} + \frac{1}{16}$

5   Converting between fractions, decimals and percentages

There are four groups of equivalent fractions, decimals and percentages below. Write down each group (beware: there are two odd ones out). For example $\frac{1}{2}$, 0.5, 50% would be a group.

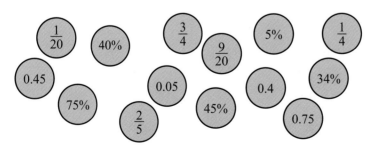

$\frac{1}{20}$ 40% $\frac{3}{4}$ $\frac{9}{20}$ 5% $\frac{1}{4}$

0.45   75%   0.05 $\frac{2}{5}$ 45%   0.4   34%   0.75

2.3 Coordinates

In this section you will:

- use coordinates with positive and negative numbers

- solve problems involving shapes

Exercise 1M

1 The map opposite shows a remote
Scottish island used for training by
the S.A.S. Write down the coordinates
of the following places:

(a) Rocket launcher

(b) H.Q.

(c) Hospital A

(d) Rifle range

(e) Officers' mess

(f) Radar control

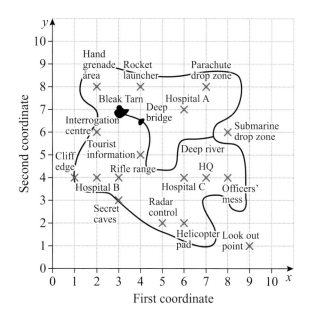

2 Make a list of the places which are
at the following points:

(a) (2, 8)   (b) (7, 8)   (c) (3, 3)

(d) (6, 4)   (e) (2, 6)   (f) (6, 2)

(g) (2, 4)   (h) (9, 1)

3 A soldier is one square to the right of the helicopter pad. The soldier reports that he is at
position (2, 7). Explain clearly whether he is correct or not.

4 A soldier starts at position (6, 3). The soldier travels 2 squares left, 3 squares up then one
square right. What are the coordinates of the soldier's position now?

5 Make up your own map and mark points of interest.

For questions 6 to 8 , plot the points given and join them up in order.
Write on the grid what the picture is.

6 Draw x and y axes with values from 0 to 14.

(a) (6, 13), (1, 3), (2, 1), (12, 1), (8, 9), (6, 5), (4, 5), (8, 13), (6, 13), (8, 13), (13, 3), (12, 1).

(b) (1, 3), (9, 3), (7, 7), (6, 5), (8, 5).

Now colour in the shape.

7 Draw axes with both x and y from 0 to 11.

(a) (7, 1), (3, 1), (1, 10), (2, 11), (3, 10), (4, 11), (5, 10), (6, 11), (7, 10), (8, 6), (8, 5), (9, $4\frac{1}{2}$), (9, 4), (8, 4), (9, 3), (5, 3), (5, 2), (7, 1).

(b) (5, 5), (4, 6), (5, 7), (6, 6), (7, 7), (8, 6), (7, 5), (6, 6), (5, 5).

(c) (5, 2), (6, 2), (6, $1\frac{1}{2}$).   (d) (7, 5), (8, 5).

(e) (7, 4), (8, 4)   (f) (3, 7), (2, $6\frac{1}{2}$), (3, 6)

(g) Put dots at (5, 6) and (7, 6).

8 Draw axes with both x and y from 0 to 18.

(a) (0, 3), (1, 4), (2,6), (4, 8), (6, 8), (8, 9), (12, 9), (13, 11), (12, 12), (12, 14), (14, 12), (15, 12), (17, 14), (17, 12), (16, 11), (17, 10), (17, 9), (16, 9), (15, 8), (14, 9), (13, 9).

(b) (16, 9), (16, 7), (14, 5), (14, 1), (15, 1), (15, 6), (13, 4), (13, 1), (12, 1), (12, 4), (11, 5), (9, 5), (9, $6\frac{1}{2}$), (9, 4), (8, 3), (8, 1), (7, 1), (7, 4), (6, 6), (6, 4), (5, 3), (5, 1), (6, 1), (6, 3), (7, 4), (6, 6), (6, 7), (3, 2), (1, 2), (0, 3).

Negative coordinates

The x axis can be extended to the left and the y axis can be extended downwards to include the negative numbers $-1, -2, -3$ etc.

The word 'BACON' can be found using the letters in the following order:

$(2, -2), (2, 3), (-2, -3), (-2, -1), (-1, 2)$

Similarly the coordinates of the points which spell out the word 'CAN' are

$(-2, -3), (2, 3), (-1, 2)$

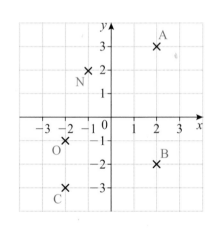

Exercise 2M

1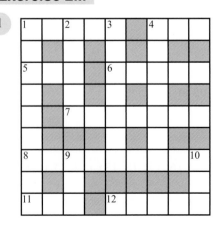

Copy the crossword grid and complete it using the clues below.

The letters are found using coordinates on the grid.

Across
1. $(-3, 4)\,(-4, -2)\,(-3, 4)\,(1, 3)\,(3, -3)$
4. $(5, 5)\,(-4, -2)\,(3, -3)$
5. $(-4, -2)\,(5, 2)\,(5, -5)$
6. $(-4, -2)\,(-3, -4)\,(3, -3)\,(-4, -2)\,(5, -5)$
7. $(2, -2)\,(3, -3)\,(-2, 5)\,(-4, 1)\,(-3, -4)\,(2, -2)\,(1, 3)$
8. $(3, -3)\,(1, 3)\,(-3, 4)\,(-3, -4)\,(4, 4)\,(0, 1)\,(-4, -2)$
   $(0, 1)\,(2, -2)$
11. German for 'THE'.
12. $(-4, 1)\,(-4, -2)\,(-2, -2)\,(5, 2)\,(0, 1)$

Down
1. $(-3, 4)\,(5, -5)\,(-4, -2)\,(-2, 2)\,(2, -2)\,(1, 3)$
   $(3, -3)\,(1, 3)\,(2, 5)$
2. $(-3, 4)\,(-2, 5)\,(5, -5)\,(5, 2)\,(2, -2)$
3. Useful for books
4. Used in mathematics
9. $(-3, 4)\,(-4, -2)\,(3, -3)$
10. $(2, -2)\,(-4, -2)\,(0, 1)$

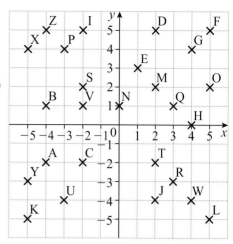

---

2 (a) Draw x and y axes from -5 to 5.

   (b) One vertex (corner) of an isosceles triangle is $(-5, -1)$.
      Draw this point and the rest of an isosceles triangle so that all the corners
      have negative coordinates.

3 Draw x and y axes with values from -5 to 5. Plot the points given and join them up in order.

   (a) $(-2, -3), (-1, -3), (0, -2), (-2, 0), (-2, 1), (-3, 2), (-4, 1), (-4, 3), (-3, 4),$
      $(-2, 4), (0, 2), (-1, 1), (-1, 0), (1, -1), (3, -1), (3, 0), (1, 2), (0, 2).$

   (b) $(2, -1), (4, -3), (3, -4), (2, -2), (0, -2).$

   (c) $(-4, 1), (-3, 3), (-3, 4), (-3, 2).$

   (d) Draw a dot at $(-2, 3)$. Colour in the shape.

Complete the shape

Two sides of a rectangle are drawn.

Find   (a) the coordinates of the fourth vertex of the rectangle

        (b) the coordinates of the centre of the rectangle.

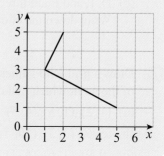

The complete rectangle is shown.

(a) Fourth vertex is at (6, 3)

(b) Centre of rectangle is at $(3\frac{1}{2}, 3)$

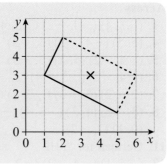

Exercise 2E

1 The graph shows several incomplete quadrilaterals.

Copy the diagram and complete the shapes.

(a) Write down the coordinates of the fourth vertex of each shape.

(b) Write down the coordinates of the centre of each shape.

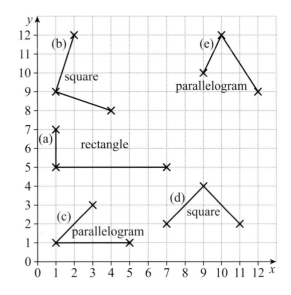

2 Copy the graph shown.

(a) A, B and F are three corners of a square. Write down the coordinates of the other corner.

(b) B, C and D are three corners of another square. Write down the coordinates of the other corner.

(c) D, E and F are three corners of a rectangle. Write down the coordinates of the other corner.

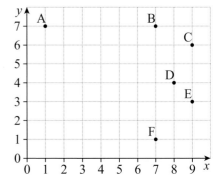

3 Draw a grid with values from 0 to 10. Plot the three points given and then find the coordinates of the point which makes a square when the points are joined up.

(a) (1, 2), (1, 5), (4, 5)

(b) (5, 6), (7, 3), (10, 5)

(c) (0, 9), (1, 6), (4, 7)

4 You are given the vertices but not
   the sides of two parallelograms
   P and Q.

   For each parallelogram find *three*
   possible positions for the fourth vertex.

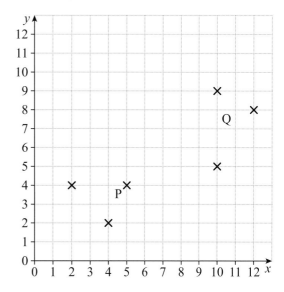

5 Copy the graph shown.

   (a) A, B and C are three corners of a square.
       Write down the coordinates of the other corner.

   (b) C, A and D are three corners of another square.
       Write down the coordinates of the other corner.

   (c) B, D and E are three corners of a rectangle.
       Write down the coordinates of the other corner.

   (d) C, F and G are three vertices of a parallelogram.
       Write down the coordinates of the other vertex.

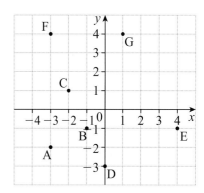

6

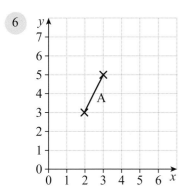

   The crosses mark two vertices of an isosceles triangle A.

   Find as many points as you can, with whole number
   coordinates, for the third vertex of the triangle.

   [There are, in fact, 12 possible points for the third vertex.
   Find as many as you can.]

7   The diagram shows one side of an isosceles triangle B.

(a) Find *six* possible points, with whole number coordinates, for the third vertex of the triangle.

(b) Explain how you could find the coordinates of several more positions for the third vertex.

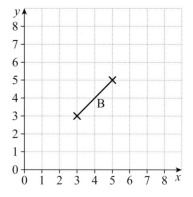

2.4 Straight line graphs

In section 2.4 you will learn about:

- lines which are parallel to the axes
- sloping lines
- drawing straight line graphs

Lines parallel to the axes

- The points P, Q, R and S have coordinates $(4, 4)$, $(4, 3)$, $(4, 2)$ and $(4, 1)$ and they all lie on a straight line. Since the x-coordinate of all the points is 4, we say the *equation* of the line is $x = 4$.

- The points A, B and C have coordinates $(1, 3)$, $(2, 3)$ and $(3, 3)$ and they all lie on a straight line. Since the y-coordinate of all the points is 3, we say the *equation* of the line is $y = 3$.

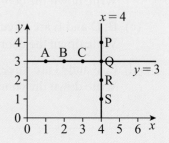

Exercise 1M

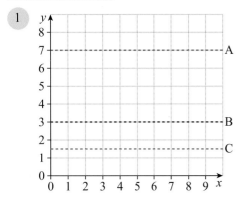

1

(a) Choose 3 points that lie on line A. Write down the coordinates of each of these points.

(b) Write down the y-values of each of the points you chose in part (a).

(c) Write down the equation '$y = ...$' for line A.

(d) Repeat parts (a), (b) and (c) for line B.

(e) Write down the equation for line C.

2 (a) Choose 3 points that lie on line P.
       Write down the coordinates of each
       of these points.
   (b) Write down the *x*-values of each of
       the points you chose in part (a).
   (c) Write down the equation '*x* = …'
       for line P.
   (d) Repeat parts (a), (b) and (c) for line Q.
   (e) Write down the equation for line R.

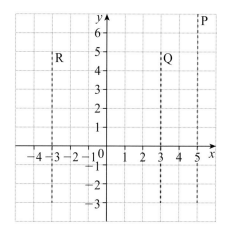

Write down the equations of lines A, B and C in each of questions 3 and 4 .

3

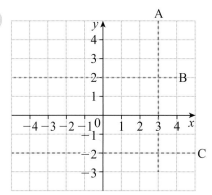

4

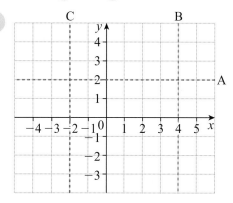

5 On squared paper, draw suitable axes then
   (a) Draw the lines *y* = 2 and *x* = 3. At what point do they meet?
   (b) Draw the lines *y* = 5 and *x* = 1. At what point do they meet?
   (c) Draw the lines *x* = 7 and *y* = 3. At what point do they meet?

6 In the diagram, E and N lie on the line with
   equation *y* = 1. B and K lie on the line *x* = 5.
   In parts (a) to (h) find the equation of the line
   passing through the points given:

   (a) A and D   (b) A, B and I

   (c) M and P   (d) I and H

   (e) L and E   (f) D, K and G

   (g) C, M, L and H   (h) P and F

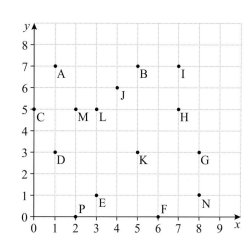

7 (a) Draw x and y axes from 0 to 6.

    (b) Mark on three points which lie on the line $x = 2$

    (c) Mark on three points which lie on the line $y = 4.5$

    (d) Write down the coordinates of the point that lies on both of the above lines.

Relating *x* and *y*

- The sloping line passes through the following points:
  (1, 1), (2, 2), (3, 3), (4, 4), (5, 5).

  For each point, the y-coordinate is equal to the
  x-coordinate.

  > The equation of the line is $y = x$ (or $x = y$)

  This is the rule for any point on the line.

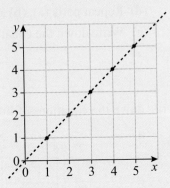

- This line passes through:
  (0, 1), (1, 2), (2, 3), (3, 4), (4, 5).

  For each point the y-coordinate is one more than
  the x-coordinate.

  > The equation of the line is $y = x + 1$

  We could also say that the x-coordinate is always one less
  than the y-coordinate. The equation of the line could then
  be written as $x = y - 1$.
  [Most mathematicians use the equation beginning '$y = $']

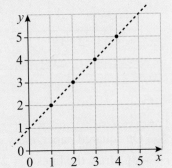

- This line slopes the other way and passes through:
  (0, 5), (1, 4), (2, 3), (3, 2), (4, 1), (5, 0).

  The sum of the x-coordinate and the y-coordinate is
  always 5.

  > The equation of the line is $x + y = 5$

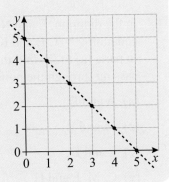

Exercise 1E

1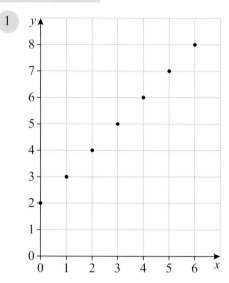

(a) Write down the coordinates of the points marked opposite.

(b) Look carefully at the x and y values then write down the equation of the line through the points.

2 Write down the coordinates of the points marked opposite then write down the equation of the line through the points.

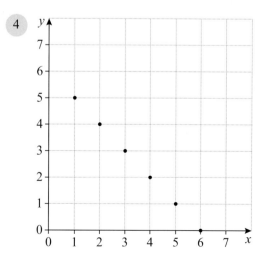

For questions ③ to ⑥ write down the coordinates of the points marked. Find the equation of the line through the points.

3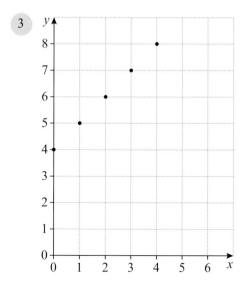

4

5

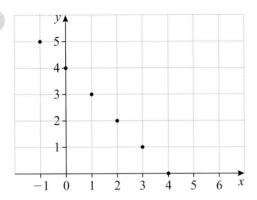

6

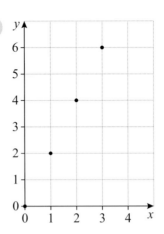

7   Polly says that the equation of the line though
the points opposite is $y = 3 - x$.

Explain clearly the mistake that Polly has made.

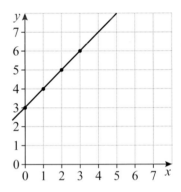

8   A line passes through the coordinates $(2, 6)$, $(3, 5)$, $(4, 4)$, $(5, 3)$ and $(n, 2)$.
    (a) Write down the equation of the line through the points.
    (b) Write down the value of n.

9   Look at the graph. Find the equation for
    (a) line A   [Hint: It starts $y = 2x + \dots$]
    (b) line B
    (c) line C
    (d) line D

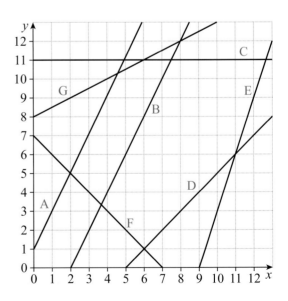

10   This is the table of the points on line G

x	0	2	4	6
y	8	9	10	11

Find the equation for line G.
[Hint: It starts $y = \frac{1}{2}x + \dots$]

11 This is the table for the points on line E.

x	9	10	11	12
y	0	3	6	9

Find the equation of line E.   [Hint: It starts $y = 3x - ...$]

12 Make a table for the points on line F.

x	0	1	2	3
y	7			

Find the equation of line F.

Drawing graphs

- The equation of a line is $y = x + 2$. Here is a list of five
  points on the line: (0, 2), (1, 3), (2, 4), (3, 5), (4, 6)

  The points are plotted on a graph and the line $y = x + 2$ is drawn.
  Notice that the line extends beyond (0, 2) and (4, 6)

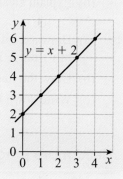

Exercise 2M

1 For the line $y = x + 6$, find the y values for
   (a) $x = 2$ (b) $x = 4$ (c) $x = 5$ (d) $x = 0$

2 For the line $y = x - 5$, find the y values for
   (a) $x = 0$ (b) $x = 1$ (c) $x = 2$ (d) $x = 3$

3 (a) The equation of a line is $y = x + 3$. Copy and complete a list of points on the line:
       (0, 3) (1, 4) (2, ☐) (3, ☐) (4, ☐), ie. find y-values for $x = 2$, $x = 3$ and $x = 4$.
   (b) Draw x and y axes.
   (c) Plot the points above and draw a line through them.

4 (a) The equation of a line is $y = x + 5$. Copy and complete a list of points on the line:
       (0, 5) (1, 6) (2, ☐) (3, ☐) (4, ☐).
   (b) Draw x and y axes.
   (c) Plot the points above and draw the graph of $y = x + 5$.

112

In questions ⑤ to ⑧ you are given the equation of a line and a list of points on the line. Fill in the missing numbers and then draw the graph.

⑤ $y = x - 2$; $(0, -2)$ $(1, -1)$, $(2, \boxed{})$, $(3, \boxed{})$, $(4, \boxed{})$

⑥ $y = 2x$; $(0, 0)$ $(1, 2)$, $(2, \boxed{})$, $(3, \boxed{})$, $(4, \boxed{})$

⑦ $y = 2x + 1$; $(0, \boxed{})$, $(2, \boxed{})$, $(4, \boxed{})$

⑧ $y = 6 - x$; $(1, \boxed{})$, $(3, \boxed{})$, $(5, \boxed{})$, $(6, \boxed{})$

⑨ Ada is asked to draw the graph of $y = 4 + x$. Her graph is shown opposite.

(a) Write down the coordinates of five points on her line.

(b) Explain clearly what mistake Ada has made.

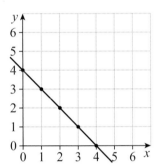

⑩ (a) Draw axes with values of x from 0 to 5 and with values of y from -1 to 7.

(b) Draw the lines $y = 5 - x$ and $y = 2x - 1$ on the same graph.

(c) Write down the coordinates of the point where the lines meet.

Need more practice with coordinates and straight line graphs?

① Draw axes with both x and y from 0 to 17. Plot the points below and join them up in order.

(a) $(5, 1)$, $(6, 6)$, $(6, 3)$, $(7, 2)$, $(6, 2)$, $(5, 1)$.

(b) $(8, 11)$, $(8, 8)$, $(10, 10)$, $(11, 12)$, $(11, 15)$.

(c) $(2, 14)$, $(1, 14)$, $(1, 15)$, $(2, 15)$.

(d) $(12, 1)$, $(11, 2)$, $(10, 2)$, $(10, 4)$, $(9, 6)$, $(8, 7)$, $(7, 10)$, $(8, 11)$, $(9, 13)$, $(11, 15)$, $(10, 17)$, $(8, 17)$, $(7, 16)$, $(4, 16)$, $(2, 15)$, $(2, 14)$, $(3, 13)$, $(5, 13)$, $(6, 12)$, $(4, 7)$, $(4, 2)$, $(3, 2)$, $(2, 1)$, $(12, 1)$.

(e) $(7, 16)$, $(7, 15)$.

(f) $(5, 13)$, $(6, 13)$.

② Calvin says that the equation of the red line shown opposite is $x = 3$.

Explain clearly whether Calvin is correct or not.

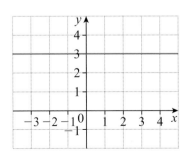

3   Draw x and y axes from 0 to 8.

The equation of a line is $y = 7 - x$.

Copy and complete the list of points below which lie on the line:

$(0, 7)$ $(1, 6)$ $(2, \square)$ $(3, \square)$ $(4, \square)$

Plot these points then draw a line through them.

In questions 4 and 5 you are given the equation of a line and a list of points on the line.
Fill in the missing numbers and then draw the graph.

4   $y = x - 4$; $(0, -4)$ $(1, -3)$, $(2, \square)$, $(3, \square)$, $(4, \square)$

5   $y = 2x + 3$; $(0, 3)$ $(1, 5)$, $(2, \square)$, $(3, \square)$, $(4, \square)$

Extension questions with coordinates and straight line graphs

1   Draw x and y axes with the values from -8 to 8.
Plot the points below and join them up in order.

(a) $(-4, -1)$, $(-2, -3)$, $(-1, -3)$, $(0, -5)$, $(1, -3)$, $(3, -3)$, $(4, -1)$, $(7, 1)$, $(7, 2)$, $(4, 3)$, $(1, 3)$, $(0, 6)$, $(-1, 3)$, $(-2, 3)$, $(-4, 1)$, $(-7, 3)$, $(-5, 0)$, $(-7, -3)$, $(-4, -1)$.

(b) $(7, 4)$, $(8, 4)$, $(8, 5)$, $(7, 5)$, $(7, 4)$

(c) $(6, 6)$, $(5, 6)$, $(5, 7)$, $(6, 7)$, $(6, 6)$

(d) $(4, 0)$, $(5, 0)$

(e) Draw a dot at $(5, 2)$. Colour in the shape.

In questions 2 and 3 you are given the equation of a line and a list of points on the line.
Fill in the missing numbers and then draw the graph.

2   $y = 2x - 2$; $(0, \square)$, $(2, \square)$, $(4, \square)$

3   $y = 3x + 2$; $(0, \square)$, $(1, \square)$, $(2, \square)$

4   For the line $y = 3x$, find the y values for
(a) $x = 2$ (b) $x = 5$ (c) $x = 0$

5   Which of the points below lie on the line $y = x + 7$?
A(3, 10)   B(6, 1)   C(5, 12)

6   Which of the points below lie on the line $y = 2x - 1$?
A(0, 1)   B(2, 3)   C(5, 9)

7 Here are two lines: $y = x + 2$ and $y = 2x$.
On which of these lines do the following points lie?

A(5, 7)   B(4, 8)   C(0, 0)

D(1, 2)   E(10, 12)   F(0, 2)

8 Here are two lines: $y = x - 3$ and $y = 3x - 2$.
On which of these lines do the following points lie?

P(2, 4)   Q(3, 0)   R(5, 2)

S(0, −2)   T(3, 7)   U(7, 4)

9 Look at the graph. Decide which of
the equations below matches each
line.

$y = x - 2$ $y = 4$

$y = 8 - x$ $y = 2x$

$x = 4$

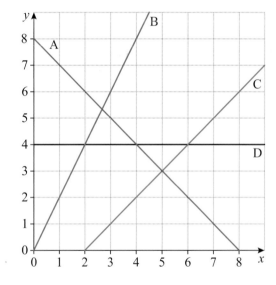

CHECK YOURSELF ON SECTIONS 2.3 AND 2.4

1 Using coordinates with positive and negative numbers

Draw a grid like this …

(a) Plot these points on the grid and
join them up in the order given:
(2, 2), (3, 3), (3, 4), (2, 5), (5, 5),
(4, 4), (4, 3), (5, 2), (2, 2)

(b) How many lines of symmetry does
the shape have?

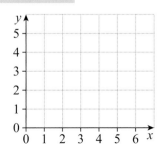

Draw a grid like the one shown.

(c) Plot the points A(−2, 1) B(2, 3) C(2, 0) D(−2, −2)

(d) Join the points to make a shape. Name the shape.

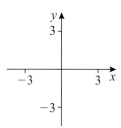

2   Solving problems involving shapes

(a) Points A, D and E are three vertices of a rectangle.
Write down the coordinates of the other vertex.

(b) C, E and D are three vertices of a square.
Write down the coordinates of the other vertex.

(c) B, C and E are three vertices of a parallelogram.
Write down the coordinates of the other vertex.

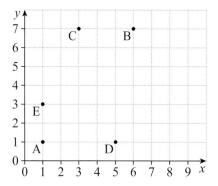

3   Lines parallel to the axes

ABCD is a rectangle.

(a) Write down the coordinates of A.

(b) Write down the equation of line AD.

(c) Write down the equation of line DC.

(d) N is in the middle of the rectangle.
What are the coordinates of N?

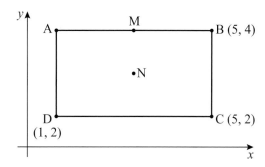

4   Drawing straight line graphs

(a) The equation of a line is $y = x + 3$.
Copy and complete a list of points on the line:

(0, 3), (1, ☐), (2, ☐), (3, ☐), (4, ☐)

(b) Draw x and y axes.

(c) Plot the points above and draw the graph of $y = x + 3$.

✕ Spot the mistakes 3 ✕

Fractions, decimals, percentages and straight line graphs

Work through each question below and *explain clearly* what mistakes have been made.
Beware – some questions are correctly done.

1 $\dfrac{3}{5} \times \dfrac{7}{8} = \dfrac{24}{40} \times \dfrac{35}{40} = \dfrac{840}{40} = 21$

2 $\dfrac{5}{8} - \dfrac{1}{3} = \dfrac{5-1}{8-3} = \dfrac{4}{5}$

3 $19\% = \dfrac{19}{100} = 0.019$

4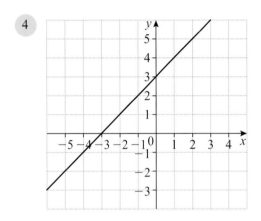

The equation of this line
is $y = x + 4$

5 $\dfrac{5}{11} + \dfrac{1}{4} = \dfrac{20 + 11}{44} = \dfrac{31}{44}$

6 $\dfrac{13}{20} = \dfrac{52}{100} = 0.52$

7 Write down the equation
of the line which the
points A, H and L lie on.

Answer: $y = 2$

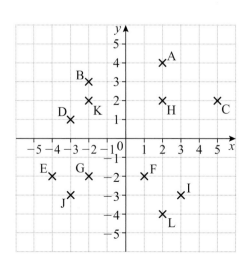

8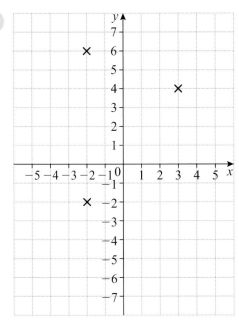

The three crosses shown can be joined with the point $(3, -4)$ to form a parallelogram.

9 $\dfrac{3}{4} \times 3 = \dfrac{9}{12} = \dfrac{3}{4}$

10 Write the numbers 0.7, $\dfrac{1}{8}$, 76%, 0.72 in order of size, starting with the smallest.

Answer: $0.7 = 0.70$, $\dfrac{1}{8} = 0.8$, $76\% = \dfrac{76}{100} = 0.76$ and 0.72

so order is 0.7, 0.72, 76%, $\dfrac{1}{8}$

2.5 Perimeter and area

In section 2.5 you will learn how to:

- find perimeters
- find areas involving rectangles
- find areas involving triangles

Perimeter

The perimeter of a shape is the distance around its edges. It is a length and is measured in units of length such as metres or centimetres.

118

Exercise 1M

1 The shapes below are drawn on 1 cm squared paper.

Find the perimeter of each shape.

(a)

(b)

2 What is the **total** perimeter of these 2 **squares**?

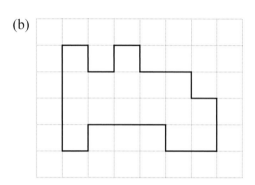

3 cm

7 cm

3 Copy and complete this table showing the measurements of rectangles.

Length	9 cm	8 cm	6 cm	8 cm	6.7 cm	
Width	7 cm	3 cm			2.9 cm	4.5 cm
Perimeter			26 cm	34 cm		37 cm

4 7 m

9 m

(a) Find the perimeter of this garden.

(b) Ed wants to put fence panels around
the entire edge of the garden.
Each fence panel is 2 m long.
How many fence panels will Ed need?
The panels can be cut if necessary.

5 The perimeter of a rectangular lawn is 50 m.
The shortest side is 8 m. How long is the longest side?

6 A picture frame has its length twice its height.
The total length of wood used in the frame is 108 cm.
Work out the length of the frame.

The shapes in questions ⑦ to ⑭ consist of rectangles joined together. Find the missing lengths and then work out the perimeter of each shape. The lengths are in cm.

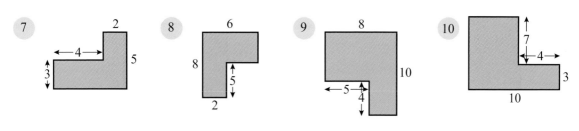

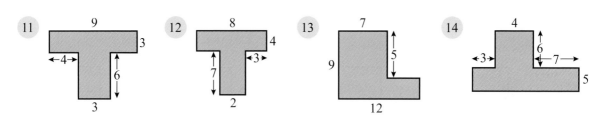

15

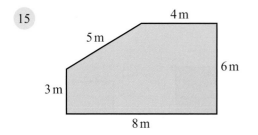

The plan of a ceiling is shown opposite.
Some coving is to be fixed around the entire edge of the ceiling.
The coving costs £3.25 per metre.
What is the total cost of the coving?

Area

The area of a shape is the amount of surface it covers. It is measured in squares, usually square metres (m²) or square centimetres (cm²).

area of rectangle = length × width

Find the area of the shape.
Split the shape into rectangles.

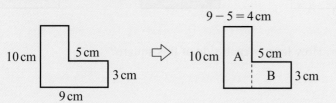

9 − 5 = 4 cm

area A = 10 × 4 = 40

area B = 5 × 3 = 15

total area = 40 + 15
= 55 cm²

120

Exercise 2M

1 Find each blue area below (the lengths are in cm).

(a)
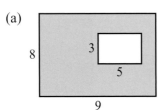

(b)
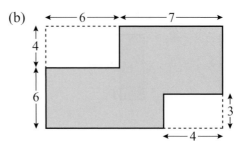

2 Find the area of each square below.

(a) 4 cm
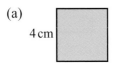

(b) 7 cm
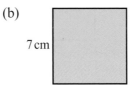

(c) 6 cm
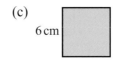

(d) 10 cm
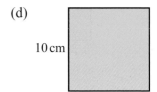

3 Find the area of each shape. The lengths are in cm.

(a)
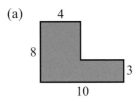

(b)
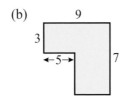

(c)
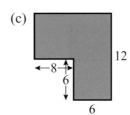

(d)
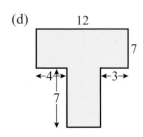

(e)
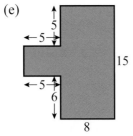

(f)
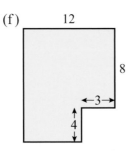

(g)
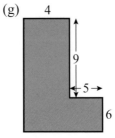

(h)
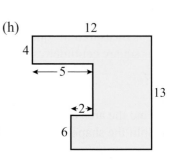

4 A square has an area of 64 cm^2. How long is each side of this square?

5 In the rectangles below, the area is written inside the shape.
   Calculate the length of the side marked x.

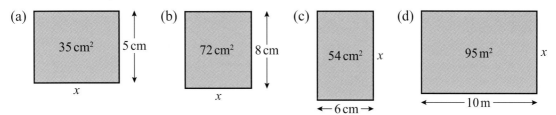

(a) 35 cm² 5 cm x

(b) 72 cm² 8 cm x

(c) 54 cm² x ← 6 cm →

(d) 95 m² x ← 10 m →

6 2 m 1.5 m

   (a) Write down the length and width in cm only.
   (b) This wall is to be covered with tiles. Each tile has a length
       of 20 cm and a width of 10 cm. How many tiles are needed
       to cover the entire wall?

7 A lawn is surrounded by a path which is 1 m wide.

   Calculate the area of the path.

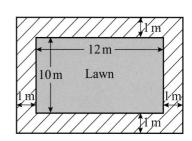

8 A rectangle has a perimeter of 28 cm and a length of 9 cm.
   What is its area?

9 Five identical squares are placed next to each
   other as shown. Each square has an area of 36 cm².
   Find the perimeter of the overall rectangle shown.

Triangles

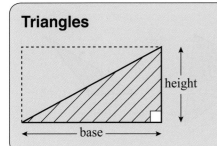

area of rectangle = base × height

area of triangle = $\frac{1}{2}$ (area of rectangle)

area of triangle = $\frac{1}{2}$(base × height)

122

Find the area of each triangle.

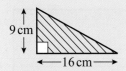

area $= \frac{1}{2}(16 \times 9) = 72$ cm²

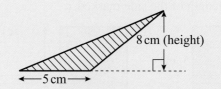

area $= \frac{1}{2}(5 \times 8) = 20$ cm²

Exercise 3M

1 Find the area of each triangle. Lengths are in cm.

(a)
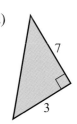

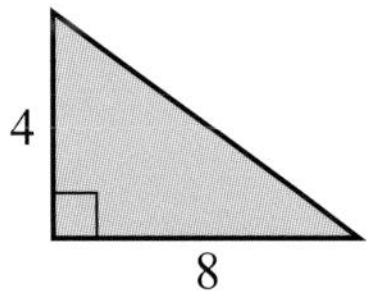

(b)

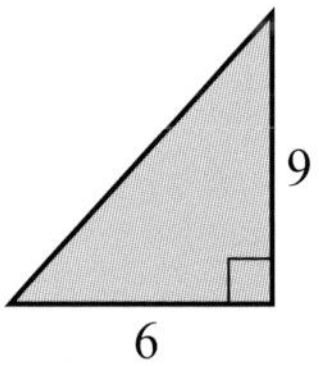

(c)

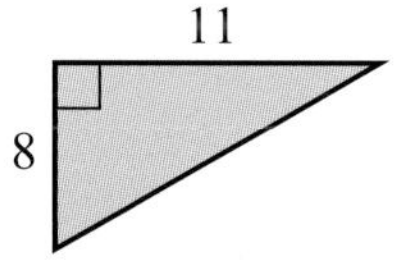

(d)

(e)

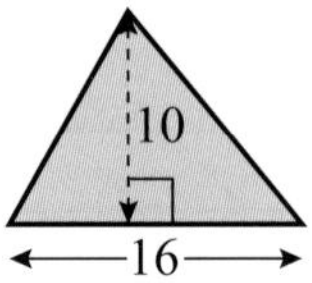

(f)

(g)

(h)

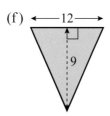
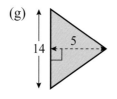
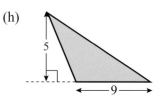

2 A triangle has a base of 8 cm and an area of 36 cm².
Calculate the height of the triangle.

3 Find the area of each triangle. Lengths are in cm.

(a)

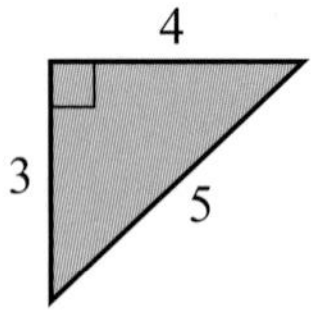

(b)

(c)

(d)

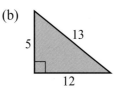
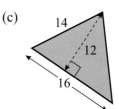
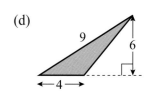

4 A triangle has a height of 18 cm and an area of 54 cm².
Calculate the base of the triangle.

5   Find the total area of each shape. Lengths are in cm.

(a)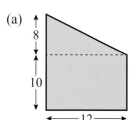

(b)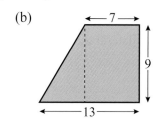

(c)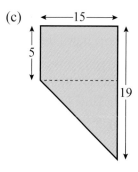

6   Find the total area of each shape. Lengths are in cm.

(a)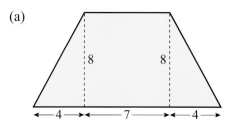

(b)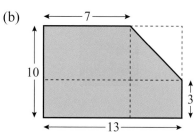

7   The base and height of a triangle are equal in length.
    How long is the base if the area of the triangle is 32 cm²?

8   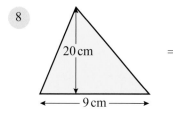   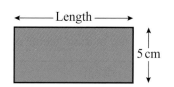   The area of the triangle is equal
    to the area of the rectangle.
    How long is the length of the
    rectangle?

9   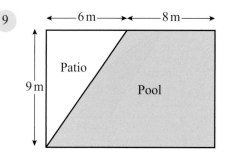   Calculate the area of the pool.

Need more practice with perimeter and area?

1. Write down the perimeter of an equilateral triangle of side length 6 cm.

2. A square has an area of 49 cm².
   (a) How long is each side of this square?
   (b) Find the perimeter of this square.

3.
   (a) Work out the perimeter of this shape.
   (b) Work out the area of this shape.

4. Work out the area of this triangle.

5. Copy and complete this table showing the measurements of triangles.

Base	6 cm	8 cm	14 cm		7 cm
Height	4 cm			30 cm	
Area		36 cm²	140 cm²	90 cm²	105 cm²

6.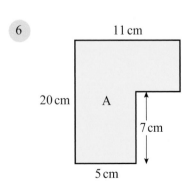
   Which shape has the greater area and by how much – A or B?
   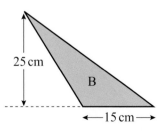

7   The area of rectangle P is
$\frac{5}{6}$ of the area of triangle Q.

Work out the width of
rectangle P.

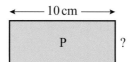

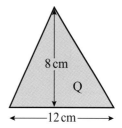

Extension questions with perimeter and area

1   Find the total area of each shape. Lengths are in cm.

(a)

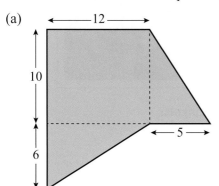

(b)

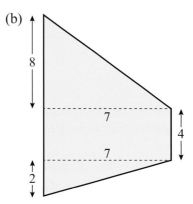

2

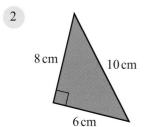

Tanya says that the area of this
triangle is 30 cm². Is she correct?
Explain your answer fully.

3

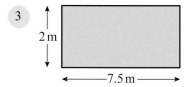

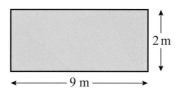

Shahanya wants to paint the two walls shown above. Each tin of paint will cover 11 m².
How many tins of paint will she need?

4 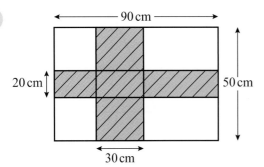 Calculate the area of the shaded cross.

5 A picture measures 12 cm by 7 cm.
   It is surrounded by a border 3 cm wide.
   What is the area of the border?

6 A floor measures 5 m by 4 m. It is to be covered by rectangular
   tiles measuring 80 cm by 50 cm. How many tiles are needed?

7 Each of the shapes here has an area of 2 cm².
   (a) On squared dotty paper draw three
       more shapes with area 2 cm².
   (b) Draw three shapes with area 3 cm².
   (c) Draw one shape with area 4 cm² *and*
       perimeter 10 cm.

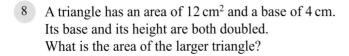

8 A triangle has an area of 12 cm² and a base of 4 cm.
   Its base and its height are both doubled.
   What is the area of the larger triangle?

9 Find the shaded area.
   All lengths are in cm.

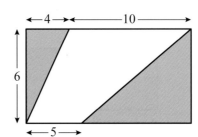

10 Hectares are used to measure large areas. 1 hectare = 10 000 m².
   A groundsman has enough grass seed to cover 1.5 hectares.
   A tennis court measures 15 m by 40 m. How many courts can he cover with seed?

Investigation – area and perimeter

You need squared paper. Each side of the rectangles below must be a whole number.

Part A

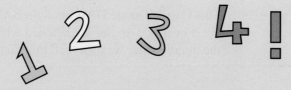

Draw four different rectangles which all have a *perimeter* of 24 cm.

Part B

Draw three different rectangles which all have an *area* of 24 cm².

Part C

Draw at least four rectangles which have a perimeter of 20 cm.
(1) Work out the area of each rectangle.
(2) Which of your rectangles has the largest area?

Part D

The perimeter of a new rectangle is 32 cm.
(1) *Predict* what the sides of the rectangle will be so that it has the largest possible area.
(2) Check by drawing different rectangles to see if your prediction was correct.

Part E

A rectangle has a perimeter of 100 cm. What are the length and width if the rectangle is to have the largest possible area? What is the largest possible area?

2.6 Angles

In section 2.6 you will:

- label angles and measure and draw them with a protractor
- calculate angles on a straight line and at a point
- calculate angles in a triangle
- calculate angles with parallel lines

128

Labelling angles

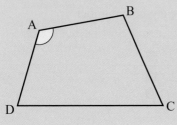

This is called angle DAB or angle BAD. We write this as DÂB or BÂD. Angles are labelled with capital letters and the middle letter wears a 'hat' to indicate an angle.

Exercise 1M

Name the shaded angles below:

1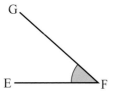

2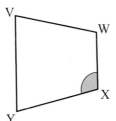

3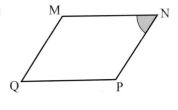

4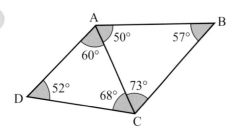

William says that AĈD = 73° and AD̂C = 52°. Is he correct?
Give reasons for your answer.

Give the measurement of each angle listed on the next page.
Remember to read the correct scale. Some questions are done for you, to remind you of this.

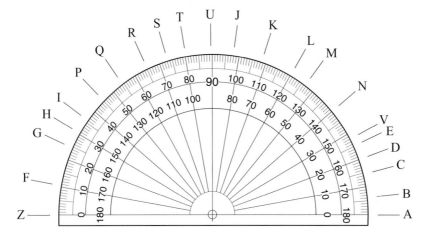

⑤ AÔD = 20°	⑥ AÔN =	⑦ AÔL = 60°	⑧ AÔK =
⑨ ZÔF =	⑩ ZÔP = 45°	⑪ ZÔR =	⑫ ZÔT = 80°
⑬ ZÔI =	⑭ ZÔG =	⑮ AÔC =	⑯ AÔV =
⑰ AÔQ = 126°	⑱ AÔP =	⑲ AÔF =	⑳ AÔB =
㉑ ZÔH =	㉒ ZÔB =	㉓ ZÔC =	㉔ ZÔD =
㉕ AÔG =	㉖ AÔH =	㉗ AÔI =	㉘ AÔM =
㉙ AÔR =	㉚ ZÔE =	㉛ ZÔJ =	㉜ ZÔK =
㉝ ZÔL =	㉞ ZÔM =	㉟ AÔE =	㊱ AÔJ =
㊲ AÔU =	㊳ AÔS =	㊴ ZÔN =	㊵ ZÔQ =
㊶ ZÔS =	㊷ ZÔU =	㊸ ZÔV =	㊹ AÔT =

Exercise 2M

Use a protractor to measure the angles indicated.

①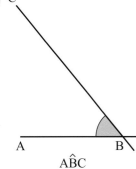

AB̂C

②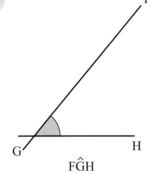

FĜH

③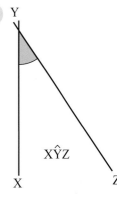

XŶZ

④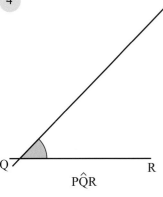

PQ̂R

⑤

DF̂E

⑥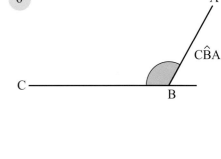

CB̂A

130

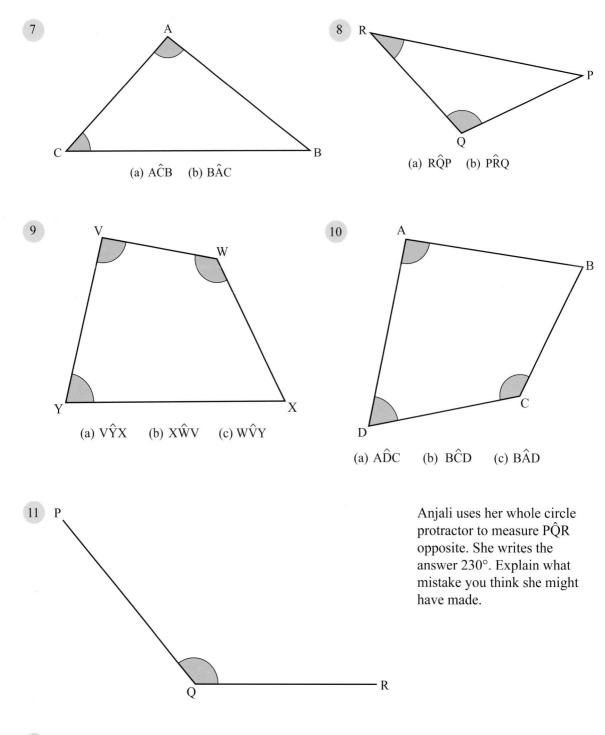

7

(a) AĈB   (b) BÂC

8

(a) RQ̂P   (b) PR̂Q

9

(a) VŶX   (b) XŴV   (c) WV̂Y

10

(a) AD̂C   (b) BĈD   (c) BÂD

11

Anjali uses her whole circle protractor to measure PQ̂R opposite. She writes the answer 230°. Explain what mistake you think she might have made.

12 Write down the instructions you would give to a younger child who needed to measure BÂD with a protractor in question 10 above.

Identifying acute, obtuse and reflex angles

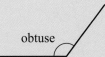

- an *acute* angle is less than 90°

- an *obtuse* angle is between 90° and 180°

- a *reflex* angle is greater than 180°

Exercise 3M

Drawing angles with a protractor

Use a protractor to draw the following angles accurately.

1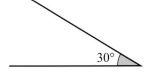

2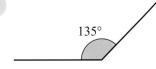

3

| 4 | 85° | 5 | 48° | 6 | 130° | 7 | 33° | 8 | 164° | 9 | 138° |
| 10 | 18° | 11 | 25° | 12 | 210° | 13 | 290° | 14 | 156° | 15 | 304° |

16 For each angle above, state whether it is acute, obtuse or reflex.

Calculating angles on a straight line and at a point

- **Angles on a straight line**

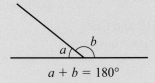

$a + b = 180°$

The angles on a straight line add up to 180°

- **Angles at a point**

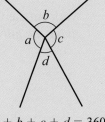

$a + b + c + d = 360°$

The angles at a point add up to 360°

- **Vertically opposite angles**

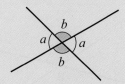

The opposite angles are equal when two lines intersect

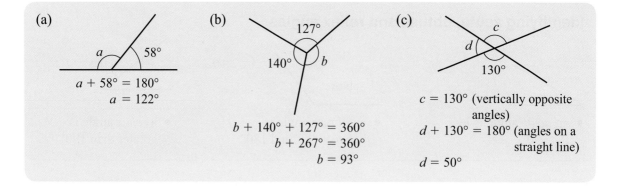

(a)

$$a + 58° = 180°$$
$$a = 122°$$

(b)

$$b + 140° + 127° = 360°$$
$$b + 267° = 360°$$
$$b = 93°$$

(c)

$$c = 130° \text{ (vertically opposite angles)}$$
$$d + 130° = 180° \text{ (angles on a straight line)}$$
$$d = 50°$$

Exercise 4M

Find the angles marked with letters.

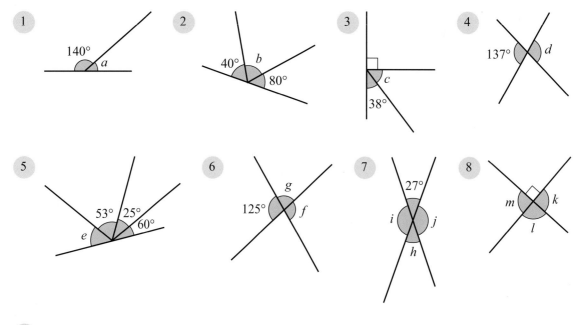

9

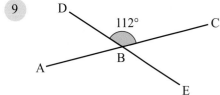

Work out the values of AB̂E and CB̂E, *giving the full reasons for your answers.*

10

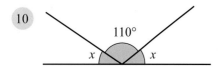

Angad says that the two angles marked x must equal 70° because all the angles on a straight line add up to 180°. This means the value of x must be 35°. Is this correct. Give a reason if it is not correct.

11 Work out the value of *n* opposite.
Give full reasons for your answers.

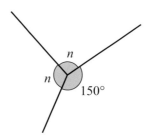

12

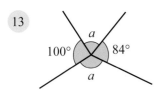

The point where all the lines meet opposite is M.
Are angles AM̂B and EM̂D vertically opposite?
Give a reason for your answer.

Find the values of the letters in questions 13 to 15.

13

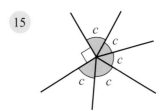

14

15

Calculating angles in a triangle

Draw a triangle of any shape on a piece of card and cut it out accurately. Now tear off the three corners as shown.

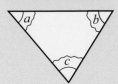

When the angles *a*, *b* and *c* are placed together they form a straight line.

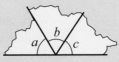

We see that:

The angles in a triangle add up to 180°

134

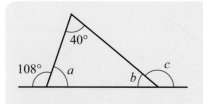

Find the angles marked with letters.
$a = 72°$ (angles on a straight line)
$b + 72° + 40° = 180°$ (angles in a triangle)
$b = 68°$
$c = 112°$ (angles on a straight line)

Exercise 5M

Find the angles marked with letters.

1

2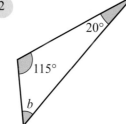

3

4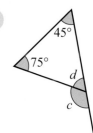

5

6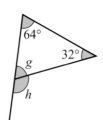

7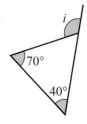

8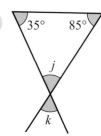

9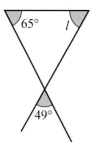

10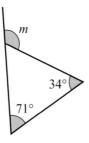

11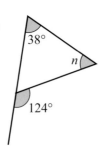

12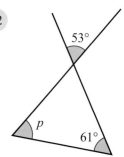

13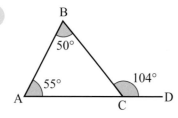

Work out AĈB.
Explain clearly why the numbers on this diagram are not possible.

14   Work out the value of SR̂T opposite.
Give full reasons for your answer.

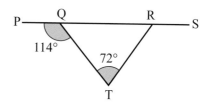

Isosceles and equilateral triangles

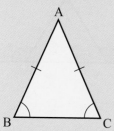

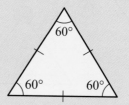

An *isosceles* triangle has two equal sides and two equal angles.

The sides AB and AC are equal (marked with a dash) so angles B̂ and Ĉ are also equal.

An *equilateral* triangle has three equal sides and three equal angles (all 60°).

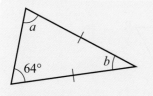

Find the angles marked with letters.

$a = 64°$ (isosceles triangle)

$b + 64° + 64° = 180°$ (angles in a triangle)

$b = 52°$

Exercise 6M

Find the angles marked with letters.

 1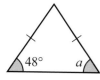

2

3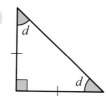

4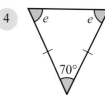

136

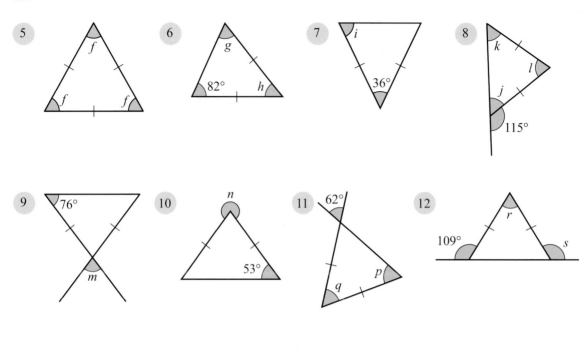

5   f, f, f

6   g, 82°, h

7   i, 36°

8   k, l, j, 115°

9   76°, m

10   n, 53°

11   62°, q, p

12   r, 109°, s

13

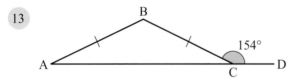

Work out the value of AB̂C,
giving full reasons for your answer.

14   Work out the value of QR̂S,
giving full reasons for your
answer.

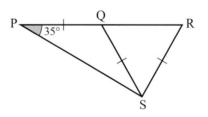

15   Joe is asked to work out the
value of BÂD in the diagram
opposite. He says that no angles
have been given so he cannot
do the question.

Explain how Joe should start
the problem then work out the
value of BÂD, giving full reasons.

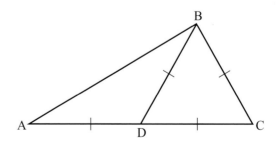

16 Julie has laid a patio with triangular slabs as shown below. She has one space to fill (yellow below). She has 3 slabs remaining. Which slab will fit perfectly into the space? Explain why.

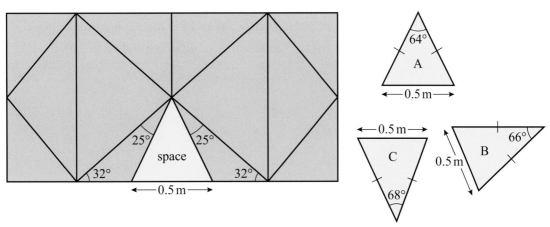

Angles and parallel lines

In this diagram all the arrow lines are parallel.

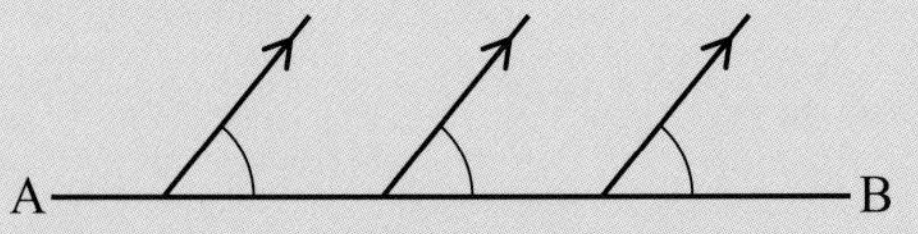

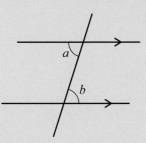

The arrows all make the same angle with the line AB. These angles are called **corresponding** angles.

angle a = angle b
These are called **alternate** angles.

Many people think of corresponding angles as 'F' angles.

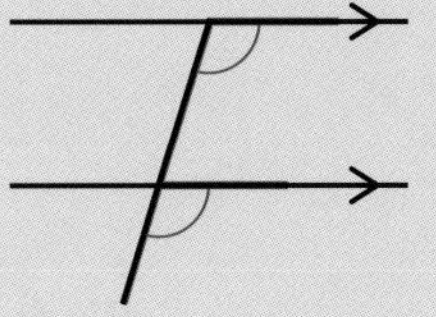

Many people think of alternate angles as 'Z' angles.

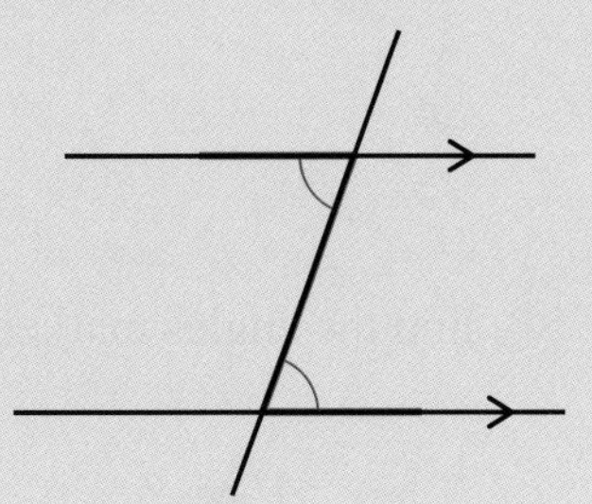

138

Find the angles marked with letters.

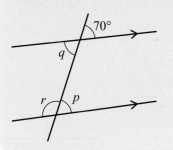

$p = 70°$ (corresponding angles)

$q = 70°$ (alternate angles or vertically opposite angles)

$r = 110°$ (angles on a straight line add up to 180°)

Exercise 7M

1. Work out the values of CÊE and CB̂M, giving reasons for your answers.

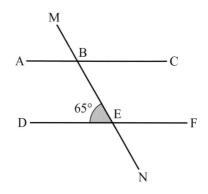

2. Work out the values of PQ̂U and SR̂V, giving reasons for your answers.

In questions ③ to ⑩ , find the angles marked with letters.

3
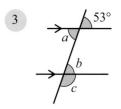

4
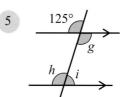

5

6
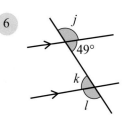

7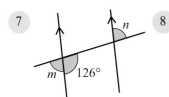

8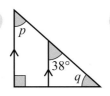

9

10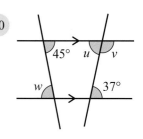

11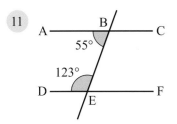

Work out the value of BÊF then explain why the lines AC and DF are *not* parallel.

12 Find the values of *x* and *y* in the diagram opposite.

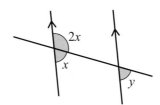

Need more practice with angles?

1 The angle at a point is split into 8 equal angles.
Write down the value of each of these angles.

2 Use the letters shown to write down the name of the angle marked as 75°.

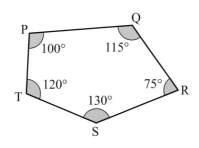

3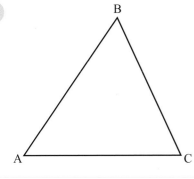

Use a protractor to measure
(a) BÂC
(b) AĈB
(c) AB̂C
(d) Add up all the angles and make sure the total is 180°.

140

4   Use a protractor to draw any 3 obtuse angles which have values which are square numbers.
    (Reminder: 3 × 3 = 9 so 9 is a square number, 8 × 8 = 64 so 64 is a square number.)

Find the angles marked with letters in questions 5 to 12 .

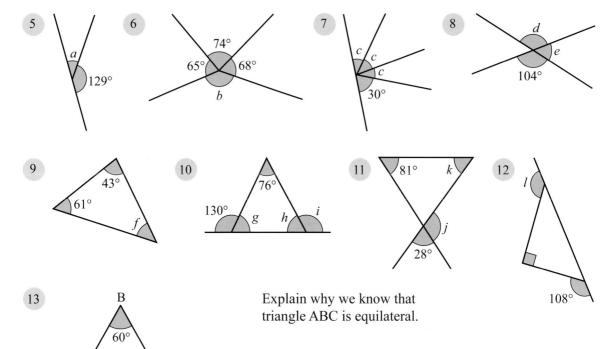

13   B

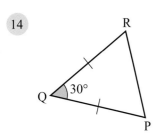

Explain why we know that
triangle ABC is equilateral.

14

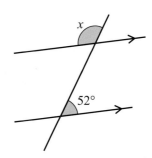

Triangle PQR is isosceles.
Work out the value of PR̂Q,
giving reasons for your answer.

15   Work out the value of x opposite.

Extension questions with angles

Find the angles marked with letters in questions ① to ⑧ .

① 15° a a a a

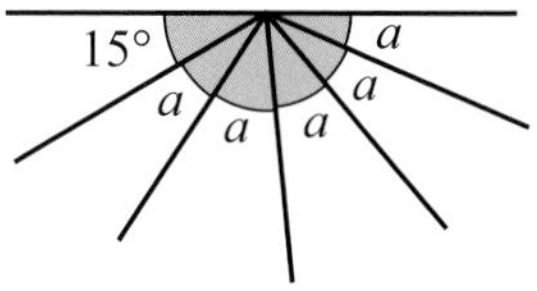

② b $3b$ $2b$

③ 86° c c 86°

④ 110° $3d$ $3d$ $3d$ d

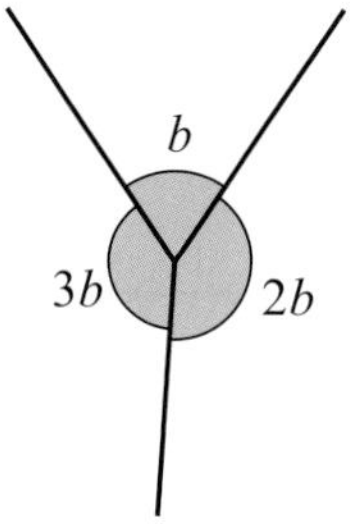

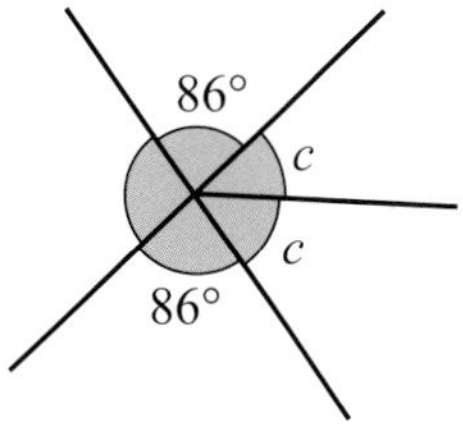

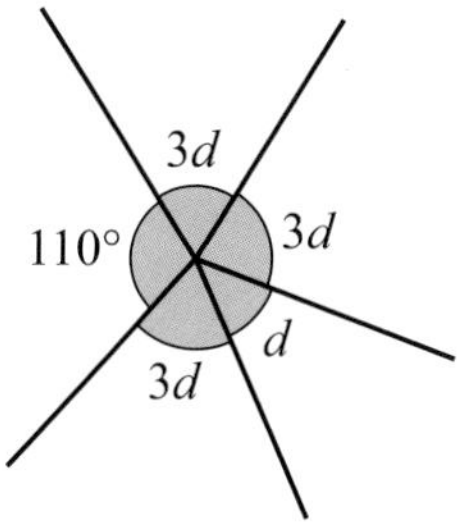

⑤ 74° f e

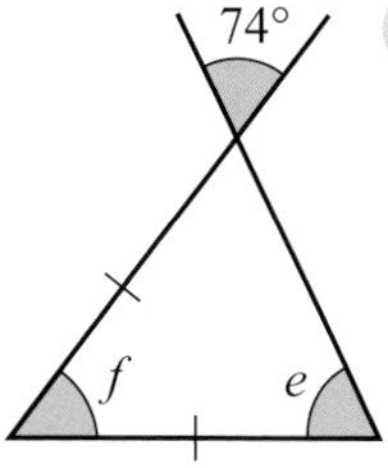

⑥ g 115° h

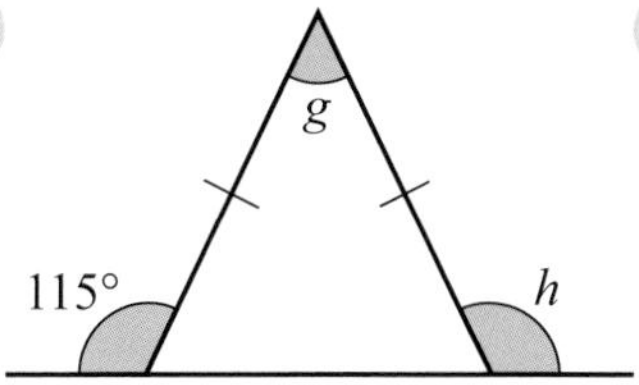

⑦ k i j 58°

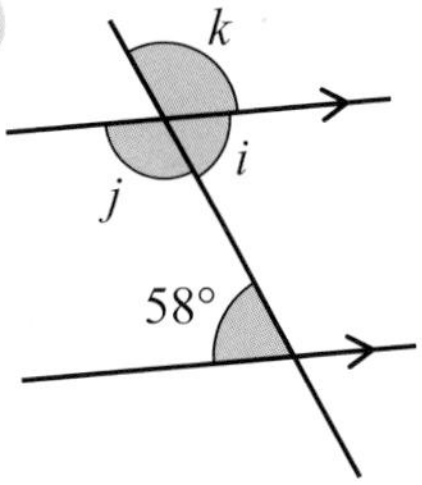

⑧ $6l$ $10l$ $2l$

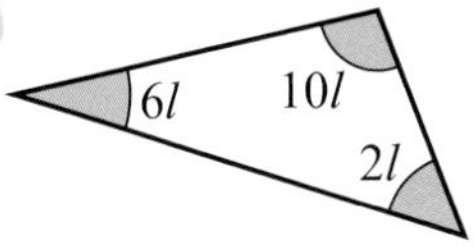

⑨ Prove that triangle BĈE opposite is isosceles. Write down your reasons clearly.

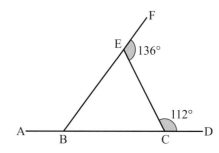

Work out the values of angles a, b, c and d opposite.

⑩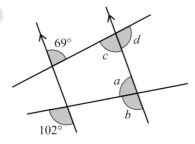

69° d c a b 102°

⑪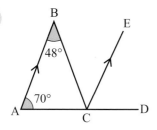

B 48° E 70° A C D

Work out the values of BĈE and DĈE, giving reasons for your answers.

12   One of the angles in an isosceles triangle is 80°.

     (a) Work out the values of the other two angles in the triangle.

     (b) Could there be a different pair of angles? If so, write down the values of these two angles.

13   Work out the values of TŜU and TÛS opposite, giving reasons for your answers.

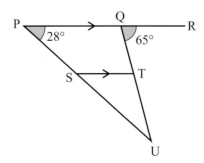

14

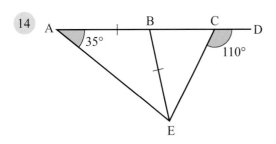

Explain clearly why triangle BĈE opposite is isosceles.

✖ Spot the mistakes 4 ✖

Perimeter, area and angles

Work through each question below and *explain clearly* what mistakes have been made. Beware – some questions are correctly done.

1

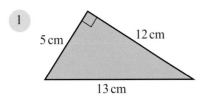

area of triangle $= \frac{1}{2} \times 13 \times 5$

                  $= 32.5 \text{ cm}^2$

2   A square has an area of 36 cm² so the length of one side $= 36 \div 4 = 9$ cm.

3

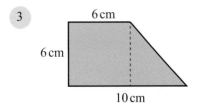

area of square $= 6 \times 6 = 36$

area of triangle $= \frac{1}{2} \times 10 \times 6 = 30$

total area $= 36 + 30 = 66 \text{ cm}^2$

4   Calculate the value of BÂC.

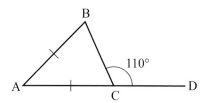

AĈB = 70° (angles on a straight
            line add up to 180°)

BÂC = 70° (two angles in an
            isosceles triangle are equal)

5   The base of a triangle is 8 cm and its area is 96 cm².
    Calculate its height.
    Answer: height = 96 ÷ 8 = 12 cm

6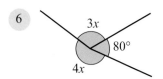

    Find the value of x.

    Answer: $3x + 4x = 360° - 80°$ (angles at a point add up to 360°)
    $$7x = 280°$$
    $$x = 40°$$

7   **12 cm**

    6 cm

    15 cm

    9 cm

    7 cm

    Work out the perimeter of the shape opposite.

    Answer: Perimeter = 6 + 12 + 15 + 7 + 9
                       = 49 cm

8   An obtuse angle added to an obtuse angle always gives a reflex angle. True or False?
    Seb says that this statement is false.

9   Calculate the total shaded area opposite.
    total shaded area = $\frac{1}{2} \times 4 \times 8 + \frac{1}{2} \times 6 \times 8$
                       = 16 + 24
                       = 40 cm²

    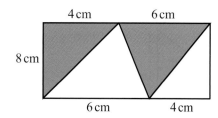

10 8 m

    Pool   4 m

    A rectangular swimming pool has length 8 m and width 4 m.

    The pool is surrounded by a path 1 metre wide.
    Work out the area of the path.

    Answer: large rectangle area = $9 \times 5 = 45$ m²
            pool area = $8 \times 4 = 32$ m²
            area of path = $45 - 32 = 13$ m²

CHECK YOURSELF ON SECTIONS 2.5 and 2.6

1   Finding perimeters

(a) Work out the perimeter of the shape opposite.

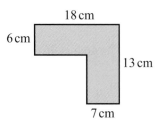

(b)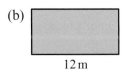

A wall of perimeter 38 m surrounds a rectangular yard of length 12 m. What is the width of the yard?

2   Finding areas involving rectangles

(a) Find the area of the shape opposite.

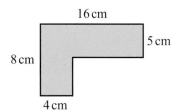

(b) A rectangular room has an area of 42 m². If the width of the room is 6 m, what is its length?

3   Finding areas involving triangles

Find the area of each shape.

(a)   (b)   (c)

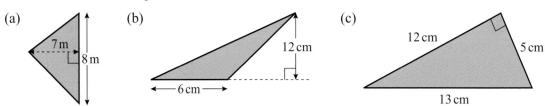

(d)

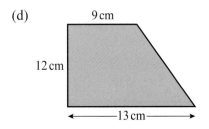

(e) A triangle has an area of 80 m². If the base of the triangle is 8 m, what is its height?

4   Labelling angles and measuring and drawing them with a protractor

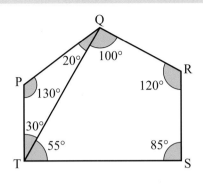

Write down the size of each angle stated below:

(a) RŜT

(b) PT̂Q

(c) RQ̂T

Use a protractor to measure the two angles below.

(d)

(e)

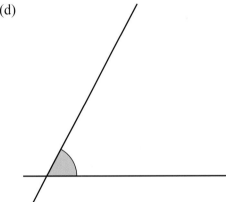

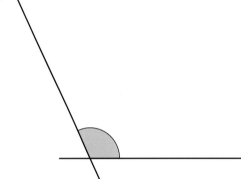

Use a protractor to draw angles of   (f) 73°   (g) 135°

5   Calculating angles on a straight line and at a point

(a)

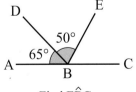

Find EB̂C

(b)

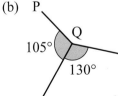

Find PQ̂R

(c)

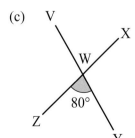

Find XŴY and VŴX

6   Calculating angles in a triangle

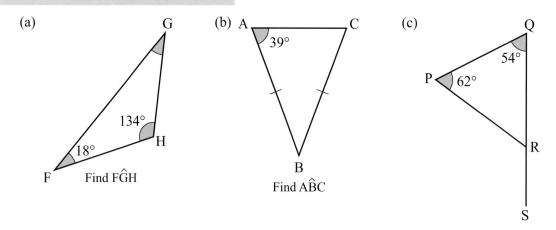

(a) Find FĜH

(b) Find AB̂C

(c) Find PR̂Q and PR̂S

7   Calculating angles with parallel lines

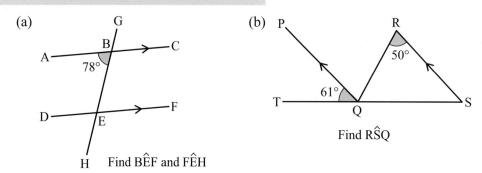

(a) Find BÊF and FÊH

(b) Find RŜQ

2.7 Applying mathematics 2

In section 2.7 you will apply maths in a variety
of situations.

1   Anil has read 97 of the 448 pages in his book.
    How many more pages must he read to reach the middle?

2   There are 15 piles of magazines. Eight piles have 20 magazines each, the other piles each have
    25 magazines. How many magazines are there altogether?

3   The area of the 'U' shape is 175 cm².

(a) Find the area of each small square.

(b) Work out the length of the perimeter of the shape.

4   An electrician uses the formula $V = IR$ to work out the voltage V.
Work out the value of V when $I = 15$ and $R = 16$.

5   Anton has £60. He spends two-fifths of this money on Monday.
$\frac{3}{8}$ of this Monday money is spent on pizza. How much money does Anton spend on pizza?

6   A floor measuring 5 m by 3.6 m is to be covered with square tiles of side 10 cm.
A packet of 20 tiles costs £18.95. How much will it cost to tile the floor?

7

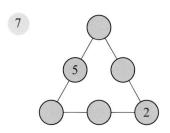

This is a number triangle.
The numbers along each edge add up to 9.

Copy and complete the triangle.

The six numbers are 1, 2, 3, 4, 5, 6.

8   Neve sells two types of robot, the A7 and the D39.
The A7 costs £11 to make and is sold for £19.
The D39 costs £17 to make and is sold for £26.
The table below shows how many robots were made and sold during October.

Robot	Number made	Number sold
A7	128	89
D39	217	175

Work out the profit that Neve made during October.

148

9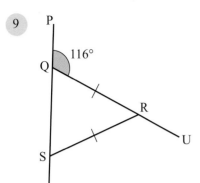

Patrick says that $S\hat{R}U = 128°$.
Is he correct?
Justify your answer fully.

10 Work out $\left(\dfrac{3}{5} + \dfrac{1}{6}\right) \times \dfrac{5}{8}$

UNIT 2   MIXED REVIEW

Part one

1 Cancel down these fractions

   (a) $\dfrac{15}{20}$ (b) $\dfrac{24}{28}$ (c) $\dfrac{36}{38}$ (d) $\dfrac{75}{200}$

2 Work out

   (a) $\dfrac{3}{5} + \dfrac{1}{5}$ (b) $\dfrac{3}{8}$ of 24   (c) $\dfrac{3}{4} - \dfrac{1}{2}$

3 Answer true or false:

   (a) $20\% = \dfrac{1}{5}$ (b) $\dfrac{1}{5} + \dfrac{1}{5} = \dfrac{2}{10}$ (c) $\dfrac{16}{20} = \dfrac{8}{10}$

4 Write down the value of the angles marked with letters.

   (a) 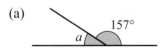   (b) 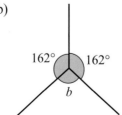   (c)   (d)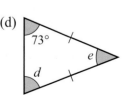

5   Find the area of each shape. The lengths are in cm.

(a) 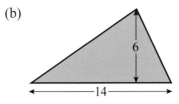   (b)

6   What is 90% as a fraction?

7   Ariana says that 0.4 is greater than 30%. Is she correct or not?
    Explain your answer fully.

8   Work out $\dfrac{2}{3} + \dfrac{2}{7} - \dfrac{1}{2}$

9   Wade has to write down the
    coordinates of a point D so
    that ABCD forms a square.
    He writes down (3, −2).
    Explain clearly the mistake
    he has made.

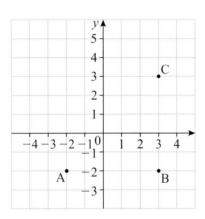

10 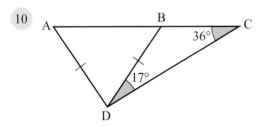   Work out the value of AD̂B.

Part two

1   Copy and complete this table showing equivalent fractions, decimals and percentages.

Fraction	Decimal	Percentage
		16%
	0.7	
$\dfrac{1}{4}$		

2 Which is larger

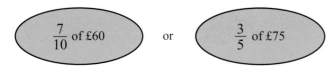

$\dfrac{7}{10}$ of £60   or $\dfrac{3}{5}$ of £75

3 If two angles are alternate, what letter do they form?

4 The letters from A to Z are shown on the grid.
Decipher the following messages

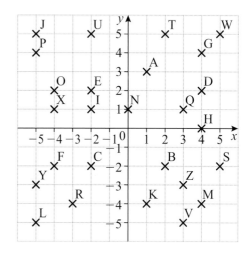

(a) $(5, 5) (4, 0) (1, 3) (2, 5) \square (4, 2) (-4, 2) \square$

$(-5, -3) (-4, 2) (-2, 5) \square (-2, -2)$

$(1, 3) (-5, -5) (-5, -5) \square (1, 3) \square (4, -4)$

$(1, 3) (0, 1) \square (5, 5) (-2, 1) (2, 5) (4, 0)$

$\square (1, 3) \square (5, -2) (-5, 4) (1, 3) (4, 2)$

$(-2, 2) \square (-4, 2) (0, 1) \square (4, 0) (-2, 1)$

$(5, -2) \square (4, 0) (-2, 2) (1, 3) (4, 2) ? \square$

$(4, 2) (-4, 2) (-2, 5) (4, 4)!$

(b) Change the seventh word to: $(5, 5) (-2, 1)$
$(2, 5) (4, 0) (-4, 2) (-2, 5) (2, 5)$.
Change the last word to: $(4, 2) (-4, 2)$
$(-2, 5) (4, 4) (-5, -5) (1, 3) (5, -2)$.

(c) $(5, 5) (4, 0) (1, 3) (2, 5) \square (4, 2) (-4, 2) \square (-5, -3) (-4, 2) (-2, 5) \square (-2, -2)$
$(1, 3) (-5, -5) (-5, -5) \square (1, 3) \square (4, 2) (-2, 2) (1, 3) (4, 2) \square (-5, 4) (1, 3)$
$(-3, -4) (-3, -4) (-4, 2) (2, 5)? \square (-5, 4) (-4, 2) (-5, -5) (-5, -3) (4, 4) (-4, 2)$
$(0, 1)!$

5 There are 72 houses in the village of Cowsley.
There are 98 houses in the village of Sefton.
Last Halloween $\frac{3}{8}$ of the houses in Cowsley
put out pumpkins and $\frac{2}{7}$ of the houses in
Sefton put out pumpkins. Which village
had more houses with pumpkins.
Show all your working out.

6   Here is a diagram of a designer's logo for 'speedo'
    training shoes:

    (a) Make an accurate drawing of the logo using
        a ruler, pencil and protractor.

    (b) Measure the length AB on your drawing.

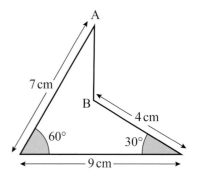

7   The perimeter of the rectangle
    opposite is $\frac{13}{18}$ m. Work out the
    length of the rectangle.

8   In the diagram opposite ... →

    (a) Measure angle $A\hat{B}D$ using a protractor.

    (b) Measure angle $A\hat{C}B$ using a protractor.

    (c) What is the length of the line DB in centimetres?

    (d) What is the length of the line AB in millimetres?

    (e) How many triangles can be seen in the diagram?

    (f) What do all the angles in any triangle add up to?

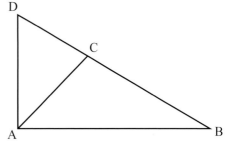

9   Find the area of each shape. Lengths are in cm.

    (a)

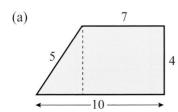

    (b)

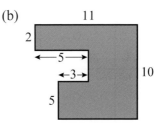

10 Use a ruler and protractor to draw this triangle accurately.
    Measure the length marked x.

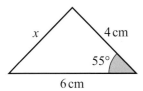

11 Draw an isosceles triangle where one angle is exactly twice the value of each of the other two angles.

12 The equation of a line is $y = x - 2$. Some points on the line are:

(0, −2) (1, −1) (2, ☐) (3, ☐) (4, ☐)

Fill in the missing numbers and then draw a set of axes and the line $y = x - 2$.

Puzzles and Problems 2

Hidden words

(a) Start in the top left box.

(b) Work out the answer to the calculation in the box.

(c) Find the answer in the top corner of another box.

(d) Write down the letter in that box.

(e) Repeat steps (b), (c) and (d) until you arrive back at the top left box.
    What is the message.

1

100	61	62	70	11	71
X	A	D	N	I	F
9 + 12	100 − 11	4 × 15	32 ÷ 8	100 − 45	37 + 22
25	52	90	89	21	9
O	I	O	N	T	E
63 + 8	2 × 7 × 5	60 − 23	45 + 17	14 + 51	88 ÷ 8
91	60	4	37	17	55
N	R	G	R	E	S
38 + 25	60 − 29	49 + 51	3 + 4 + 5	5 × 9	100 ÷ 4
45	65	59	31	63	12
H	H	F	U	N	S
48 + 42	22 − 5	28 + 33	82 + 9	37 + 15	9 ÷ 1

2

90	29	68	91	50	48
X	A	Q	L	R	B
$90 - 82$	$(2 \times 15) + 4$	$70 - 3$	3×13	$60 - 17$	$25 - 16$
1	46	17	28	34	5
A	O	T	E	N	U
30×3	$10 + 2 - 7$	$65 - 43$	$98 - 81$	$18 \div 18$	$27 - 11$
16	41	40	77	33	23
A	P	E	N	A	O
$47 - 29$	$75 - 27$	$16 + 34$	$71 - 42$	$16 + 75$	$91 - 50$
22	43	18	39	8	9
H	E	R	T	Y	A
5×8	$10 + 11 + 12$	$41 - 13$	$65 - 42$	$66 - 20$	$94 - 17$

3

41	60	81	45	54	9
X	A	E	A	R	E
4×7	$31 - (5 \times 5)$	$26 \div 2$	7×9	6×7	7×7
28	63	6	49	10	17
A	T	L	E	Y	L
$55 + 45$	$81 - 42$	$3 \times 3 \times 3$	$200 - 145$	$70 - 18$	$13 + 15 + 17$
0	13	100	39	92	77
A	N	N	O	C	P
$73 + 19$	$20 - (4 + 7)$	$100 \div 10$	$29 + 25$	5×12	$13 \div 13$
52	27	55	30	33	42
O	C	D	N	U	?
$9 + 10 + 11$	$99 \div 3$	$0 \div 7$	9×9	$68 \div 4$	$27 + 14$

4

100	19	84	6	81	56
X	I	E	L	S	W
12×7	9×9	$90 \div 15$	12×8	8×7	$72 \div 8$
96	144	121	97	116	25
V	D	F	W	T	S
$8 + 9 + 41$	$10 \times 2 \times 5$	$84 \div 7$	7×5	$43 - 10 - 7$	$102 - 5$
40	91	101	58	22	5
O	R	D	I	L	U
$20 \div 4$	$71 - 49$	$6 + 7 + 44$	$32 - 7$	$3 \times 4 \times 12$	$67 + 49$
12	35	26	9	85	1
T	A	O	O	H	S
$38 + 47$	$17 \div 17$	11×11	$49 + 42$	$58 - 39$	$2 \times 2 \times 5 \times 2$

5

337	121	356	1	100	180
X	R	S	S	F	E
17×5	$5 \times (31 - 22)$	$7 + 77 + 777$	$1011 \div 3$	$(28 - 19) \times 9$	$17 + 18 + 19$
58	108	472	23	85	321
I	S	E	T	M	E
$4557 \div 7$	$80 - 37$	$8 \times 5 - 39$	$90 - 17 - 38$	$237 - 189$	11×11
35	266	99	45	210	43
R	W	G	S	A	P
$5 \times 6 \times 7$	$10000 \div 100$	59×7	$900 \div 5$	$813 - 547$	$100 - (7 \times 6)$
48	81	54	651	861	745
O	L	A	D	T	I
$3204 \div 9$	$745 \div 1$	$(9 \times 8) - 49$	$1 + 20 + 300$	$3 \times 3 \times 6 \times 2$	$800 - 328$

A long time ago! 2

Napier's rods

An early calculator was invented by John Napier in the sixteenth century. It was made of rods which were marked as shown below. Each rod shows the 'times table' for the number at the top.

	1	2	3	4	5	6	7	8	9
1	0/1	0/2	0/3	0/4	0/5	0/6	0/7	0/8	0/9
2	0/2	0/4	0/6	0/8	1/0	1/2	1/4	1/6	1/8
3	0/3	0/6	0/9	1/2	1/5	1/8	2/1	2/4	2/7
4	0/4	0/8	1/2	1/6	2/0	2/4	2/8	3/2	3/6
5	0/5	1/0	1/5	2/0	2/5	3/0	3/5	4/0	4/5
6	0/6	1/2	1/8	2/4	3/0	3/6	4/2	4/8	5/4
7	0/7	1/4	2/1	2/8	3/5	4/2	4/9	5/6	6/3
8	0/8	1/6	2/4	3/2	4/0	4/8	5/6	6/4	7/2
9	0/9	1/8	2/7	3/6	4/5	5/4	6/3	7/2	8/1
10	1/0	2/0	3/0	4/0	5/0	6/0	7/0	8/0	9/0

To multiply two numbers together eg. 678×7, place the rods together with 6, 7 and 8 at the top. Place next to the blue rod with the numbers 1 to 9.

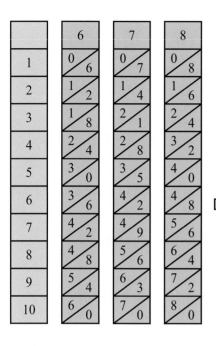

We are multiplying by 7 so look at row 7. Add the numbers diagonally moving from right to left.

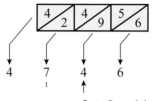

$$678 \times 7 = 4746$$

Exercise

1   Draw and cut out a set of Napier's rods. Your teacher will tell you how long to make the rectangles.

2   Use your Napier's rods to work out the following:

   (a) 368×4 (b) 427×6 (c) 592×7

   (d) 4276×9 (e) 56392×4 (f) 684539×7

   (g) A builder uses 4965 bricks for each of 8 houses. How many bricks does he use in total?

   (h) The Army has to pay 3 shillings each to 27483 soldiers. How many shillings in total is this?

3   **RESEARCH:** Find out:

   (a) When were Napier's rods most widely used?

   (b) In which kinds of jobs were they used?

   (c) How can Napier's rods be used to multiply by 2-digit numbers?

   (d) Can Napier's rods be used for division?

Mental Arithmetic Practice 2

Here are two sets of mental arithmetic questions. Ideally a teacher will read out each question twice, with pupils' books closed. Each test of 20 questions should take about 20 minutes.

Test 1

1. What is thirty multiplied by ten?

2. The side of a square is seven metres. What is the area of the square?

3. What number is eleven more than sixty-nine?

4. Change twenty metres into centimetres.

5. What is one quarter of sixty-four?

6. If I buy a notepad for forty-five pence and a rubber for twenty-two pence, how much change do I get from one pound?

7. How many five pence coins make two pounds?

8. What is twenty per cent of twenty pounds?

9. What is three quarters of forty-four euros?

10. The perimeter of a square is twenty centimetres. What is the area of the square?

11. What number is squared to make forty-nine?

12. What decimal number is fifty-five divided by one hundred?

13. How many faces has a cube?

14. How many minutes is it from nine forty-five till noon?

15. What is the angle between the hands of a clock at two o'clock?

16. What is the perimeter of a rectangle which measures thirteen metres by six metres?

17. Write down one half of three hundred and thirty.

18. What is one fifth of two hundred?

19. Two angles in a triangle add up to ninety-four degrees. What is the size of the third angle?

20. A lottery prize of twenty million pounds is shared equally between forty people. How much does each winner receive?

Test 2

1. Write three hundredths as a decimal number.

2. How many thirds are there in two whole ones?

3. Work out twenty per cent of fifty-five pounds.

4. If you have four thousand pence, how much do you have in pounds?

5. Answer true or false: 'Ten per cent of two thousand pounds is twenty pounds.'

6. What is the next prime number after seven?

7. Write down all the factors of eight.

8. Subtract twenty centimetres from two metres, giving your answer in metres as a decimal number.

9 What is ten multiplied by nought point nought seven?

10 Write three quarters as a decimal.

11 Add together seven, seventeen and twenty-seven.

12 Forty-two per cent of the pupils at a school are boys. What percentage are girls?

13 The temperature is four degrees celsius at noon. Six hours later the temperature has fallen twenty degrees. What is the new temperature?

14 Write in figures the number four hundred and two thousand and twelve.

15 How many sixes are there in fifty-four?

16 What five coins make forty-five pence?

17 A train leaves London at eleven thirty a.m. and arrives in Paris at two p.m. How long does the journey take?

18 What is the sum of six, sixteen and sixty?

19 Find the change from a five pound note when you spend two pounds sixty-nine pence.

20 Write down the next number in the sequence: one, two, four, eight.

UNIT 3

3.1 Properties of numbers

In section 3.1 you will:

- review prime numbers
- use factors and multiples of numbers
- learn about square numbers and cube numbers

Prime numbers

A prime number has 2 factors only (i.e. it is divisible by only two different numbers: by itself and by one).

The first six prime numbers are 2, 3, 5, 7, 11 and 13.

Note that 1 has only one factor so is *not* a prime number.

Exercise 1M

1   Draw a number square like the one shown.

(a) Cross out in pencil the number 1.

(b) Cross out in pencil all the even numbers, but leave the number 2.

(c) Draw a red circle around all the numbers divisible by 3, but leave the number 3.

(d) Cross out in pencil all the numbers divisible by 5, but leave the number 5.

(e) Draw a green circle around all the numbers divisible by 7, but leave the number 7.

(f) Cross out in red all the numbers divisible by 11, but leave the number 11.

1	2	3	4	5	6	7	8	9	10
11	12	13	14	15	16	17	18	19	20
21	22	23	24	25	26	27	28	29	30
31	32	33	34	35	36	37	38	39	40
41	42	43	44	45	46	47	48	49	50
51	52	53	54	55	56	57	58	59	60
61	62	63	64	65	66	67	68	69	70
71	72	73	74	75	76	77	78	79	80
81	82	83	84	85	86	87	88	89	90
91	92	93	94	95	96	97	98	99	100

The numbers which have been left blank are all the prime numbers between 1 and 100.
You have drawn a square for finding prime numbers known as the 'sieve of Eratosthenes'.
Eratosthenes was a famous Greek mathematician working over 2000 years ago.

2 Write down the one number in each list which is prime.

(a) 6,   7,   8,   9,   10

(b) 18,   19,   20,   21,   22

(c) 36,   37,   38,   39,   40

(d) 84,   85,   86,   87,   88,   89

> Prime numbers are used to generate codes and are used for security in credit cards and internet banking.

3 How many prime numbers are there between 1 and 100?

4 Write down two prime numbers which add up to another prime number. Do this in three ways.

5 Find three pairs of prime numbers with a difference of 4 between the numbers.

6 (a) List the prime numbers ending in 1 which are smaller then 100.

(b) List the prime numbers ending in 7 which are smaller then 100.

(c) Apart from 5 why do no prime numbers end in 5?

7 Answer *true* or *false* for the statement below:

'For all whole numbers greater than one there is at least one prime number between that number and its double.'

8 A rectangle has an area of 23 cm².
Its length and width are both a whole number of centimetres.
What is the perimeter of the rectangle?

9 Find three prime numbers which add up to another prime number.

Multiples

The *multiples* of 5 divide by 5 with no remainder.

The first four multiples of 5 are 5, 10, 15, 20.

The first four multiples of 6 are 6, 12, 18, 24.

> The multiples of 5 are the numbers in the 5 times table

Factors

The *factors* of 8 are 1, 2, 4, 8 because 1×8 = 8 and 2×4 = 8

Exercise 2M

1 Copy and complete

(a) 25, 30, 35 and 60 are all multiples of ☐

(b) 14, 21, 35 and 70 are all multiples of ☐

(c) 8, 12, 20 and 28 are all multiples of ☐ and ☐

2 Which number below is not a multiple of 7?

49, 77, 91, 105, 18

3 Fran says that 2, 12, 9 and 8 are all factors of 36.
Is she correct? Give a reason for your answer.

4 Write down *all* the factors of:

(a) 10   (b) 18   (c) 32   (d) 31   (e) 63

5 Find two 1-digit numbers that have 4 factors.

6 Find three numbers that are multiples of both 2 and 5.

7 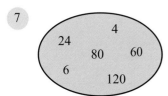 Write down the numbers in the hoop which are:

(a) multiples of 12

(b) factors of 12

8 Find two numbers less than 20 that have 6 factors.

9 Find three numbers that are multiples of 2, 3 and 5.

10 Mary buys boxes of chicken drumsticks
in boxes of 8 and Lana buys the
drumsticks in boxes of 12.
What is the least number of boxes they
each buy so that they have exactly the
same number of drumsticks?

11   The number in each circle is the product of the numbers in the squares on either side.
     Find the missing numbers.

(a)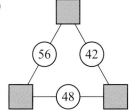

(b)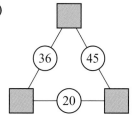

(c)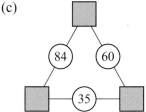

(d)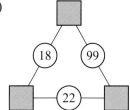

Prime factors

Factors of a number which are also prime numbers are called *prime factors*.

$24 = 2 \times 2 \times 2 \times 3$ Numbers can be written as products
$60 = 2 \times 2 \times 3 \times 5$ of prime factors as shown opposite.

These prime factors can be found by using a 'factor tree' as shown below.

Factor trees

(a) Here is a factor tree for 60

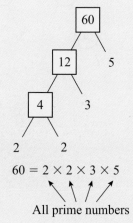

$60 = 2 \times 2 \times 3 \times 5$

All prime numbers

Use pairs of
factors to make
each number.

(b) Here is a factor tree for 24

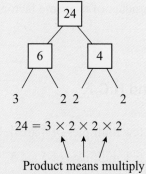

$24 = 3 \times 2 \times 2 \times 2$

Product means multiply

Exercise 3M

1. Copy and complete these factor trees.

   (a)

   (b)

   (c)

2. Write the following numbers as products of their prime factors.

   (a) 30   (b) 70   (c) 100

3. William draws the factor tree below for 90.

   Ava draws the factor tree below for 90.

   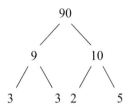

   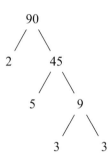

   Which factor tree is correct? Give reasons for your answer.

4. Write each number below as a product of its prime factors by first drawing a factor tree.

   (a) 28   (b) 32   (c) 34   (d) 81
   (e) 84   (f) 216   (g) 294   (h) 200

5. Find the values of a, b, c and d in the factor tree shown opposite.

6. Draw a factor tree then express 2464 as a product of its prime factors

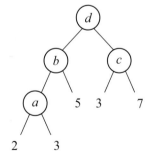

L.C.M. and H.C.F.

The first few multiples of 4 are 4, 8, 12, 16, (20), 24, 28…

The first few multiples of 5 are 5, 10, 15, (20), 25, 30, 35 …

The *Least Common Multiple* (L.C.M) of 4 and 5 is 20.

It is the lowest number which is in both lists.

Exercise 4M

1 (a) Write down the first six multiples of 3
   (b) Write down the first six multiples of 5
   (c) Write down the L.C.M. of 3 and 5

2 (a) Write down the first four multiples of 4
   (b) Write down the first four multiples of 12
   (c) Write down the L.C.M. of 4 and 12

3 Find the L.C.M. of
   (a) 6 and 9   (b) 8 and 12   (c) 14 and 35
   (d) 2, 4 and 6   (e) 3, 5 and 10   (f) 4, 7 and 9

The factors of 12 are 1, 2, 3, ④, 6, 12

The factors of 20 are 1, 2, ④, 5, 10, 20

The *Highest Common Factor* (H.C.F.) of 12 and 20 is 4

It is the highest number which is in both lists.

4 The table shows the factors and common factors of 24 and 36

number	factors	common factors
24	1, 2, 3, 4, 6, 8, 12, 24	} 1, 2, 3, 4, 6, 12
36	1, 2, 3, 4, 6, 9, 12, 18, 36	

Write down the H.C.F. of 24 and 36.

5 The number 6 is the H.C.F. of two numbers x and y.
   Write down possible values for x and y.

6 The table shows the factors and common factors of 18 and 24

number	factors	common factors
18	1, 2, 3, 6, 9, 18	} 1, 2, 3, 6
24	1, 2, 3, 4, 6, 8, 12, 24	

Write down the H.C.F. of 18 and 24.

7 Find the H.C.F. of
   (a) 12 and 18   (b) 22 and 55   (c) 45 and 72
   (d) 12, 18 and 30   (e) 36, 60 and 72   (f) 20, 40 and 50

8   The number 20 is the H.C.F. of the numbers 80 and n.
    Write down a possible value for n.

9   Don't confuse your L.C.M. s with your H.C.F. s!
    (a) Find the H.C.F. of 12 and 30.
    (b) Find the L.C.M. of 8 and 20.
    (c) Write down two numbers whose H.C.F. is 11
    (d) Write down two numbers whose L.C.M. is 10

    Hint: make a table like that in question ⑥

10 Some people play the game Fizzbuzz. They count up through the numbers in turn starting at 1.
    If the number is a multiple of 5, the person must sat 'Fizz' and if the number is a multiple of 7,
    the person must say 'Buzz'. If the number is a multiple of both 5 and 7, the person must say
    'Fizzbuzz'.
    Write down the number reached when 'Fizzbuzz' is shouted out for the *second* time?

11 One musician busks outside the library every
    40 minutes. Another musician busks outside
    the library every 50 minutes. If they are both
    outside the library at 10:30 am, when will
    they both be outside the library again at the
    same time?

Square numbers and cube numbers

A *square number* is obtained by multiplying a number by itself.

3×3 is written 3^2 (We say '3 squared ...')

4×4 is written 4^2

$3^2 = 9$

A *cube number* is obtained by multiplying a number by itself three times.

$1 \times 1 \times 1 = 1^3 = 1$ (We say '1 cubed')

$2 \times 2 \times 2 = 2^3 = 8$ (We say '2 cubed')

$3 \times 3 \times 3 = 3^3 = 27$ (We say '3 cubed')

The numbers 1, 8, 27 are
the first three cube numbers.

Exercise 5M

1   Work out
    (a) 5^2 (b) 8^2 (c) 10^2 (d) 1^2

2   Work out
    (a) $3^2 + 4^2$ (b) $1^2 + 2^2 + 3^2$ (c) $9^2 + 10^2$

3   The sum of the square numbers 9 and 81 is 90.
    Find a pair of square numbers with a sum of
    (a) 13   (b) 73   (c) 40   (d) 181
    (e) 125   (f) 97   (g) 74   (h) 113

4   Here is a 6×6 square divided into 9 smaller squares.
    Draw a 5×5 square and design a pattern which divides
    it into nine smaller squares.

    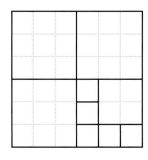

5   Which square number is between
    (a) 50 and 70   (b) 70 and 100   (c) 150 and 180?

6   Which numbers below are *not* square numbers?
                1   4   8   25   49   84

7   Write down the value of 4 cubed.

8   Work out
    (a) 5^3 (b) 7^3 (c) 10^3 (d) 6^3

9   Look at the numbers in the pentagon.
    Write down the numbers which are:
    (a) factors of 16
    (b) prime numbers
    (c) multiples of 3
    (d) square numbers
    (e) cube numbers

    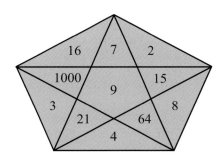

10 Write down two square numbers which are also cube numbers.

Exercise 6M

1   Find a pair of square numbers with a difference of:

(a) 7   (b) 80   (c) 84   (d) 300

2   (a) Write down this sequence and fill in the missing numbers

$$1 = 1 = 1^2$$
$$1 + 3 = 4 = 2^2$$
$$1 + 3 + 5 = \square = \square^2$$
$$1 + 3 + 5 + 7 = \square = \square^2$$

(b) Write down the next five lines of the sequence.

3   (a) Does $(2 + 3)^2$ equal $2^2 + 3^2$? Show working out.

(b) Does $(5 + 6)^2$ equal $5^2 + 6^2$? Show working out.

4   What number when multiplied by itself gives

(a) 49   (b) 121   (c) 169

5   The *square root* of a number is the number which is multiplied by itself to give that number. The symbol for square root is $\sqrt{}$ so $\sqrt{9} = 3$ and $\sqrt{100} = 10$.

Work out

(a) $\sqrt{25}$ (b) $\sqrt{81}$ (c) $\sqrt{49}$ (d) $\sqrt{1}$

6   Copy the following and fill in the spaces

(a) $7^2 = 49$, $\sqrt{49} = \square$ (b) $14^2 = 196$, $\sqrt{196} = \square$

(c) $21^2 = 441$, $\sqrt{\square} = 21$ (d) $3.3^2 = 10.89$, $\sqrt{\square} = 3.3$

7   The difference between two cube numbers is 61. Write down the two cube numbers.

8   The odd numbers can be added in groups to give an interesting sequence:

$$1 = 1 = 1^3$$
$$3 + 5 = 8 = 2^3$$
$$7 + 9 + 11 = 27 = 3^3$$

Write down the next three rows of the sequence to see if the sum of each row always gives a cube number.

9   What number multiplied by itself three times gives 512?

10

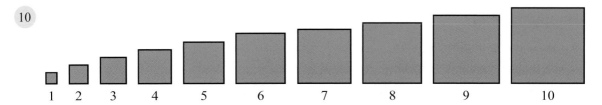

| 1 | 2 | 3 | 4 | 5 | 6 | 7 | 8 | 9 | 10 |

Find the sum of the areas of the 10 squares shown above.
Each length shown is in cm.

Satisfied numbers

The number 4 is an even number *and* a square number. It *satisfies* both categories.

1 Copy the grid below and use a pencil for your answers (so that you can rub out mistakes).

Write the numbers from 1 to 9, one in each box, so that all the numbers satisfy the conditions for both the row and the column.

	Number between 5 and 9	Square number	Prime number
Factor of 6	6	?	?
Even number	?	?	?
Odd number	?	?	?

2 Copy the grid and write the numbers from 1 to 9, one in each box.

	Prime number	Multiple of 3	Factor of 16
Number greater than 5			
Odd number			
Even number			

3 This one is more difficult. Write the numbers from 1 to 16, one in each box.
There are several correct solutions. Ask a friend to check yours.

	Prime number	Odd number	Factor of 16	Even number
Numbers less than 7				
Factor of 36				
Numbers less than 12				
Numbers between 11–17				

4 Design a grid with categories of your own and ask a friend to solve it.

Happy numbers

- (a) Take any number, say 23.
  - (b) Square the digits and add: $2^2 + 3^2 = 4 + 9 = 13$
  - (c) Repeat (b) for the answer: $1^2 + 3^2 = 1 + 9 = 10$
  - (d) Repeat (b) for the answer: $1^2 + 0^2 = 1$
    23 is a so-called 'happy' number because it ends in one.

- Take another number, say 7.
  Write 7 as 07 to maintain the pattern of squaring and adding the digits.
  Here is the sequence:

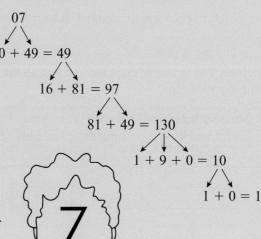

$$07$$
$$0 + 49 = 49$$
$$16 + 81 = 97$$
$$81 + 49 = 130$$
$$1 + 9 + 0 = 10$$
$$1 + 0 = 1$$

So 7 is a happy number also.

With practice you may be able to do the arithmetic in your head and write:

$07 \rightarrow 49 \rightarrow 97 \rightarrow 130 \rightarrow 10 \rightarrow 1$.

You may find it helpful to make a list of the square numbers $1^2, 2^2, 3^2, \ldots 9^2$.

- Your task is to find all the happy numbers from 1 to 100 and to circle them on a grid like the one shown. This may appear to be a very time-consuming and rather tedious task! But remember: Good mathematicians always look for short cuts and for ways of reducing the working.

  So think about what you are doing and good luck!

  As a final check you should find that there are 20 happy numbers from 1 to 100.

1	2	3	4	5	6	7	8	9	10
11	12	13	14	15	16	17	18	19	20
21	22	23	24	25	26	27	28	29	30
31	32	33	34	35	36	37	38	39	40
41	42	43	44	45	46	47	48	49	50
51	52	53	54	55	56	57	58	59	60
61	62	63	64	65	66	67	68	69	70
71	72	73	74	75	76	77	78	79	80
81	82	83	84	85	86	87	88	89	90
91	92	93	94	95	96	97	98	99	100

Need more practice with properties of numbers?

1. When two prime numbers are added the answer is 22.

   What could the two numbers be?

2. Which number is not a multiple of 12?   36, 84, 132, 118, 156

3. Write each line with either 'multiple' or 'factor' in the space.

   (a) 15 is a [   ] of 5

   (b) 8 is a [   ] of 32

   (c) 9 is a [   ] of 90

   (d) 6 is a [   ] of both 18 and 30

4. Find two numbers that are multiples of 2, 4 and 6.

5. Write down all the factors of the following numbers

   (a) 50   (b) 44   (c) 100   (d) 29

6. How many of the prime numbers are even?

7. What is the smallest number with exactly 3 factors?

8. Henry needs to express the number 3300 as the product of its prime factors. He draws the factor tree shown opposite and writes $3300 = 3 \times 3 \times 5 \times 5 \times 11$
   Explain clearly what mistake he has made in his tree.

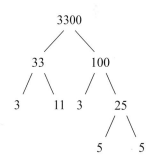

9. Write each number below as a product of its prime factors by first drawing a factor tree.

   (a) 60   (b) 210   (c) 390   (d) 112

10. Find a pair of square numbers with a difference of:

    (a) 45   (b) 32   (c) 39   (d) 105

11. Write down two prime numbers between 30 and 40.

170

Extension questions with properties of numbers

1 What is the smallest number with exactly

(a) 4 factors?　　　　(b) 5 factors?

2 $30 = 2 \times 3 \times 5$ and $165 = 3 \times 5 \times 11$
3 and 5 are both factors of 30 and 165 so the highest common factor of 30 and 165
is $3 \times 5 = 15$.

(a) If $315 = 3 \times 3 \times 5 \times 7$ and $273 = 3 \times 7 \times 13$, find the highest common factor of 315 and 273.

(b) If $1386 = 2 \times 3 \times 3 \times 7 \times 11$ and $858 = 2 \times 3 \times 11 \times 13$, find the highest common factor of 1386 and 858.

3 The factor tree for 1365 is shown opposite.

(a) Draw a factor tree for 650.

(b) Find the highest common factor for 650 and 1365.

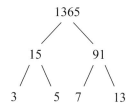

4 *Lagrange's theorem.* A famous mathematician called Lagrange proved that every whole number could be written as the sum of four or fewer square numbers.

For example:　$21 = 16 + 4 + 1$
$19 = 16 + 1 + 1 + 1$
$35 = 25 + 9 + 1$

Check that the theorem applies to the following numbers.

(a) 10　　　(b) 24　　　(c) 47　　　(d) 66　　　(e) 98

(f) 63　　　(g) 120　　　(h) 141　　　(i) 423

If you can find a number which needs more than four squares you will have disproved Lagrange's theorem and a new theorem will be named after you.

5 Rory can swim a length in 40 seconds and Arlo can swim a length in 70 seconds. They both start swimming from one end of the pool at the same time.

How many more lengths will Rory have completed than Arlo when they are both back for the first time at that end of the pool at the same time?

6   Use a calculator to find which of the following are prime numbers.

(a) 143   (b) 108   (c) 221

(d) 293   (e) 493   (f) 323

(g) 151   (h) 1999

Hint: Divide by the prime
      numbers 2, 3, 5, 7, ...

3.2 Further arithmetic

In section 3.2 you will:

- Practise arithmetic with whole numbers and decimals

Reminder

327×45

$$
\begin{array}{r}
327 \\
\times\ 45 \\
\hline
1635 \\
13080 \\
\hline
14715 \\
\end{array}
$$

(327 × 5)
(327 × 40)

$1161 \div 27$

$$
\begin{array}{r}
4\,3 \\
27\overline{)1161} \\
-\ 108\downarrow \\
\hline
81 \\
-81 \\
\hline
0 \\
\end{array}
$$

(27 × 4)

(27 × 3)

Exercise 1M

1   Work out

(a) 36×29 (b) 54×21 (c) 312×24

(d) 207×32 (e) 27×27 (f) 241×32

2   Copy and complete

(a)
$$
\begin{array}{r}
3\ 2 \\
11\overline{)3\ 5\ 2} \\
-\ \square\square\downarrow \\
\hline
2\ 2 \\
\square\square \\
\end{array}
$$
(3 × 11)

(2 × 11)

(b)
$$
\begin{array}{r}
5\ \ 3\ \text{remainder}\ \square \\
13\overline{)6\ 9\ 1} \\
-\ \square\square\downarrow \\
\hline
4\ 1 \\
\square\square \\
\hline
\square \\
\end{array}
$$
(5 × 13)

(3 × 13)

3   Work out

(a) $480 \div 15$ (b) $714 \div 21$ (c) $962 \div 26$

4 Copy and complete

(a) $32 \times 17 = \square\square\square$

(b) $11 \times \square\square\square = 3575$

(c) $\square\square \times 17 = 408$

(d) $22 \times 55 = \square\square\square\square$

5 56 people decide to go to an Amusement Park.
A ticket for the day is £48 per person.
42 of the people travel by coach which
costs £16 per person.
The rest of the people travel in 4 cars.
The petrol for each car is £28.
All the 56 people agree to pay an equal
amount for the Park ticket and the travel.
How much does each person pay?

6 A box of 15 golf balls costs 975 pence. How much does each ball cost?

7 There are 23 rooms in a school and each room has 33 chairs.
How many chairs are there altogether?

8 At a restaurant menu A costs £24 per person and menu B costs £45 per person.
During one evening each person chooses menu A or menu B. If 36 people choose menu A and
the restaurant takes £2169 in total, how many people choose menu B?

Exercise 2M

Work out and give the remainder where necessary.

1 $267 \div 12$

2 $409 \div 11$

3 $637 \div 15$

4 $714 \div 23$

5 $819 \div 25$

6 $561 \div 37$

7 Eggs are packed twelve to a box. How many boxes are needed for 444 eggs?

8 Bambi the cat eats one tin of cat food every day.
How much will it cost to feed Bambi for 31 days if each tin costs 45p.

9 How many 23-seater coaches will be needed for a school trip for a party of 278?

10 In this multiplication the missing digits are 2, 3, 4, 5.
Find the missing numbers

$$
\begin{array}{r}
\square\,\square \\
\times \ \square\,\square \\
\hline
1\ 2\ 4\ 2 \\
\end{array}
$$

11 A prize of 470 chocolate bars is shared equally between 18 winners.
How many bars does each winner get and how many are left over?

12 Angelina pays a £1500 deposit for a holiday
to Italy followed by 12 monthly instalments
of £367.
How much does she pay in total for her
holiday?

13 Each class of a school has 31 pupils plus one teacher and there are 15 classes in the school.
The school hall can take 26 rows of chairs with 18 chairs in a row.
Is that enough chairs for all the pupils and teachers?

14 When Philip was digging a hole in his garden he
struck oil! The oil came out at a rate of £17 for
every minute of the day and night.
How much does Philip receive in a 24-hour day?

15 If $84 \times 63 = 5292$, write down
the value of $5292 \div 63$.

Reminder

Adding and subtracting decimals – line up the decimal points.

$2.\underline{1} \times 0.\underline{0\,3} = 0.\underline{0\,6\,3}$ because $21 \times 3 = 63$ then the number of digits after the decimal
point in the answer must be the same as the total number of digits
after the decimal points in the question.

Exercise 3M

1 Work out
(a) $6 - 1.37$ (b) 0.8×0.04 (c) $7.32 \div 3$
(d) 0.7^2 (e) $8.82 \div 7$ (f) 0.09×0.04

2 Arrange the numbers in order of size, smallest first.
(a) 0.062, 0.06, 0.53, 0.7, 0.065
(b) 0.38, 0.039, 0.327, 0.42, 0.356

3 Which is greater and by how much:
0.4^2 or $15.2 \div 100$?

4 A 3 metre length of steel is cut into three pieces.
   Two of the pieces of steel measure 1.2 m and 0.53 m in length.
   How long is the third piece?

5 Eight ice-creams can be bought for £13.60.
   How many ice-creams can be bought for £22.10?

6 Hattie says that 3.62 + 0.7 is equal to 3.69.
   Explain clearly why Hattie is not correct.

7 Work out the 3 questions below and put the
   answers in order of size, starting with the smallest.

   | A | 5.024 ÷ 8 | | B | 3.46 + 2 + 0.8 | | C | 1.56 × 0.4 |

8 Given that 26 ÷ 8 = 3.25, write down the values of:

   (a) 3.25×8 (b) 32.5×8 (c) $2.6 \div 0.8$

9 Wire costs £5.60 per metre. How much does 2.8 m of wire cost?

10 The perimeter of a square is 3.6 m. Calculate the area of the square.

✗ Spot the mistakes 5 ✗

Number properties and arithmetic

Work through each question below and *explain clearly* what mistakes have been made.
Beware – some questions are correctly done.

1 The lowest common multiple of 18 and 30 is 6.

2 $3^3 = 9$

3 Work out 5542 ÷ 17 so $17\overline{)55^24^72}$ $\overset{3\ 1\ 4\ r4}{}$ so the answer is 314 remainder 4

4 $0.072 = \dfrac{72}{100} = \dfrac{18}{25}$

5 Express 13923 as a product
    of its prime factors.

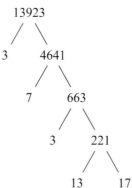

$$13923 = 3 \times 3 \times 7 \times 13 \times 17$$

6 Is 51 a prime number?
    Answer: 51 is prime because it only has 2 factors 1 and 51.

7 $0.32 \times 0.6 = 1.92$

8 Find the 14th largest cube number.
    Answer: $14^3 = 14 \times 14 \times 14$

    14th cube number $= 2744$

$$
\begin{array}{r}
14 \\
\times\ 14 \\
\hline
56 \\
140 \\
\hline
196 \\
\end{array}
\qquad
\begin{array}{r}
196 \\
\times\ 14 \\
\hline
784 \\
1960 \\
\hline
2744 \\
\end{array}
$$

9 $\sqrt{22.09} = 4.7$
    because $4.7 \times 4.7 = 22.09$

$$
\begin{array}{r}
47 \\
\times\ 47 \\
\hline
329 \\
1880 \\
\hline
2209 \\
\end{array}
$$

10 A box contains 24 iPads. Each iPad is worth £349. Imi has 26 boxes.
    What is the value of these 26 boxes?

    Number of iPads $= 26 \times 24$
                           $= 624$

$$
\begin{array}{r}
26 \\
\times\ 24 \\
\hline
104 \\
520 \\
\hline
624 \\
\end{array}
$$

    Value $= 624 \times 349$
           $= £49\,296$

$$
\begin{array}{r}
624 \\
\times\ 349 \\
\hline
5616 \\
24\,960 \\
18\,720 \\
\hline
49\,296 \\
\end{array}
$$

CHECK YOURSELF ON SECTIONS 3.1 AND 3.2

1 Reviewing prime numbers

(a) Write down all the prime numbers between 50 and 60.

(b) Write 30 as the sum of two prime numbers.

2 Using factors and multiples of numbers

(a) List all the factors of 24.

(b) Find the lowest common multiple of 8 and 12.

(c) Find the highest common factor of 45 and 60.

(d) Draw a factor tree then express 150 as a product of its prime factors.

3 Square numbers and cube numbers

Work out

(a) 7^2 (b) 1^3 (c) $3^3 + 4^2$ (d) $10^2 - 2^3$

Find a pair of square numbers with a difference of:

(e) 13   (f) 16   (g) 99

4 Arithmetic with whole numbers and decimals

(a) 27×16 (b) 38×427 (c) $1872 \div 13$

(d) It costs £744 to hire a coach for 31 football supporters. How much does each person pay?

(e) 0.07×0.8 (f) $17 - 0.18$ (g) $22.56 \div 6$

(h) The perimeter of the rectangle shown is 29.4 cm.
Work out the area of the rectangle.

6.7 cm

3.3 Averages and range

In section 3.3 you will:

- review the mean, median, mode and range

- compare sets of data using averages and range

The mean
All the data is added and the total is divided by the number of items.

The median
When the data is arranged in order of size, the median is the one in the middle.
If there are two 'middle' numbers, the median is in the middle of these two numbers.

The mode
The number which occurs most often.
A set of data may have more than one mode.

The range
The difference between the largest value and the smallest value.
The range is a measure of how *spread out* the data is. The range is *not* an average.

The shoe sizes of 8 people were: 8, 4, 6, 10, 7, 6, 6, 9

(a) mean shoe size $= \dfrac{8 + 4 + 6 + 10 + 7 + 6 + 6 + 9}{8} = \dfrac{56}{8} = 7$

(b) arrange the shoe sizes in order: 4 6 6 6 7 8 9 10

$\uparrow$

the median is the $\frac{1}{2}$–way number   median $= \dfrac{6 + 7}{2} = 6.5$

(c) mode $= 6$ because there are more 6s than any other number

(d) range $=$ highest number $-$ lowest number $= 10 - 4 = 6$

Exercise 1M

1   In four different shops the price of a
    pound of apples is 89p, 67p, 76p and 84p.
    What is the mean price of the apples?

2   In eight mental arithmetic tests,
    Carl scores 13, 15, 9, 14, 15, 10, 13 and 15.
    What is Carl's mean mark?

3   Harry played a computer game nine times. His scores are below.

| 43 000 | 37 800 | 46 500 | 48 150 | 33 800 |
| 39 170 | 45 700 | 49 060 | 46 350 | |

    Find his median score.

4 The children in class 7C list how many pets they have.

2	6	3	2	0	1	8	2	1	3	5	2	2
0	3	2	0	1	8	4	2	5	6	1	6	3

(a) Which number of pets is the mode?

(b) Write down the range for these numbers.

5 The shoe sizes of 8 people are: 8, 4, 6, 10, 7, 6, 6, 9

Find   (a) the mean   (b) the median

         (c) the mode   (d) the range

6 Nine dogs weigh 207 kg in total. Find the mean average weight of the dogs.

7 The range for nine numbers on a card is 56.
One number is covered by a piece of blu-tac.
What could that number be?

55	22	13
38	61	10
24	44	

8 Carys and Nina play cricket. During one month they score the runs shown below.

(a) Find the mean score for Carys.   (b) Find the mean score for Nina.

Carys			
28	15	41	38
18	3	13	51
39	14		

Nina			
2	23	9	74
46	12	34	16

(c) Who has the higher mean score and by how much?

9 Rena throws a dice ten times and wins 50p if the median score is more than 4.
The dice shows 5, 6, 5, 2, 1, 4, 6, 3, 6, 2. Find the median score.
Does she win 50p?

10 (a) Calculate the mean of the numbers 8, 5, 3, 8, 7, 5, 6

(b) Calculate the new mean when the lowest number is removed.

Exercise 1E

1 Colin has 5 cards. The mean of the five cards is 7.
The range of the five cards is 8.
What numbers are on the two other cards?

7	7	7		

2

The temperatures in seven towns across the UK were recorded at 03:00.

Grantham	−1°C	Taunton	0°C
Aberdare	1°C	Burnley	−5°C
Loughborough	−2°C	Portrush	−4°C
Perth	−7°C		

What was the median temperature?

3 (a) Copy and complete: 'For the set of numbers 7, 7, 8, 10, 11, 12, 12, 13, there are ▢ modes. The modes are ▢ and ▢.'

(b) Find the mode or modes for this set of numbers 2, 3, 3, 3, 5, 5, 7, 8, 8, 8, 10, 10, 11, 11, 12, 12, 12, 14, 15.

4 (a) Sid has 3 cards. Find the mean. | 5 | 2 | 11 |

(b) Sid takes another card and the mean goes up by 2. | 5 | 2 | 11 | ▢ |
What number is on the new card?

5 Cath has 5 cards. There are two modes which are 11 and 16.
The total on all five cards is 69.

(a) Write down the number on each card.

(b) Write down the median.

6 There were 5 people living in a house. The *median* age of the people was 21 and the range of their ages was 3. Write each sentence below and write next to it whether it is *True*, *Possible* or *False*.

(a) Every person was either 20 or 21 years old.

(b) The oldest person in the house was 24 years old.

(c) The mean age of the people was less than 21 years.

7 Will has 4 cards. The mean for three of the cards is 7.
When the fourth card is included, the mean for all four cards is 6.
Write down the number on the fourth card.

8 Meg has 4 cards. The mean of the four cards is 5. | 3 | 6 | 8 | ▢ |
What number is on the final card?

180

9 The mean age of a group of 10 young people is 13.
One person leaves and the mean age of the 9 remaining people is 12.
How old was the person who left the group?

10 Think of five numbers which have a mean of 6 and a median of 4.
Ask a friend to check your answer.

11 Make a list of 9 numbers (not all the same!) so that the mode, the median and the mean are all the same value (for example: the set of numbers 5, 6, 7, 7, 10 have mode, median and mean equal to 7). Ask a friend to check your list.

Comparing sets of data

The table below shows how many portions of fruit and vegetables are eaten by Calvin and Amy from Monday to Friday one week.

	M	T	W	Th	F
Calvin	1	2	3	4	5
Amy	3	3	3	3	3

Calvin mean $= \frac{15}{5} = 3$

Amy mean $= \frac{15}{5} = 3$

They both have the same average but clearly their pattern of eating is different. To compare the data we use a measure of how *spread out* the data is in addition to comparing an average.

Calvin range $= 5 - 1 = 4$ Amy range $= 3 - 3 = 0$

Amy's portions each day are the same because the range is 0. Calvin's portions each day can differ by up to 4 on any one day.

Comparing sets of data

To compare 2 sets of data, always write at least 2 things:

1. Compare an average (ie. mean, median or mode).
2. Compare the range of each set of data (this shows how spread out the data is).

Exercise 2M

1 12 pupils in Year 7 and 12 pupils in Year 11 were asked how many hours of TV they watched each day. The results are recorded below:

Year 7　　6　7　4　4　2　6　4　5　7　1　3　3

Year 11　　2　1　1　5　3　5　6　8　4　3　1　2

(a) Work out the median and range for each of Year 7 and Year 11.

(b) Write a sentence to compare the number of hours of TV watched each day by pupils in Year 7 and Year 11.

2 Some children in Year 7 were asked how many portions of fruit and vegetables they ate each day. The following were recorded:

Class 7C: mean = 2.3   range = 7

Class 7D: mean = 2.1   range = 6

Copy and complete the sentence below to compare portions eaten by children in class 7C and class 7D.

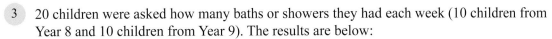

'The mean portion for class 7C is .... than the mean portion for class 7D and the range of portions for class 7C is ....
than the range of portions for class 7D.'

3 20 children were asked how many baths or showers they had each week (10 children from Year 8 and 10 children from Year 9). The results are below:

(a) Work out the mean and range for Year 8.

(b) Work out the mean and range for Year 9.

(c) Write a sentence to compare the number of baths or showers taken by children in Year 8 and Year 9.

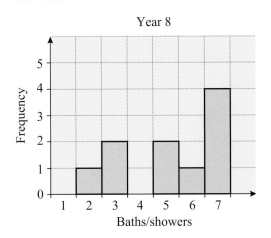

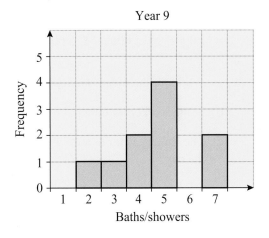

4 The amount (in pounds) that 3 sales people have sold in each of the last five months is shown below.

Olga	7500	6300	6100	8900	8300
Austin	7200	6600	6000	6100	6500
Mia	6700	7900	7300	6900	7200

(a) Find the mean, median and range for each person.

(b) The manager is thinking of promoting Olga or Mia.
Who do you think deserves to be promoted and why?

182

5　The heights (in metres) of the players in two football
squads are shown below:

Catcott: 1.85, 1.95, 1.66, 1.98, 1.88, 1.9l, 1.81, 2, 1.82,
　　　　1.93, 1.88, 1.81, 1.89, 1.95, 1.86

Tipperton: 1.87, 1.99, 1.93, 1.85, 1.94, 1.86, 1.87, l.96,
　　　　　1.92, 1.93, 1.85, 1.99, 1.97, 1.89, 1.96

(a)　Find the median height for Catcott.

(b)　Find the range for Catcott.

(c)　Find the median height for Tipperton.

(d)　Find the range for Tipperton.

(e)　Which team generally has taller players?
　　　Give reasons for your answers.

6　The yearly salaries of people working in Carwells Bakery is shown below.

| £14 000 | £12 000 | £12 000 | £13 000 | £14 000 | £12 000 |
| £13 000 | £12 000 | £75 000 | £13 000 | £12 000 | £14 000 |

(a)　Work out the mean, median and mode for these salaries.

(b)　Some workers want a pay rise. Which average should they use to support their argument?

(c)　The Bakery want to attract more workers. Which average should they use to advertise
　　　the pay?

Need more practice with averages and range?

1　The ages of 5 children are 3, 9, 2, 8, 3

　　Find　(a) the mean　　　　(b) the median

　　　　　(c) the mode　　　　(d) the range

2　In a science test the marks for the boys were 13, 16, 9, 13, 18, 15
and the marks for the girls were 12, 16, 19, 17.

Is the mean mark for the boys greater than the mean mark for the whole class?
Justify your answer fully.

3 Lynne caught twelve fish.
Their masses were:

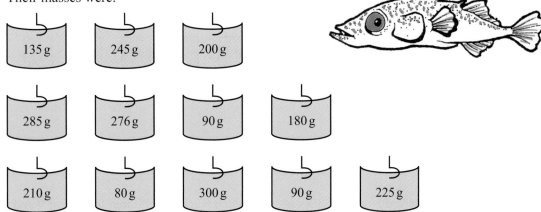

135 g   245 g   200 g

285 g   276 g   90 g   180 g

210 g   80 g   300 g   90 g   225 g

(a) Find the modal mass (the mode).

(b) Find the median mass.

(c) Find the range.

(d) Find the mean mass.

4 The total height of 4 children is 660 cm.
Find the mean height of the children

5

A golfer records his scores for seven rounds
of golf as below:

79   87   79   83   89   79   78

He tells his friends that his average score is 79.
Is he telling the truth? Explain your answer fully.

6 The mean average pocket money received by 4 children is £8 each week.
Three of the children receive £6, £10 and £7 each.
How much pocket money does the fourth child receive each week?

7
| ? | ? | ? | ? | ? |

The five numbers above have a mean average equal to 8.
The mode is 11 and the median is 9.
Write down all the numbers if the range is 8.

8 Mark has thrown a dice 9 times and the mean score on the dice has been 3.
He scores a 6 with his next throw. What is the mean score for all 10 throws?

9 Is the median less than, equal to or greater than the mean for the numbers 2, 11, 11, 2, 11, 10, 2? Show your working out.

10 The seven numbers opposite have a mode of 3 and 10. Their range is 8. Write down what the missing numbers could be.

| 10 | 10 | 10 | ? | ? | ? | ? |

Extension questions with averages and range

1 18 children were asked how often they ate meat each week (10 children from Year 9 and 8 children from Year 11). The results are below:

(a) Work out the mean and range for Year 9.

(b) Work out the mean and range for Year 11.

(c) Write a sentence to compare the number of times meat is eaten each week by children in Year 9 and Year 11.

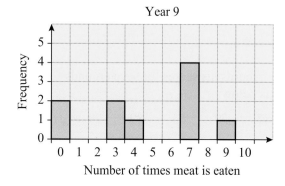

Year 9

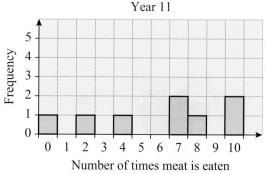

Year 11

2

Helen and Nadia record their best ten times for a swimming race. The times (in seconds) are shown below:

Helen: 75, 70, 69, 70, 74, 69, 73, 69, 67, 74

Nadia: 78, 81, 80, 76, 80, 79, 69, 79, 80, 78

(a) Find the mean time for Helen.

(b) Find the range for Helen.

(c) Find the mean time for Nadia.

(d) Find the range for Nadia.

(e) Who is generally quicker?
Give reasons for your answers.

3 **Investigation** – averages and range

Part A. Look at the class register and ask the first half of the pupils for their height or weight or number of pencils/pens they have or anything of your choice.

Part B. Find the mean, median, mode and range of the data listed in Part A.

Part C. Ask the other half of the pupils for the same data.

Part D. Find the mean, median, mode and range of the data listed in Part C.

Part E. Compare the two sets of data using the averages and range.

CHECK YOURSELF ON SECTION 3.3

1   Reviewing the mean, median, mode and range

Consider 9, 13, 8, 3, 15, 4, 8, 12

Find the   (a) mean   (b) median   (c) mode   (d) range

(e) The three numbers opposite have a mean average
     of 7 and a range of 14. Write down all three numbers.

| ? | 5 | ? |

2   Comparing sets of data using averages and range

The Warriors and the Sabres are 2 basketball teams.
The ages (in years) of the players in each team are listed below:

| The Warriors: | 24 | 22 | 17 | 28 | 22 | 19 | 31 | 27 | 21 | 27 |
| The Sabres: | 28 | 24 | 18 | 20 | 19 | 30 | 27 | 19 | 24 | 18 |

Use the mean and range to write a sentence to compare the ages of the players for the Warriors and the Sabres.

3.4 Displaying and interpreting data

In section 3.4 you will:
- review charts
- draw and use stem and leaf diagrams
- display data in groups
- use pie charts

Reviewing charts

Exercise 1M

1 In a survey children were asked to name their favourite sport.

(a) What was the most popular sport?

(b) How many children took part in the survey?

(c) How many more children chose swimming than netball?

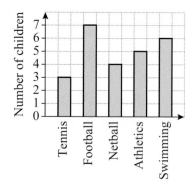

2 This table shows the number of different sorts of snacks sold by a shop.

(a) How many snacks were sold on Thursday?

(b) Each Aero costs 65p. How much was spent on Aeros in the whole week?

(c) Draw a bar chart to show the number of each kind of snack sold in a week.

	Mon	Tue	Wed	Thur	Fri
Mars	3	1	0	0	3
Snickers	0	4	1	2	2
Twix	2	2	1	3	4
Aero	5	0	0	1	4
Crunchie	2	3	4	1	1
Kit Kat	5	0	2	1	1

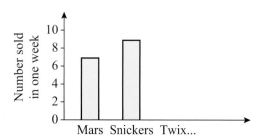

3 The number of people staying in two different hotels in each month of the year is shown below.

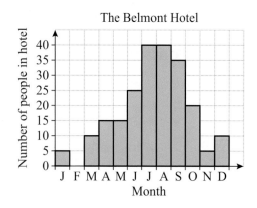

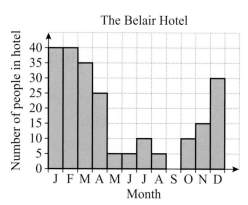

(a) How many people stayed in the 'Belmont' in July?

(b) How many people stayed in the 'Belair' in July?

(c) What was the total number of people staying in the two hotels in April?

(d) One hotel is in a ski resort and the other is by the seaside. Which is in the ski resort?

4   People are asked about their favourite pets.
The results are below (C – cat, D – dog, R – rabbit, O – other).

C   D   D   R   D   A tally chart is made to show these results.

D   C   O   C   C

D   D   C   O   C

O   D   O   R   D

Pet	Tally	Total
Cat	|||||||	6
Dog	|||| ||	7
Rabbit	||	2
Other	||||	4

Two mistakes have been made in the chart. Identify both mistakes.

5   The bar charts show the sale of different things over a year but the labels on the charts have been lost. Decide which of the charts A, B, C or D shows sales of:

(a) Christmas trees   (b) Crisps   (c) Flower seeds

(d) Greetings cards [including Christmas, Valentine's Day, etc.]

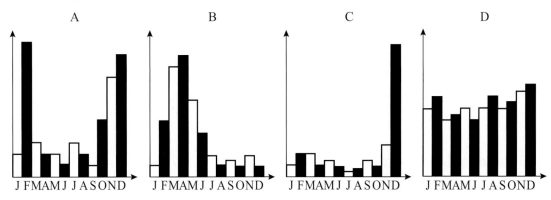

6   Some people were asked to state which was their favourite T.V. programme from the list below.

East Enders   E

MTV   M

Football Highlights   F

Neighbours   N

The Simpsons   S

The replies were:

```
S  N  S  M  N  E  M  F  N  M  E  M  M  E  N
F  S  N  M  M  E  S  E  N  S  E  N  N  E  N
N  M  E  N  N  E  M  F  N  S  E  M  N  F  N
```

(a) Make a tally chart and then draw a bar chart to show the results

		Tally	Total
East Enders	E		
MTV	M		
Football Highlights	F		
Neighbours	N		
The Simpsons	S		

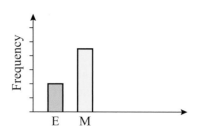

(b) Which programme was the most popular?

(c) How many more people liked East Enders compared to the Simpsons?

7

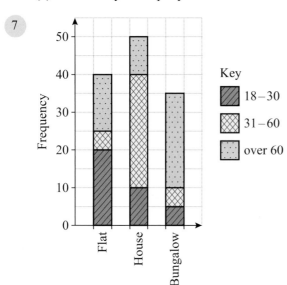

The bar chart opposite shows the type of dwelling people of different age groups live in. This is for one small area in a town.

(a) How many 31–60 year olds live in a house?

(b) A 70 year old is looking for somewhere to live. Which type of dwelling would you most expect this person to be interested in? Give a reason for your answer.

(c) Which type of dwelling is most popular with the 18–30 year olds? Why do you think this is?

Stem and leaf diagrams

Data can be displayed in groups in a stem and leaf diagram.

Here are the marks of 20 girls in a science test.

```
47  53  71  55  28  40  45  62  57  64
33  48  59  61  73  37  75  26  68  39
```

Stem (tens)	Leaf (units)
2	
3	
4	7
5	3 5
6	
7	1

We will put the marks into groups 20–29, 30–39 … 70–79.

We will choose the tens digit as the 'stem' and the units as the 'leaf'.

The first four marks are shown [47, 53, 71, 55]

The complete diagram is below … and then with the leaves in numerical order:

Stem	Leaf
2	8 6
3	3 7 9
4	7 0 5 8
5	3 5 7 9
6	2 4 1 8
7	1 3 5

'unordered' stem and leaf

Stem	Leaf
2	6 8
3	3 7 9
4	0 5 7 8
5	3 5 7 9
6	1 2 4 8
7	1 3 5

'ordered' stem and leaf

A key is needed.

Key
4|7 means 47 in the test

The diagram shows the shape of the distribution.

Exercise 2M

1 The marks of 24 children in a test are shown

41	23	35	15	40	39	47	29
52	54	45	27	28	36	48	51
59	65	42	32	46	53	66	38

Stem	Leaf
1	
2	3
3	5
4	1
5	
6	

Key
3|5 means 35 marks

(a) Draw an ordered stem and leaf diagram. The first three entries are shown.

(b) Write down the range for these marks.

2 Here is the stem and leaf diagram showing the masses, in kg, of some people on a bus.

(a) Write down the range of the masses.

(b) How many people were on the bus?

(c) What is the median mass?

Stem (tens)	Leaf (units)
3	3 7
4	1 2 7 7 8
5	1 6 8 9
6	0 3 7
7	4 5
8	2

Key
7|4 means 74 kg

3 In this question the stem shows the units digit and the leaf shows the first digit after the decimal point.

Draw the ordered stem and leaf diagram using the following data:

2.4	3.1	5.2	4.7	1.4	6.2	4.5	3.3
4.0	6.3	3.7	6.7	4.6	4.9	5.1	5.5
1.8	3.8	4.5	2.4	5.8	3.3	4.6	2.8

Key
3|7 means 3.7

Stem	Leaf
1	
2	
3	
4	
5	
6	

(a) What is the median?

(b) Write down the range.

4 The ages of people in a swimming pool are recorded at two different times of the day.
The information is shown below:

8:30 am

24	52	31	55	40	37	58	61	25	46	45
44	67	68	75	73	28	20	59	65	39	

7:45 pm

30	41	53	22	72	54	35	47	59
44	67	46	38	59	29	47	28	

Stem	Leaf
2	
3	
4	
5	
6	
7	

(a) Draw an ordered stem and leaf diagram for each set of data.
You must include a key for each.

(b) Use the medians and ranges to compare the ages of the people at the two times of the day.

5 The lengths of tadpoles in two ponds are measured.
The stem and leaf diagram for these lengths from
pond A is shown opposite.

Stem	Leaf
3	4 5 5 6
4	1 2 3 3 3 6 7 7 9
5	2 4 5 8 8 8 9 9
6	0 1 1 4 5 5 8 9
7	2 2 2 3 7
8	0 1

Key: 6|8 means 6.8 cm

The lengths (in cm) from pond B are shown opposite.

(a) Draw an ordered stem and leaf diagram for the
lengths from pond B.

(b) In which pond are the lengths generally greater?
Give full reasons for your answer (ie. consider
averages and the spread).

4.3	4.5	5.2	6.8	3.6	7.2
4.0	4.6	3.9	4.1	3.5	4.8
5.9	3.6	4.5	4.4	5.6	6.3
3.8	9.1	4.0	6.8	4.5	4.8
5.6	3.5	4.3	3.6	3.9	

Displaying data in groups

- Here are the ages of the people at a wedding.

33 11 45 22 50 38 23 54 18 72   5 58
37   3 61 51   7 62 24 57 31 27 66 29
25 39 48 15 52 25 35 18 49 63 13 74

With so many different numbers over a wide range
it is helpful to put the ages into *groups*.

Inequalities can be used to identify a *group*.

For example, let Age = A

The group $10 \leqslant A < 20$ means all ages from 10 to 20, including 10 but not including 20.

> Ages are *continuous* data because any age value can be taken.
>
> *Discrete* data is when there can be no values between the data values. For example a family can have 2 or 3 children but not 2.4 children!

• A tally chart can be drawn up.

Ages (A)	Tally	Total (Frequency)
$0 \leqslant A < 10$	|||	3
$10 \leqslant A < 20$	Ж	5
$20 \leqslant A < 30$	Ж ||	7
$30 \leqslant A < 40$	Ж		6
$40 \leqslant A < 50$	|||	3
$50 \leqslant A < 60$	Ж		6
$60 \leqslant A < 70$	||||	4
$70 \leqslant A < 80$	||	2

• Draw a frequency diagram.

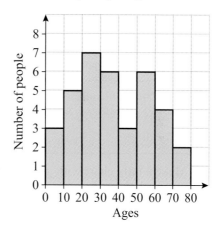

Exercise 3M

1 The heights, in cm, of 30 children are shown below

$$134 \quad 146 \quad 141 \quad 147 \quad 151 \quad 141 \quad 137 \quad 159 \quad 142 \quad 146$$

$$151 \quad 157 \quad 143 \quad 154 \quad 146 \quad 143 \quad 149 \quad 151 \quad 141 \quad 148$$

$$136 \quad 144 \quad 147 \quad 152 \quad 147 \quad 137 \quad 133 \quad 140 \quad 139 \quad 155$$

(a) Put the heights into groups

(b) Draw a frequency diagram

Class interval	Frequency
$130 \leqslant h < 135$	
$135 \leqslant h < 140$	
$140 \leqslant h < 145$	
$145 \leqslant h < 150$	
$150 \leqslant h < 155$	
$155 \leqslant h < 160$	

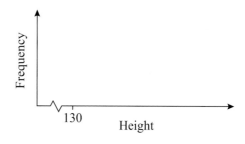

(c) How many children were *more than* 139 cm tall?

2   Tom has lots of snakes and he likes to weigh them
    every week. The weights are shown.

    (a) How many snakes weigh between 60 and 80 grams?

    (b) How many snakes weigh less than 40 grams?

    (c) How many snakes does he have altogether?

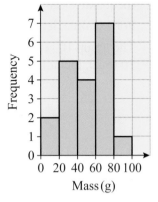

3   The ages (A) of people in a Sports Club at 4:30 pm one day is shown below.
    The ages are in years.

15	24	29	41	34	20	13	12	38
34	11	45	63	13	22	45	32	11
24	17	20	35	13	29	17	20	54

    (a) Make a tally chart with groups $10 \leqslant A < 20$, $20 \leqslant A < 30$, etc.

    (b) Draw a frequency diagram.

    (c) Draw a stem and leaf diagram.

    (d) Write down the median age.

    (e) Which diagram is most useful – the frequency
        diagram or the stem and leaf diagram?
        Give reasons for your answer.

    (f) Describe what happens to the number of
        people as the ages increase.

4   Farmer Gray rears pigs. As an experiment, he decided to feed half of his pigs with their normal
    diet and the other half on a new high fibre diet. The diagrams show the weight of the pigs in
    the two groups.

Normal diet

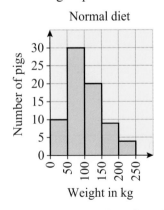

High fibre diet

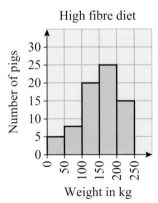

In one sentence describe what effect the new diet had.

Using pie charts

Exercise 4M

1 In a survey children said what pets they had at home.

   (a) What fraction of the children had a hamster?

   (b) What fraction of the children had a dog?

   (c) 40 children took part in the survey.
       How many of these children had a pet spider?

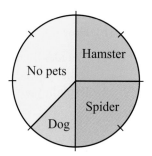

2 The pie chart shows the results of a survey in which 80 people
were asked how they travelled to work.
Copy this table and fill it in.

Method	car	walk	train	bus
Number of people				

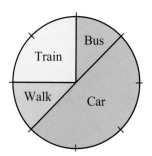

3

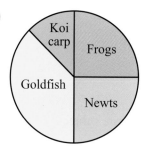

Jodie counted the different animals in her pond.
Altogether there were 200 animals or fish.

   (a) *About* how many frogs were there?

   (b) *About* how many goldfish were there?

4 In 2017 and 2018 children were asked in a survey to say which country they would most like
to go to for a holiday. The pie charts show the results.

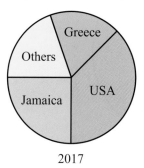

2017

100 children
answered in
each year

Countries in the
'others' section
had only one or
two votes each.

2018

   (a) Which was the most popular country in the 2017 survey?

   (b) Which country was less popular in 2018 than in 2017?

   (c) *Roughly* how many children said 'Jamaica' in the 2017 survey?

5   Lara earns £720 each month.
    The pie chart opposite shows how she spends her money.

    (a) How much money does she save each month?

    (b) How much rent does she pay each month?

    (c) She ideally needs £250 each month for her
         'other' spending. Does she have enough money?
         Explain your answer fully.

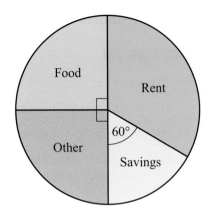

6   In a survey children were asked what *pests* they had at home.
    Five twelfths of the children said, 'my sister'.
    What angle would you draw for the 'my sister' sector on a pie chart?

7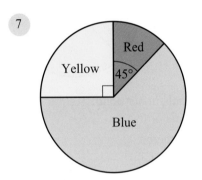

    This pie chart shows the favourite
    colour of 24 pupils in class 7B.
    How many pupils chose blue?

8   The pupils in Years 7 and 8 in a school were asked to state their favourite subject.
    Here are the results.

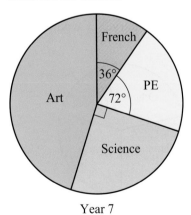

Year 7

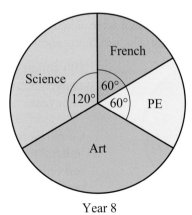

Year 8

There are 280 pupils in Year 7 and 270 pupils in Year 8.

John says 'more pupils in Year 7 chose PE than in Year 8.'
Is John correct? Explain your answer fully.

Need more practice with displaying and interpreting data?

1

Rainfall in cm (y-axis: 0, 5, 10, 15, 20, 25, 30, 35, 40, 45, 50)

Months of the Year (x-axis: J F M A M J J A S O N D)

The monthly rainfall in the Lake District is shown on the left.

(a) How much rain fell in August?

(b) Which was the driest month in the year?

(c) Which was the wettest month in the year?

(d) In which months did 25 cm of rain fall?

(e) How much more rain fell in November compared to June?

2 Here is a *bar-line graph* showing the number of children in the families of children in a school.

(a) How many families had three children?

(b) How many families were there altogether?

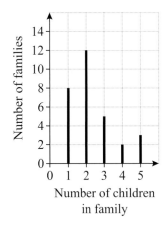

Number of families (y-axis: 0, 2, 4, 6, 8, 10, 12, 14)

Number of children in family (x-axis: 0, 1, 2, 3, 4, 5)

3 Collect your own data for a bar line graph like the one in question **2**.
Ask lots of people to state the number of children in their families.

Draw a graph of the results and use colour to make it more attractive.

4 The stem and leaf diagram below shows the test marks (out of 50) for a class.

Stem	Leaf
0	8 9
1	3 3 6 9
2	4 5 5 5 7 7 8
3	1 1 2 2 3 5 6 6 8 8 9 9
4	2 3 3 6 7

(a) Mitchell says that the median mark is 31.
Is he correct?
Explain your answer fully?

(b) Describe what is missing from the stem and leaf diagram.

5 A teacher has a theory that pupils' test results are affected by the amount of T.V. watched at home.
With the willing cooperation of the children's parents, the pupils were split into two groups:

Group X watched at least two hours of T.V. per day.

Group Y watched a maximum of half an hour per day.

The pupils were given two tests: one at the start of the experiment and another test
six months later. Here are the results:

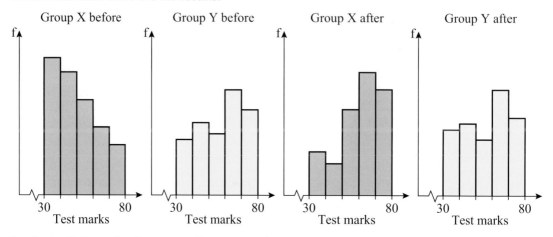

Look carefully at the frequency diagrams. What conclusions can you draw?
Was the teacher's theory correct? Give details of how the pupils in group X and in group Y
performed in the two tests.

6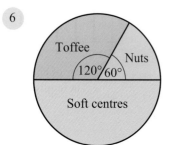

The pie chart shows the contents of a box of chocolates.

Mary eats all the toffees in the box. She eats 12 toffees.

How many soft centres are in the box?

7 This diagram shows the
temperature and rainfall
readings in one week.

The rainfall is shown as
the bar chart.

The temperature is shown
as the line graph.

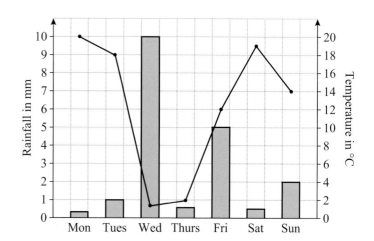

(a) Use both graphs to describe the weather on Monday.

(b) On which day was the weather cold and wet?

(c) Compare the weather on Thursday and Saturday.

8   Shruti started with one frog but it laid eggs and now she has lots!
One day she measures all her little pets. Here are the lengths in mm.

    82 63 91 78 27 93 87 48 22 15
    42 28 84 65 87 55 79 66 85 38

(a) Make a tally chart and then draw the frequency diagram.

Length (mm) (L)	Tally	Frequency
$0 < L \leqslant 20$		
$20 < L \leqslant 40$		
$40 < L \leqslant 60$		
$60 < L \leqslant 80$		
$80 < L \leqslant 100$		

(b) Draw a stem and leaf diagram for this data.

(c) Write down the median length.

(d) Which diagram is most useful for finding the median? Justify your answer.

9   If $\frac{3}{8}$ of a pie chart is red, what angle would be used for this red sector?

Extension questions with displaying and interpreting data

1   A drug company claims that its new nutrient pill helps people to improve their memory.
As an experiment two randomly selected groups of people were given the same memory test.
Group A took the new pills for a month while group B took no pills.
Here are the results of the tests: (A high score indicates a good memory).

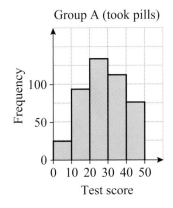

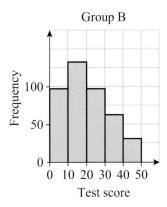

Does it appear that the new pills did in fact help to improve memory?

2 A farmer divides his land into three parts. He uses 5 acres for corn, 3 acres for carrots and 2 acres for pigs. Draw a pie chart to show this information.

Method:

(a) Find the total number of acres: $5 + 3 + 2 = 10$ acres.

(b) Find the angle in a pie chart for 1 acre.

Total 10 acres $= 360°$ total angle in pie chart.

$$1 \text{ acre} = \frac{360}{10} = 36°$$

(c) Find each angle for the pie chart.

For corn, 5 acres $= 5 \times 36° = 180°$

For carrots, 3 acres $= 3 \times 36° = 108°$

For pigs, 2 acres $= 2 \times 36° = 72°$

The pie chart is then drawn as shown opposite.

(d) Draw a pie chart for 16 acres of corn, 7 acres of carrots and 13 acres for pigs.

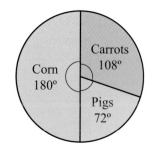

3 Three people get some money.

Jack gets £25, Abi gets £37 and Charlotte gets £10.

This information is to be shown on a pie chart.

Work out what angle is used for each person.

In questions 4 , 5 and 6 work out the angle for each sector and draw a pie chart.

4 Number of programmes per night.

Programme	Frequency
News	2
Soap	5
Comedy	4
Drama	5
Film	2

5 Pupils' favourite sports.

Sport	Frequency
Rugby	5
Football	7
Tennis	4
Squash	2
Athletics	3
Swimming	3

6 Periods per subject

Subject	Frequency
Maths	5
English	5
Science	6
Humanities	4
Arts	4
Others	16

7 A hidden observer watched Anna in a 60 minute maths lesson.

This is how she spent her time:

Looking for a calculator	8 minutes
Sharpening a pencil	7 minutes
Talking	32 minutes
Checking the clock	2 minutes
Working	4 minutes
Packing up	7 minutes

Draw an accurate pie chart to illustrate Anna's lesson.

8

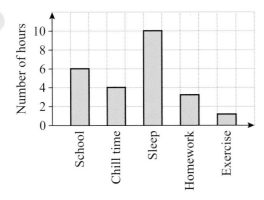

The bar chart shows an average day for Lamara. She draws the pie chart below to show this information but makes a mistake. Describe fully what she has done wrong.

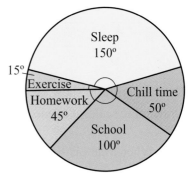

3.5 Probability 1

In this section you will learn about:

- the probability scale
- experimental probability
- expected probability

In probability we ask questions like …

'How likely is it?'

'What are the chances of …?'

Here are some questions where we do not know the answer …

'Will it rain tomorrow?'

'Who will win the next World Cup?'

'Will the school be struck by lightning?'

Some events are certain. Some events are impossible.

Some events are in between certain and impossible.

The probability of an event is a measure of the chance of it happening.

The probability (or chance) of an event occurring is measured on a scale like this …

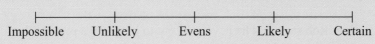

Impossible   Unlikely   Evens   Likely   Certain

Exercise 1M

Draw a probability scale like this ...

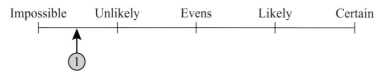

Draw an arrow to show the chance of the events listed below happening.
Draw more scales if needed. [The arrow for question ① has been done for you.]

1   When a card is selected from a pack it will be an 'ace'.

2   When a coin is tossed it will show a 'head'.

3   The letter 'a' appears somewhere on the next page of this book.

4   When a drawing pin is dropped it will land 'point up'.

5   There will be at least one baby born somewhere in Great Britain on the first day of next month.

6   You have the same birthday as the Prime Minister.

7   The day after Monday will be Tuesday.

8   There will be a burst pipe in the school heating system next week and the school will have to close for 3 days.

9   You will blink your eyes in the next minute

10 You will be asked to tidy your room this week.

11 When a slice of toast is dropped, it will land on the floor buttered side down.

12 You will discover a tarantula in your bed tonight.

13 England will win the next World Cup at football.

14 Your maths teacher has a black belt in Judo.

15 You will be captured by aliens tonight.

16 It is 24th December. Rob says that he is very likely to be given a present the following day. Comment on what he has said.

17   Octavia is on holiday in Spain in the Summer. On the Tuesday it is very sunny. Octavia says 'it will probably rain tomorrow because it was so sunny today.' Comment on what she has said.

18   Ben draws an arrow to show the chance of getting a prime number when one dice is thrown. Explain fully why you think he is correct or not correct.

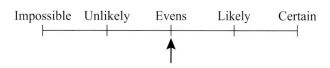

Probability as a number

Different countries have different words for saying how likely or unlikely any particular event is.

All over the world people use probability as a way of doing this, using numbers on a scale instead of words.

The scale looks like this

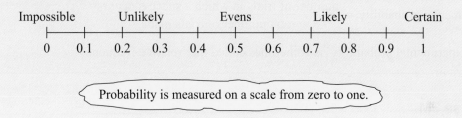

Probability is measured on a scale from zero to one.

Exercise 2M

Look at the events in the last exercise and for each one estimate the probability of it occurring using a probability from 0 to 1.

As an example in question 1 you might write 'about 0.1'. Copy each question and write your estimate of its probability at the end.

Experimental probability

The chance of certain events occurring can easily be predicted. For example the chance of tossing a head with an ordinary coin. Many events, however, cannot be so easily predicted.

Experiment: To find the experimental probability that the third word in the third line on any page in this book contains the letter 'a' (You could use a non-mathematical book if you prefer.)

Step 1. We will do 50 *trials*. Write down at random 50 page numbers between 1 and 180 (say 3, 15, 16, 21, 27, etc.).

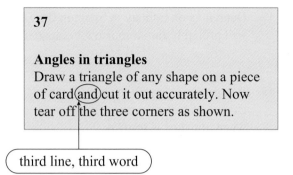

37

Angles in triangles
Draw a triangle of any shape on a piece of card and cut it out accurately. Now tear off the three corners as shown.

Step 2. For each page look at the third word in the third line. This is a *trial*. If there is not a third word on the third line it still counts as a trial. (The third line might be all numbers.)

third line, third word

Step 3. If the word contains the letter 'a' this is a *success*.

Step 4. Make a tally chart like this …

Number of trials	Number of successes
ЦЖ ЦЖ II	ЦЖ II

Step 5. Find the experimental probability that the third word in the third line on any page in this book contains the letter 'a' by doing the calculation shown below.

$$\text{Experimental probability} = \frac{\text{number of trials in which a success occurs}}{\text{total number of trials made}}$$

The 'experimental probability' is sometimes called the 'relative frequency'.

Exercise 3M

Carry out experiments to work out the experimental probability (relative frequency) of some of the following events.

Use a tally chart to record your results. Don't forget to record how many times you do the experiment (the number of 'trials').

1 Roll a dice. What is the chance of rolling a six? Perform 100 trials.

2 Toss two coins. What is the chance of tossing two tails? Perform 100 trials.

3 Pick a counter from a bag containing counters of different colours. What is the chance of picking a red counter? Perform 100 trials.

4 Roll a pair of dice. What is the chance of rolling a double? Perform 100 trials.

5 Alice throws a coin 100 times. Explain why Alice may not get 50 heads and 50 tails.

6   Sasha throws a dice 400 times. He scores a three 100 times.
    Do you think the dice is fair? Justify your answer.

Expected probability

For simple events, like throwing a dice or tossing a coin, we can work out the expected probability of an event occurring.

For a fair dice the *expected probability* of throwing a '3' is $\frac{1}{6}$

Getting a score on a dice is called an *outcome*.

> If all outcomes have an equal chance of happening then
>
> $$\text{Expected probability} = \frac{\text{the number of ways the event can happen}}{\text{the number of possible outcomes}}$$

Random choice: If a card is chosen at random from a pack it means that every card has an equal chance of being chosen.

Nine identical discs numbered 1, 2, 3, 4, 5, 6, 7, 8, 9 are put into a bag.

One disc is selected at random.

In this example there are 9 possible equally likely outcomes of a trial.

(a) The probability of selecting a '4' $= \frac{1}{9}$

   This may be written p (selecting a '4') $= \frac{1}{9}$

(b) p (selecting an odd number) $= \frac{5}{9}$

(c) p (selecting a number greater than 5) $= \frac{4}{9}$

Exercise 4M

1   What is the probability of getting blue on each spinner?

(a) 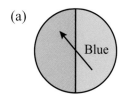   (b) 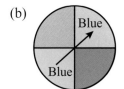   (c) 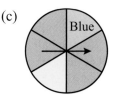   (d)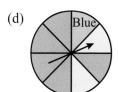

2   A pencil case contains pencils of the following colours:- 6 red, 3 black, 1 green and 1 blue. One pencil is selected without looking. Find the probability that the pencil is

(a) red   (b) black   (c) green

3   One peg is selected at random from those shown.
    What is the probability of selecting the one red peg?

4   Eight identical discs numbered 1, 2, 3, 4, 5, 6, 7, 8 are put into a bag.
    One disc is selected at random.
    Find the probability of selecting

    (a) a '5'   (b) an odd number   (c) a number less than 6

5   Ten people are trying to hit the bullseye on a dartboard. Julian says he has an equal probability
    to Chloe of hitting the bullseye. Is he correct? Give a reason for your answer.

6   I buy a fish at random from a pond containing 3 piranhas,
    2 baby sharks and 7 goldfish. Find the probability that the
    fish I chose is

    (a) a goldfish

    (b) a baby shark

    (c) dangerous

    (d) glad I rescued it!

7   A bag contains 4 red balls and 7 white balls.
    One ball is selected at random.
    Find the probability that it is
    (a) red   (b) white

8   A bag contains 2 red balls, 4 white balls and 5 blue balls.
    One ball is selected at random.
    Find the probability of selecting
    (a) a red ball   (b) a white ball   (c) a blue ball

9   Helga has a bag containing 7 blue balls and 3 red balls.
    Suraj has a box containing 15 blue balls and 5 red balls.
    They each take out one ball at random.
    Who is more likely to take out a red ball?
    Give a reason for your answer.

10 There are 14 discs in a bag. Grayson says that the probability of taking a blue disc
    when he randomly removes a disc from the bag is $\frac{1}{3}$.
    Explain clearly why Grayson cannot be correct.

Need more practice with probability?

1 For each spinner what is the probability of getting blue?

(a) 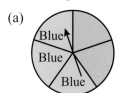 (b) 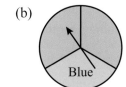 (c) 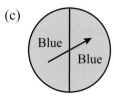 (d)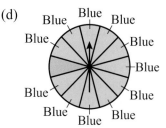

2 Evelyn throws a fair dice five times and gets scores of 2, 5, 6, 1 and 3.
   She throws the dice one more time. What is the probability that she will get a 4?

3 Nine identical discs numbered 1, 3, 4, 5, 7, 8, 10, 11, 15 are put into a bag.
   One disc is selected at random.
   Find the probability of selecting

   (a) a '10' (b) an even number (c) a number more than 6

4

   Ten identical discs numbered 1, 2, 3, 4, 5, 6, 7, 8, 9, 10 are put into a bag.
   One disc is selected at random.
   Copy the number line above then mark with an arrow the probability of
   selecting a square number.

5 I roll an ordinary dice. Find the probability that I score

   (a) 3

   (b) 1

   (c) less than 5

6 A box of crayons contains the following colours.

2 red	6 yellow
8 blue	3 orange
1 green	4 brown

   A crayon is chosen at random.
   Which colour has a probability $\frac{1}{3}$ of being chosen?
   Justify your answer

7 What is the probability of spinning?

   (a) yellow (b) green

   (c) pink or yellow (d) blue

   (e) not blue?

   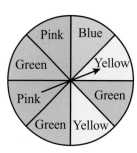

8 Maya throws a coin 600 times and it lands on tails 311 times.
   Do you think the coin is fair?
   Give a reason for your answer.

9 The probability of Wetton United winning a football game is $\frac{2}{3}$.
   What is the probability of Wetton United not winning a football game?

10 A bag contains numbered discs as shown.
    One disc is selected at random.
    Write down the probability of choosing a prime number.

Extension questions with probability

1 One card is selected at random from the cards shown.
   Find the probability of selecting
   (a) the king of hearts
   (b) a joker
   (c) a 2
   (d) an ace

2 A bag contains fifty balls numbered from 1 to 50.
   One ball is selected at random.
   Find the probability that it is
   (a) a multiple of 10   (b) a square number
   (c) a prime number   (d) divisible by 9
   (e) a cube number   (f) a factor of both 7 and 15

3 The horse 'Optimist' wins seven races
   out of seven. Owen says that 'Optimist'
   is dead certain to win the next race.
   Is Owen correct?
   Explain your answer fully.

4 Fiona has a bag containing 7 yellow beads and 5 green beads.
Hector has a bag containing 20 yellow beads and 16 green beads.
They each take out one bead at random.
Who is more likely to take out a yellow bead?
Give a reason for your answer.

5

The alphabet bricks are put in a bag and
one brick is selected at random.
Find the probability that the letter chosen is

(a) a vowel

(b) the 'Z'

(c) a letter in the word 'HAT'

(d) a letter in the word 'MUSIC'

6 The probability of Omar winning a game of chess is 0.3 and the probability of drawing is 0.2.
What is the probability of Omar losing?

7 50 Christmas presents are given out randomly to some elderly people in a Care home.
Five of the presents are radios, 20 are books and the rest are boxes of chocolates.

(a) Mr Jackson is the first person to open a present.
What is the probability that he gets a radio?

(b) What is the probability that Mr. Jackson does not get a book?

(c) Mr Jackson in fact gets a box of chocolates.
Mrs Perkins opens her present next. What is the probability that she gets a radio?

8 For this question you need a dice.

(a) Copy the table below and fill in the second row.

Number of rolls of dice	12	24	36	48	60
Number of 4s expected					
Actual number of 4s					

(b) Now roll the dice 60 times, filling in the third row every 12 rolls.

(c) Why do you think that the third row results are different to the second row values?

9 Sienna has a bag containing 8 blue balls, 6 yellow balls and 18 red balls.
Reuben has a box containing 9 yellow balls, 27 red balls and 12 blue balls.
They each take out one ball at random.
Who is more likely to take out a red ball? Give a reason for your answer.

10 There are n balls in a bag. Five of the balls are red. The remaining balls are blue.
One ball is selected at random.
Write down an expression for the probability of choosing:

(a) a red ball   (b) a blue ball

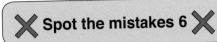

Spot the mistakes 6

Data and probability

Work through each question below and *explain clearly* what mistakes have been made.
Beware – some questions are correctly done.

1 Callum examines the numbers

    7   12   9   1   14   7   2   11

Callum works out that the mode is equal to the median.

2 The pie charts below show the proportion of students who study foreign languages at two schools.

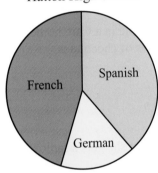

Hatton High School

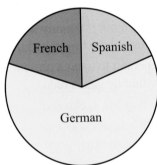

Barchester School

Alyssa says that more students study spanish in Hatton High School than in Barchester School.

3 A bag contains 8 green beads and 4 yellow beads.
A bead is randomly removed from the bag.
What is the probability of removing a yellow bead?

Answer: $\dfrac{4}{8} = \dfrac{1}{2}$

4

Number of pets	Frequency
0	8
1	7
2	14
3	11
4	5
5	2

The table opposite shows how many pets are owned by each family in a small village.

Kiara says that the mode for this data is 14.

5   A cricketer has a mean average score of 34 after 9 innings.
    The cricketer scores 49 in the next innings.
    What is the new mean average score?

    Answer: mean average $= \dfrac{34 + 49}{2} = \dfrac{83}{2} = 41.5$

6   A spinner has the numbers 1 to 4 written on it.
    When the spinner is used, what is the probability
    of it landing on a square number?

    Answer: Square numbers are 1 and 4

    $$\text{probability} = \frac{2}{4} = \frac{1}{2}$$

    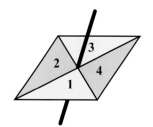

7   There are 20 people in a football squad.
    Four of them are left-footed and six of them wear orange football boots.
    Julia says that if one person is randomly chosen then the probability of that person being
    left-footed or wearing orange football boots is $\frac{10}{20}$ so $\frac{1}{2}$.

8   The ages (in years) of some people are given below. Draw a frequency diagram.

11	32	17	29	24	34	12
29	43	26	29	14	30	45
38	23	25	18	36	17	22

Frequency table is:

Age (A)	Frequency
$10 \leqslant A < 20$	6
$20 \leqslant A < 30$	9
$30 \leqslant A < 40$	4
$40 \leqslant A < 50$	2

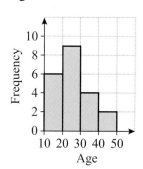

9   Some people are asked where they would most like to go on holiday.
    Their responses are shown in the pie chart below.

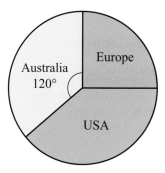

$\frac{1}{4}$ of the people chose Europe.

What fraction of the people chose USA?

Solution: Australia fraction $= \frac{120}{360} = \frac{1}{3}$

Australia + Europe fraction $= \frac{1}{3} + \frac{1}{4} = \frac{4}{12} + \frac{3}{12}$

$= \frac{7}{12}$

USA fraction $= 1 - \frac{7}{12} = \frac{5}{12}$

10   The weights of some dogs are shown in the stem and leaf diagram below.

Stem	Leaf
21	6 7 7
22	2 3 3 3 5 8
23	4 5 7 7 7
24	8 9
25	3 3 6 7

Key: 23|7 means 23.7 kg

Harvey calculates that the mean average weight is equal to the median weight.

CHECK YOURSELF ON SECTIONS 3.4 AND 3.5

1   Reviewing charts

(a) This chart shows the number of packets of different flavours of crisps sold by a shop.

	M	Tu	W	Th	F
Ready Salted	3	1	2	4	0
Salt 'n Vinegar	4	2	5	3	1
Cheese 'n Onion	5	1	3	1	4
Roast Beef	3	2	6	4	1
Prawn	1	1	2	4	4

(i)   How many packets of crisps were sold on Wednesday?

(ii) Each packet of Ready Salted crisps costs 65p. How much was spent on Ready Salted crisps in the whole week?

(iii) This is a graph of one flavour of crisps. Which flavour is it?

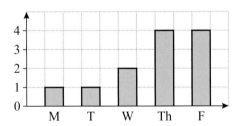

(b)

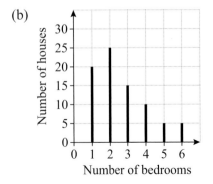

This bar line graph shows the number of bedrooms in the houses in one road.

(i)   How many houses had 4 bedrooms?

(ii) How many houses are in the road?

(iii) Why would it not be sensible to join the tops of the bars to make a line graph?

2 Stem and leaf diagrams

Draw an ordered stem and leaf diagram for the ages given below.

33	45	76	59	57	64	48	63	55	65
64	45	31	52	73	57	68	57	44	52

3 Displaying data in groups

At a medical inspection the 11/12 year-olds in a school have their heights measured. The results are shown.

136.8, 146.2, 141.2, 147.2, 151.3, 145.0, 155.0, 149.9, 138.0, 146.8, 157.4, 143.1, 143.5, 147.2, 147.5, 158.6, 154.7, 144.6, 152.4, 144.0, 151.0.

(a) Put the heights into groups

Class interval	Frequency
$135 \leqslant h < 140$	
$140 \leqslant h < 145$	
$145 \leqslant h < 150$	
$150 \leqslant h < 155$	
$155 \leqslant h < 160$	

(b) Draw a frequency diagram

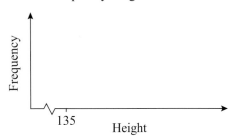

4 Pie charts

In a survey the children at a school were asked to state their favourite sport in the Olympics.

(a) Estimate what fraction of the children chose gymnastics?

(b) There are 120 children in the school. Estimate the number of children who chose athletics.

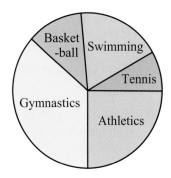

5 The probability scale and experimental probability

(a) Draw a probability scale like this …

Impossible   Unlikely   Evens   Likely   Certain

(b) Draw an arrow to show the chance of the events below happening.
   (i) A dice will show a six on its next roll.
   (ii) Your school will be struck by lightning tomorrow.

(c) Describe a simple experiment where the probability of success is very high.

6   Expected probability

(a) Here are two spinners. Say whether the
    following statements are true or false.
    Explain why.

Gill's spinner   Nick's spinner

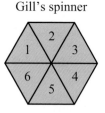

(i)   'Gill is more likely than Nick to spin a 4.'

(ii) 'Gill and Nick are equally likely to spin
      an even number.'

(iii) 'If Nick spins his spinner eight times he is bound to get at least one 8.'

(b) A bag contains 1 blue ball, 3 red balls and 7 white balls.

(i)   If I select a ball at random from the bag without looking,
      what colour ball am I most likely to select?

What is the probability I select:

(ii) a white ball?

(iii) a red ball?

(iv) a green ball?

(v)   a blue ball?

3.6 Applying mathematics 3

In section 3.6 you will apply maths in a variety
of situations.

1   It cost six people a total of £25.50 for a taxi.
    What did it cost each person?

2   A school can afford to put down 4500 m² of astroturf.
    Can the school afford to put down astroturf on the
    whole area of land shown opposite?

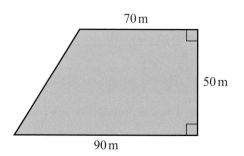

3   Work out the missing numbers

(a) $204 + 360 = \square$ (b) $270 + \square = 800$ (c) $25 \times \square = 500$

(d) $\square + 305 = 500$ (e) $\square - 220 = 450$ (f) $\square \div 12 = 8$

4 Work out the area of the whole rectangle shown opposite.

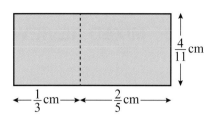

5 The five numbers opposite have mode 2 and median 3.

One more number is added to these which makes the mean equal 5.

Write down the value of this extra number which is added to the list.

6 In this calculation use each of the digits 1, 2, 3, 4, 5, 6. Put one digit in each box to make the statement true.

7 Mel needs to substitute the value $a = -3$ into the expression $a^2 + 4$.
She gets the answer -13.
Is she correct? Explain your answer fully.

8 A mixed school has a total of 852 pupils.
There are 24 more girls than boys.
How many girls are there?
[Hint: check your answer.]

9 CBE is a straight line in the diagram opposite.
ACB and BDE are isosceles triangles.
Work out the value of $A\widehat{B}D$, giving your reasons.

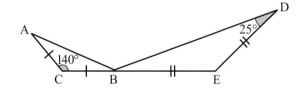

10 (a) Which is the equation of line C?

$y = 2x$, $\qquad$ $y = x$, $\qquad$ $y = x - 2$

Write down the equation of

(b) line A

(c) line B

(d) Which of the points below lie on the line $y = x + 1$?

P(4, 5) $\qquad$ Q(6, 5) $\qquad$ R(0, 1)

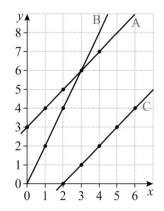

UNIT 3 MIXED REVIEW

Part one

1. (a) Write down the first five multiples of 4.
   (b) Write down the factors of 12.
   (c) Which of the factors of 12 are prime numbers?

2. One dice is thrown.
   What is the probability of not getting a six?

3. Different batteries were tested to see how long
   a set of 'chattering teeth' keep working.
   The winning battery worked for eight minutes.
   Each battery costs 90p. How much would it
   cost to keep the teeth chattering for four hours?

4. 112   (a) Copy and complete the factor tree for 112.
   / \   (b) Express 112 as a product of its prime factors.
   2   56

5. A bag contains 4 balls. The probability of selecting a white ball from the bag is 0.5.
   A white ball is taken from the bag and left on one side.
   What is the probability of selecting a white ball from the bag now?

6. Find the number.

   (a)
a 2-digit number
a multiple of both 3 and 4
the sum of its digits is 15

   (b)
a 3-digit number
a square number
the product of its digits is 2

7. Copy and complete
   (a) $0.71 \times 10 = \square$ (b) $1.52 \times \square = 152$ (c) $86.2 \div \square = 8.62$
   (d) $406 \div \square = 0.406$ (e) $0.014 \times \square = 1.4$ (f) $0.1 \times 1000 = \square$

8. This pie chart shows how 72 people travelled to the
   same hotel. Write down how many people travelled by:
   (a) train   (b) car   (c) plane

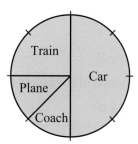

9　Answer true or false:

(a) $4^2 = 2^4$　　　　　　　(b) $2^3 > 3^2$　　　　　　　(c) $3^3 > 4^2$

10　(a) Find the mean of the numbers　　6, 3, 4, 8, 9

(b) Find the median of the numbers　8, 6, 8, 4, 1, 7, 5

(c) Find the mode of the numbers　　8, 6, 7, 5, 7, 6, 5, 7

(d) Find the range of the numbers　　5, 3, 9, 17, 13, 4

11　The frequency diagram shows
the weights of some children.

(a) How many children weighed
between 50 and 55 kg?

(b) How many children weighed
over 55 kg?

(c) How many children were
there in total?

12　Tariq has six cards.

The mean of the six cards is 8.

| 7 | 4 | 12 | 9 | 10 | |

What number is on the final card?

Part two

1　What is the probability of spinning a shaded section on each spinner?

(a)　　　　　　　　　(b)　　　　　　　　　(c)

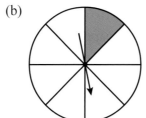
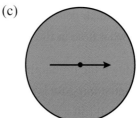

2　A crate contains 36 packets.
There are 242 full crates. The crates are emptied and all the packets are put into boxes.
What is the least number of boxes needed for all the packets if one box holds 25 packets?

3　Find the number.

(a)
> a multiple of 11
> a multiple of 7
> the product of its digits is 6

(b)
> a square number
> a 3-digit number
> the product of its digits is 20

4  It is not easy to burn a match completely.
In fact it takes thirteen seconds.
A box contains 47 matches.
How long would it take to completely burn
the matches, one after another, in 10 boxes?

5 (a) Write down the first seven multiples of four.
(b) Write down the first six multiples of seven.
(c) Write down the lowest common multiple of four and seven.

6 The line graph below shows the fuel gauge reading of a car at different times throughout
a day.

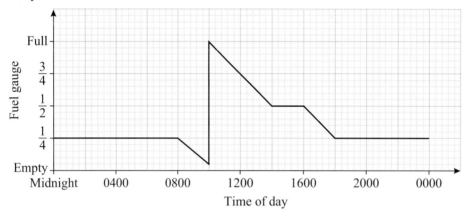

(a) Was the car moving or stationary between midnight and 8.00 am?
(b) What happened to the car at 10.00 am?
(c) How much petrol was used between 10.00 am and 2.00 pm?
(d) At what time in the evening was the car put in the garage?

7 Write down the probability of the following events occurring.
(a) When a fair coin is tossed it will come down 'heads'.
(b) You will roll a number greater than 4 on a fair dice.
(c) From a bag containing six red balls and one yellow ball, you select a red ball.

8 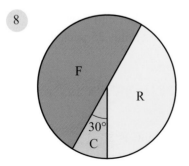 F – Football, R – Rugby, C – Cricket

The pie chart shows which sports are most
popular amongst a group of children.
12 children choose cricket.
How many children choose rugby?

9   An ice cream and a can of drink together cost 85p.
    Two ice creams and a can of drink cost £1.40.

    (a) How much does one ice cream cost?

    (b) How much would you pay for three ice creams and two cans of drink?

10 Kelly has 5 cards.

    The mean of the five cards is 8.

    The range of the five cards is 6.

    What numbers are on the other two cards?

11 Bag A contains 8 white balls, 10 red balls and 6 green balls.
    Bag B contains 11 white balls, 15 red balls and 10 green balls.
    One ball is randomly selected from each bag
    Sophie says that there is an equal probability of selecting a red ball from both bags.
    Is she correct or not?
    Explain your answer fully.

12 The stem and leaf diagram shows the heights
    of some people. Calculate the difference
    between the median and the mean height.

Stem	Leaf
16	4 6 6
17	3 4 5 5 5 8
18	2 2 4 5 6 6 9
19	0 2 5 6

Key: 17|5 means 1.75 m

Puzzles and Problems 3

1   The totals for the rows and columns are given. Unfortunately some of the
    totals are hidden by blue ink blots. Find the values of the letters.

(a)

A	A	A	A	28
A	B	C	A	27
A	C	D	B	30
D	B	B	B	

     25 30 24

(b)

A	B	A	B	B	18
B	B	E	C	D	21
A	B	B	A	B	18
C	B	C	B	C	19
E	B	D	E	D	26

     27 10 25 23 17

218

(c)

A	A	A	A	24
C	A	C	D	13
A	B	B	A	18
B	B	D	C	12

18 15 18

This one is more difficult

(d)

A	B	B	A	22
A	A	B	B	22
A	B	A	B	22
B	B	A	B	17

27 17 22 17

2   In these triangle puzzles the numbers *a*, *b*, *c*, *d* are connected as follows:

$a \times b = c$

$c \times b = d$

For example:

Copy and complete the following triangles:

(a)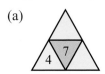

(b)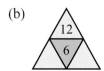

(c)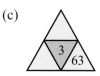

(d)

(e)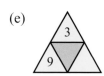

(f)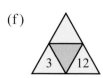

3   Draw four straight lines which pass through all 9 points, without taking your pen from the paper and without going over any line twice. [Hint: Lines can extend beyond the square].

4   Write the digits 1 to 9 so that all the answers are correct.

5   Draw six straight lines to pass through all 16 points, subject to the same conditions as in question 3 .

A long time ago! 3

Pounds, shillings and pence

In horse racing, the length of a race is often measured in furlongs.
Do you know how many furlongs make one mile?

A person throwing a party might buy a firkin of beer.
How many gallons would this be?
These are imperial units which are covered later in this book.
Actually 8 furlongs make one mile and 9 gallons make one firkin.

Your grandparents (and maybe parents!) used to buy things with shillings, tanners and two bob coins.
One penny was written as 1d. 12 pennies made 1 shilling (written as 1s.)
20 shillings made 1 pound.
21 shillings made 1 guinea.
(A 'tanner' was a 6d. coin and 2s, was sometimes called a 'two bob' coin)

> 1s. = 12d.
> £1 = 20s.

Mary wants to buy a car for £27 16s. 4d,
and a bike for 5s. 10d.
How much does she spend in total?

```
 £  s.  d.
27 16   4
     5 10
28  2   2
 1     1
```

Add the pennies first. Every 12 pennies are carried over as 1 shilling.
Next add the shillings. Every 20 shillings are carried over as 1 pound.

Mary spends a total of £28 2s. 2d.

Exercise

Try these questions from a 1927 arithmetic test.

1
```
  £  s.  d.
  5  3   7
+ 2  5   9
```

2
```
  £  s.  d.
  3 14   8
+ 6 12   3
```

3
```
  £  s.   d.
  8 13    4
+ 4 17   10
```

4
```
        £  s.  d.
from    8 19   3
take    4 13   9
```

5
```
        £  s.  d.
from   16  4   8
take    7 10   4
```

6
```
        £  s.  d.
from   17  3   2
take   10 14   8
```

7 How many $\frac{1}{2}$d. stamps could I buy with a 'two bob' coin?

8 How many oranges can I get for 3s. at the cost of seven oranges for 6d.?

9 How much must be added to 15s. 6d. to make a guinea?

10 I have bought a cake for 1s. 3d. and some jam for 5d.
How much change should I have out of 2 shillings?

11 I have been for a week's holiday and spent 6d. a day
while I was away. How much should I have left out of 4s.?

RESEARCH: There were many units used in the nineteenth century for length, weight and
capacity. Examples are 'barleycorns' and 'kilderkins'.

(a) How many different units can you find?

(b) Can you discover where any of the names come from?

Mental Arithmetic Practice 3

There are two sets of mental arithmetic questions in this section. Ideally a teacher will read out each
question twice, with pupils' books closed. Each test of 20 questions should take about 20 minutes.

Test 1

1 What is three quarters of sixty pounds?

2 What is the product of ten and thirty-five?

3 What is nought point two as a percentage?

4 How much change from a ten pound note will I receive if I spend three pounds and sixty-nine pence?

5 What is the sum of 6, 7, 8, 9, 10?

6 Two angles in a triangle are thirty-five and seventy-five degrees. What is the third angle?

7 Change seventeen thirty-five into twelve hour clock time.

8 How many 2p coins are worth the same as forty 5p coins?

9 How many centimetres are equal to eighty-five millimetres?

10 What is the area of a triangle with a base of 6 cm and a height of 8 cm?

11 I am facing south-east and turn through one right angle in a clockwise turn. In which direction am I now facing?

12 What is the next prime number after eleven?

13 I bought a magazine for 79p and paid with a £1 coin. My change consisted of five coins. What were they?

14 What is the probability that I will roll an odd number on a fair dice?

15 What is the perimeter of a square whose area is four centimetres squared?

16 Write down the number that is halfway between twenty-three and sixty-seven.

17 How many seconds are there in one hour?

18. Answer true or false: 1 km is longer than 1 mile.

19. A 'lottery' win of four million pounds is shared equally between one hundred people. How much does each person receive?

20. What is the mean average of 8, 12 and 13?

Test 2

1. What is the area of a rectangle eight metres by seven metres?

2. Round off six hundred and fifty-seven to the nearest hundred.

3. How many twelve pence pencils can you buy for one pound?

4. Write the number three thousand two hundred and nine in figures.

5. One quarter of a number is nine. What is the number?

6. How many twenty pence coins make four pounds?

7. What number is 10 less than one thousand?

8. How many thirds are there in one and two-thirds?

9. Write down a sensible estimate for eleven multiplied by forty-nine.

10. What is the probability of scoring more than a one on a fair dice?

11. Write seven tenths as a decimal number.

12. Write a hundred million pence in pounds.

13. I think of a number, divide it by six and the answer is five. What number did I think of?

14. What decimal number is forty-seven divided by one hundred?

15. What is the name given to a triangle which has two sides the same length and a pair of equal angles.

16. What number is squared to produce sixty-four?

17. How many millimetres are there in one metre?

18. In a survey seven tenths of people like watching soaps. What percentage of people like watching soaps?

19. What is the median of 6, 7 and 4?

20. How many hours are two hundred and forty minutes?

UNIT 4

4.1 Percentages

In section 4.1 you will:

- review the conversion of fractions, decimals and percentages
- review common percentages
- work out percentage increases and decreases

Fractions, decimals and percentages review

Reminder

$$\frac{3}{10} = 0.3 \qquad\qquad \frac{7}{100} = 0.07 \qquad\qquad \frac{9}{25} = \frac{36}{100} = 0.36$$

> Convert denominator to 10, 100, etc

$$0.35 = \frac{35}{100} = \frac{7}{20} \qquad\qquad 28\% = \frac{28}{100} = \frac{7}{25}$$

> Cancel down fractions

> 'Per cent' means 'out of 100'

$$\frac{19}{50} = \frac{38}{100} = 38\% \qquad\qquad 64\% = \frac{64}{100} = 0.64$$

Exercise 1M

1 Copy and complete the following statements.

(a) $\dfrac{3}{5} = \dfrac{\square}{10} = 0.\square$

(b) $\dfrac{11}{20} = \dfrac{\square}{100} = 0.\square\square$

(c) $0.9 = \dfrac{\square}{10} = \dfrac{\square\square}{100} = \square\square\%$

(d) $0.17 = \dfrac{\square\square}{100} = \square\square\%$

2   5% of people who go to the beach get sunburnt.

What fraction of people who go to the beach get sunburnt?

3   Change these percentages into decimals.
(a) 37%   (b) 60%   (c) 6%
(d) 19%   (e) 45%

4   Write True or False for each of the following statements.

(a) $0.09 = \dfrac{1}{9}$ (b) $0.25 > \dfrac{1}{4}$ (c) $0.2 = \dfrac{1}{5}$

(d) $0.4 > 4\%$ (e) $65\% = 0.65$ (f) $\dfrac{3}{5} = 35\%$

5   Change these decimals into fractions. Give the fractions in their most simple form.
(a) 0.8   (b) 0.47   (c) 0.16   (d) 0.85   (e) 0.75

6   Which test mark below is the greater percentage?
11 out of 25 or 9 out of 20

7   Write down which fractions are equivalent to
the given percentage.

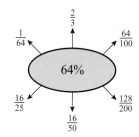

8   Convert these percentages into fractions.
(a) 49%   (b) 8%   (c) 56%   (d) 15%

9   A grandparent leaves some money in a will. 25% is left to Sam, 0.4 of the money is left to
Ursula and $\dfrac{7}{20}$ of the money is left to the cat.
Who gets the most money? Explain your answer fully.

10   Megan says that 0.3 is equivalent to 3%.
Explain clearly why this is not correct.

11   Mary uses 39 out of 52 cards to build a tower of cards.
(a) What fraction of all the cards did she use?
(b) What percentage of all the cards did she use?

12 There are five groups of *equivalent* fractions, decimals and percentages below. Write down each group. For example, $\frac{3}{4}$, 0.75, 75% would be a group (beware: there are two odd ones out).

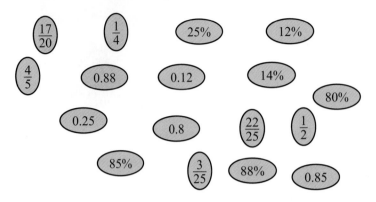

Common Percentages

Remember:

$25\% = \dfrac{1}{4}$ $\qquad\qquad$ $50\% = \dfrac{1}{2}$ $\qquad\qquad$ $75\% = \dfrac{3}{4}$

$33\tfrac{1}{3}\% = \dfrac{1}{3}$ $\qquad\qquad$ $66\tfrac{2}{3}\% = \dfrac{2}{3}$

$10\% = \dfrac{10}{100} = \dfrac{1}{10}$ $\qquad\qquad$ $20\% = \dfrac{20}{100} = \dfrac{1}{5}$

Exercise 2M

1 Mylie ate one third of her sweets.
What *percentage* of her sweets did she still have?

2 Becky spends 80% of her money shopping. What *fraction* of her money does she have left?

For each shape in question ③ to ⑥ , (a) what *fraction* is shaded?
(b) what *percentage* is shaded?

3  4 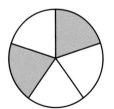 5 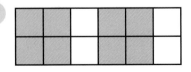 6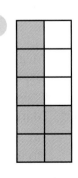

7 Draw a diagram of your own design and shade in 30%.

8 Three tenths of Lorna's books were Science Fiction.
What *percentage* of her books were *not* Science Fiction?

9 What percentage could be used in each sentence below?

  (a) Four in five adults think children should spend
      more time outdoors in the fresh air.
  (b) Zak scored 12 out of 20 in a test.
  (c) Three quarters of the students in Year 7 went
      on a school trip.
  (d) Half the people in a pub were over 40 years old.
  (e) One in three people ride a bike each week.

10 25% of 180 people are travelling to Tadcaster by bus.
$66\frac{2}{3}\%$ of the people on the bus are female.
How many people on the bus are male?

11 These pictures show how much petrol is in a car.
E is Empty and F is Full.

What percentage of a full tank is in each car?

(a) E   F
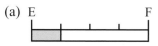

(b) E   F

(c) E   F

(d) E   F
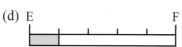

  (e) If the petrol tank in part (d) takes 55 litres of petrol when full, how many litres of petrol
      are needed to fill the tank?

Percentage increases and decreases

Use common percentages

(a) Increase 36 by 25%

    25% of 36 $= \frac{1}{4} \times 36$

            $= 9$

    Increase so $36 + 9$

            $= 45$

(b) Decrease 30 by $66\frac{2}{3}\%$

    $66\frac{2}{3}\%$ of 30 $= \frac{2}{3}$ of 30

                $= (30 \div 3) \times 2$

                $= 20$

    Decrease so $30 - 20 = 10$

Use multiples of 10%: $10\% = \frac{1}{10}$

To work out 20%, find 10% then multiply by 2

To work out 30%, find 10% then multiply by 3 and so on.

Exercise 3M

Do not use a calculator.

1. Work out
   (a) 25% of £60
   (b) 75% of £24
   (c) 10% of £70
   (d) 20% of £70
   (e) 30% of £90
   (f) $33\frac{1}{3}$% of £60

2. There are 48 dolphins in a pod.
   Seventy-five per cent of the
   dolphins are adults.
   How many adult dolphins are there?
   [The word for a group of dolphins is 'pod'.]

3. Matt scores 40% in a test.
   If full marks in the test were 50,
   how many marks did Matt get?

4. There are 220 children in a school.
   60% of the children have school meals.
   How many children have school meals?

5. A hammer costs £12. A shop decides to 'knock' 25% off the price of the hammer.
   How much will the hammer now cost?

6. A car is worth £5200. After an accident, its value falls by 40%.
   How much is the car worth now?

7. The price of a caravan is £9400. One year later the price has dropped by 10%.
   What is the new price of the caravan?

8. In a particular area, there are 4000 penguins.
   Six months later the population has decreased by 20%.
   How many penguins are there now?

9. A train company increases its prices by 15%.
   If a ticket costs £40 now, how much will it
   cost after the price increase?

10. A marathon runner weighs 60 kg at the start of a race.
    During the race his weight is reduced by 5%.
    How much does he weigh at the end of the race?

11. A shop 'slashes' its pries by $66\frac{2}{3}$%.
    Find the reduced price of a guitar costing £390.

12 Two shops sell the same make of television.
Videostore sells each TV for £580 then increases the price by 20%.
Viewmac sells the TV for £600 then increases the price by 15%.
How much money would you now save if you bought the TV from Viewmac rather than Videostore?

13 Find the sale price for each item below:
(a)
Jacket
£70
30% off

(b)
iPad
£360
5% off

(c)
Cooker
£720
$33\frac{1}{3}$% off

14 People often have to pay Value Added Tax (VAT) when they buy things.
The usual rate of VAT is 20%.
A computer costing £800 + VAT will cost £800 + £160 (20% of 800) = £960.
How much will each item below cost if VAT is added?
(a) TV £520   (b) fridge £240   (c) sofa £1400   (d) bed £650

Harder percentages of a number

$1\% = \frac{1}{100}$. To find 1% of a number, divide the number by 100.

Find 16% of a number.

Divide the number by 100 to find 1% then multiply by 16 to find 16% of the number.

(a) Work out 29% of £18.
   1% of 18 = 18 ÷ 100
   29% of 18 = (18 ÷ 100) × 29
              = 5.22 = £5.22

(b) Increase a price of £60 by 8%.
   1% of 60 = 60 ÷ 100
   8% of 60 = (60 ÷ 100) × 8
             = 4.8 = £4.80
   New price = £60 + £4.80
             = £64.80

Exercise 4M

Use a calculator when needed.

1 Work out 1% of £2600.

2 Find 1% of:
(a) £375   (b) £370   (c) £49   (d) £180

3 Work out
   (a) 8% of £460   (b) 3% of £690   (c) 32% of £240
   (d) 73% of £3800   (e) 19% of £510   (f) 94% of £1200

4 A hen weighs 3 kg. After laying an egg,
   her weight is reduced by 2%.
   How much does she weigh now?

5 A plane ticket is advertised as being £160.
   It is then increased by 14%.
   What is the new plane ticket price?

6 John weighs 80 kg. Over the next year his weight
   increases by 6%. What is his new weight?

7 2700 people watch a film. 12% of the people did not enjoy the film. How many people did not
   enjoy the film?

8 Which is larger? (8% of £23) or (9% of £21)

9 Toni earns £340 each week. She is given a 7% pay rise.
   How much does she earn each week after the pay rise?

10 A ticket to New York City costs £230.
    The price of the ticket is increased by 4%.
    What is the new price of the ticket?

11 A mail order firm reduces its prices by 7%.
    What will be the reduced price of each of
    the following items?
    (a) fridge £230   (b) TV £750
    (c) dishwasher £470   (d) cooker £860

12 (a) Increase £70 by 16%.   (b) Decrease £190 by 2%.   (c) Decrease £280 by 28%.

13 At the Chapel School there are 150 boys and 125 girls in Year 7. During the Summer the
    number of boys decreases by 4% and the number of girls increases by 4%.
    Tami says that the total number of children in Year 7 remains the same.
    Is she correct? Explain your answer fully.

14 In 2018 the entrance fee to an exhibition of famous
    jewellery was £5 and 37 840 visitors came.
    In 2019 the entrance fee was reduced by 5% and
    the number of visitors increased by 12.5%.
    How much was paid in entrance fees in 2019?

15 Increase 90 by 8% then decrease the answer by 8%.
    Does this answer surprise you?

Need more practice with percentages?

1   Work out without using a calculator:
    (a) 80% of £200   (b) $66\frac{2}{3}$% of £33   (c) 70% of £400
    (d) 20% of £60   (e) 5% of £80   (f) 15% of £80

2   Copy and complete this table.

	Fraction	Decimal	Percentage
(a)	$\frac{7}{10}$		
(b)			24%
(c)		0.46	
(d)			95%
(e)	$\frac{3}{20}$		

3   What percentage of these apples is green?

4   One Saturday 320 people go to the cinema.
    40% more people go on the following Saturday.
    How many people go to the cinema on the
    following Saturday?

5   Which is larger? (30% of £40) or (25% of £60)

6   Convert these fractions into percentages.
    (a) $\frac{17}{50}$ (b) $\frac{19}{25}$ (c) $\frac{13}{20}$ (d) $\frac{90}{200}$

7   Find the odd one out
    (a) 75% of £200   (b) 70% of £210   (c) 30% of £500

230

8 What percentage of this shape is shaded?

9 Find the sale price of each item below. The normal prices are shown in boxes.

   (a) £60
      30% off
      marked price

   (b) £36
      $33\frac{1}{3}$ % discount
      off the shown price

   (c) £700
      20% off
      normal price

   (d) £62000
      5% off
      normal price

10 Use a calculator to work out the following, giving the correct units in your answers.

   (a) 73% of 3000 kg   (b) 14% of 530 km   (c) 3% of $235
   (d) 86% of 17 km   (e) 47% of 600 m   (f) 98% of 7100 g

11 A footballer earns £130 000 per week. How much does he earn after a 4.8% pay rise?

12 Alvin has a credit card and owes £180. Each month he must pay back 2% of what he owes or £5 – whichever amount is the greater. How much will Alvin have to pay back this month? Explain your answer fully.

Extension questions with percentages

1 Jack and Maddy take delivery of 2200 poppies to sell for charity.
Jack takes 65% of the poppies.
He then sells 80% of these poppies.
How many poppies does Jack end up with unsold?

2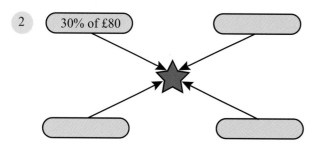

Write down three more percentage questions which give the same answer as the one shown above.

3 A computer costs £585 plus VAT at 20%.
How much does the computer cost in total?

4 The bill for a meal is £42.
The restaurant adds on a service charge
of 15% of the meal price. How much will
the meal cost including the service charge?

5 During the day a person might shrink in height by 0.5% to 1%. Donald is 1.8 m when he
wakes up. If he shrinks by 0.7% during the day, how tall is he at the end of the day?

6 Write the numbers below in order of size, smallest first.

(a) $\frac{3}{4}$, 0.8, $\frac{7}{10}$ (b) 0.57, $\frac{11}{20}$, 60% (c) 24%, $\frac{1}{4}$, $\frac{1}{5}$ (d) $\frac{21}{25}$, 0.8, 82%

7 The base and the height of a triangle
are increased by 30%.
Work out the area of the
larger triangle.

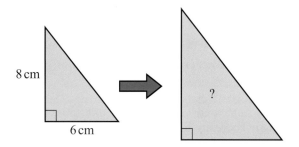

8 cm

6 cm

?

8 Murphy works at a market. He buys fleeces at £16 each and tries to sell them at £20 each.
He finds that he is not selling many so reduces the selling price by 12%.
Will he still make money if he sells the fleeces at this new price? Explain your answer fully.

9 Put the following questions in order of size of each answer, starting with the smallest.

| A | $66\frac{2}{3}$% of 21 | | B | $\frac{4}{7}$ of 28 | | C | 7% of 230 |

10 Engineer A earns £630 each week but
has to take a pay cut of 3.5%.
Engineer B earns £590 each week and
gets a pay rise of 3.5%.
Who now earns more money and by how much?

11 A Star Wars DVD costs £11. Ronata is given $\frac{1}{4}$% of £5000. Does she have enough money to buy the DVD? Explain your answer clearly.

12

| 35% deposit |
| ➕ |
| 10 equal monthly instalments |

A shop does the deal shown opposite.
A vacuum cleaner costs £282.
How much is one of the monthly instalments?

4.2 Proportion and ratio

In section 4.2 you will learn how to:

- tackle problems involving proportion
- use ratios

Proportion

Proportion is used to compare part of something to the whole.
A proportion is expressed as a fraction, decimal or percentage.

(a) There are 8 boys and 11 girls in a class of 19 children.
     The proportion of girls in the class is $\frac{11}{19}$.

(b) The proportion of cotton in the material to make a shirt is 80%

Exercise 1M

1 There are 40 people on a bus. 23 people are female. What proportion of the people are male?

2

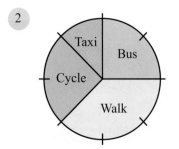

The chart shows how children travel to Maxwell High School.

(a) What proportion travel by bus?

(b) What proportion walk?

3 A soup contains 150 g of water and 50 g of vegetables.
What proportion of the soup is vegetables?

4 Count the children in your class.
What proportion of the class went to the same junior school as you?

5 42% of Year 7 love football. Another 26% of Year 7 love rugby.
What proportion of Year 7, as a percentage, do not love football or rugby?

6 The diagram shows how the government spends
money on transport. Estimate, as a percentage,
what proportion is spent on roads.

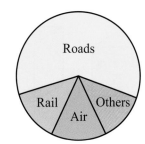

7 £30 can be exchanged for 48 dollars.
How many dollars can be exchanged for £150?

8 £30 can be exchanged for 51 euros.
How many euros can be exchanged for £90?

9 £1 is worth 1.92 dollars. How many dollars will I get for £100?

10 Jack uses 32 litres of petrol to travel 270 km. How much petrol does Jack use to travel 810 km?

11 £1 is worth 196 yen (money used in Japan). How many yen will I get for £40?

12 10 bags of corn will feed 60 hens for 3 days. Copy and complete the following:

(a) 30 bags of corn will feed ☐ hens for 3 days.

(b) 10 bags of corn will feed 20 hens for ☐ days.

Direct proportion

If 4 bottles of lemonade contain 10 litres, how much lemonade is there in 7 bottles?

4 bottles contain 10 litres

1 bottle contains 10 ÷ 4 = 2.5 litres

7 bottles contain 2.5 × 7 = 17.5 litres

Exercise 2M

1 Diving masks cost £200 for 10. Find the cost of 5 diving masks.

2 Five oranges cost 95p. How much will 9 oranges cost?

3 Eight coats cost £560. Find the cost of 11 coats.

4 5 tea pots cost £7.50. Find the cost of 50 tea pots.

5 Find the cost of 7 skateboards if 4 skateboards cost £168.

6 A machine fills 800 bottles in 5 minutes.
How many bottles will it fill in 20 minutes?

7 Seven bikes cost £1750. How much will 3 bikes cost?.

8 The total cost of 8 magazines is £12. What is the total cost of 12 magazines?

9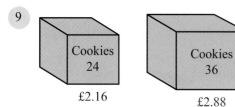

Cookies are sold in two sizes of box.
The number of cookies in each box is
shown opposite.
Which box is the better value?
You must show all working out to explain
your answer.

10 A recipe states that 180 g of flour is needed to make 12 biscuits. Marlon has 500 g of flour.
Is this enough to make 30 biscuits? Explain your answer fully.

11 Usually it takes 12 hours for 5 men to build a wall.
How many men are needed to build a wall twice as big in 12 hours?

12 12 boxes weigh 14.4 kg and 15 packets weigh 18.75 kg.
Which weighs more, 7 boxes or 6 packets?
Explain your answer fully.

13 Gideon makes puppets. He takes 5 hours
to paint 8 bodies, 2 hours to paint 5 heads
and $1\frac{1}{2}$ hours to paint 4 pairs of feet.

(a) How long will it take Gideon to paint
the bodies, heads and feet on 15 puppets?

(b) What assumptions do you have to make
to answer part (a)?

14

Makes 12 biscuits
100 g butter
50 g caster sugar
100 g soft brown sugar
25 g black treacle
175 g flour
1 tablespoon ground ginger

A biscuits recipe is shown opposite.

(a) How much of each ingredient is needed to
make 48 biscuits?

(b) A chef has 40 g of black treacle. Is this enough to
make 18 biscuits?

(c) Another chef has 250 g butter. What is the greatest
amount of biscuits the chef could make?

Ratio

Ratio is used to compare parts of a whole.

> There are 29 children in a class. 16 are boys and 13 are girls.
>
> The ratio of boys to girls is written as $16 : 13$
>
> The ratio of shaded squares to unshaded squares is $3 : 2$.
>
> The ratio of shaded squares to unshaded squares is $4 : 10$.
>
> Each part of the ratio can be multiplied or divided by the same number. This does not change the ratio.
> $4 : 10$ is the same ratio as $2 : 5$ (divide each part of the ratio by 2)
>
> $2 : 5$ is the simplest form for this ratio.

$5 : 10 : 30$ simplifies to $1 : 2 : 6$ (divide each number by 5)

$0.5 : 4$ simplifies to $1 : 8$ (multiply each number by 2)

Exercise 3M

1   There are 27 children in a class. 11 are boys and 16 are girls.
    Write down the ratio of boys to girls.

2   One evening a vet sees 10 dogs and 6 cats. Find the ratio of dogs to cats.

3   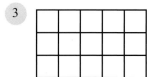 Copy this diagram. Colour in so that the ratio of black squares to white squares is $2 : 3$.

4   Make diagrams like question ③ to show the ratio of black squares to white squares is:

    (a) $3 : 2$ (b) $7 : 3$ (c) $4 : 5$

5   There are 33 people on a bus. 19 are men. Write down the ratio of men to women.

6   There are 30 people in a cinema. $\frac{3}{5}$ of the people are female.
    What is the male to female ratio?

7   Harper has 13 weeks holiday each year. She spends the rest of the year at school.
    Write down the ratio of holiday time to school time.

8   At one moment in a chess match, there are 10 black
    pieces on the board and 14 white pieces. Write down
    the ratio of black pieces to white pieces in its
    simplest form.

9   Write these ratios in simplified form.
    (a) $5:20$ (b) $8:10$ (c) $4:44$
    (d) $16:12$ (e) $10:8:6$ (f) $21:35$
    (g) $65:25$ (h) $16:24:80$ (i) $5:15:33$

10 Carl says that the ratio of his mother's age to his sister's age can never be $1:1$. Is he correct?
    Justify your answer.

11 For each pair of ratios below, write down the value of n which makes the ratios *equivalent* to
    each other.
    (a) $8:2 = n:1$ (b) $4:12 = 1:n$ (c) $70:40 = n:4$
    (d) $24:30 = 12:n$ (e) $22:33 = 2:n$ (f) $48:32 = 6:n$

12 John is 1.8 m tall and Alice is 135 cm tall. Write down the ratio of John's age to Alice's age.
    Give the ratio in simplified form.

Share £35 in the ratio $5:2$
The ratio $5:2$ means we are dividing into '$5 + 2$' = 7 parts.
£35 is split into 7 parts so 1 part = £5.
5 parts = $5 \times £5 = £25$ and 2 parts = $2 \times £5 = £10$

Exercise 4M

1   Share £50 in the ratio   (a) $1:4$ (b) $3:2$ (c) $3:7$

2   Share £75 in the ratio   (a) $2:3$ (b) $11:14$ (c) $8:7$

3   There are 28 children in a class. The ratio of boys to girls is $4:3$.
    (a) How many boys are in the class?
    (b) How many girls are in the class?

4   Sasha mixes some blue paint and some yellow paint in the ratio $7:4$ to make up 33 litres of
    paint. How much yellow paint did she use?

5   There are 30 chocolates in a box. The ratio of dark chocolates to milk chocolates is 2 : 3.
    How many milk chocolates are in the box?

6   Natasha and Ning are given some money
    in the ratio 5 : 3. If Ning receives £24,
    how much does Natasha get?

7   In a hall, the ratio of chairs to tables is 9 : 2.
    If there is a total of 99 chairs and tables,
    how many chairs are there?

8   Mark and Amy share some sweets in
    the ratio 4 : 5. If Mark gets 28 sweets,
    how many sweets do they share out in total?

9   Neil, Pippa and Mel have newspaper rounds. Each week they earn a total of £28 in the ratio
    3 : 5 : 6. How much money does Pippa earn?

10 In a kitchen drawer, there is a total of 36 knives, forks and spoons in the ratio 4 : 3 : 5.
    How many knives are there?

11 Baldeep, Millie and Mike work for a number of hours in the ratio 7 : 3 : 2. Baldeep worked for
    42 hours, which was the most. How many hours did Millie and Mike work for in total?

12 Sachin and Ellie have a total of £60 between them. Sachin has three times as much money as
    Ellie. How much money does Sachin have?

13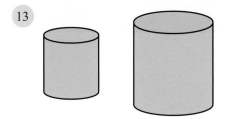
    The volumes of two cans are in the ratio 3 : 5.
    The volume of the larger can is 600 ml.
    What is the volume of the smaller can?

14 On a bus, the ratio of children to adults is 4 : 1. What proportion of the people are adults?

Need more practice with proportion and ratio?

1   Hatton United score 5 goals. Eden scores three of these goals.
    What proportion of the team's goals are scored by Eden?

2   9 pens cost £5.76. What is the total cost of 15 pens?

3

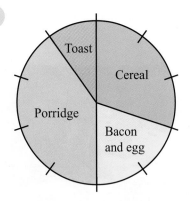

The chart shows what various children had for breakfast one day.

(a) What proportion ate cereal?

(b) What proportion ate porridge?

4 Ayden and Stella each do a newspaper round.
In total they deliver 275 newspapers split between Ayden and Stella in the ratio 4 : 7.
How many newspapers does Stella deliver?

5 Which of the four ratios below is the odd one out?

(28:24)   (7:6)   (21:16)   (35:30)

6 The ratio of red crayons to blue crayons in a pencil case is 2 : 5.
What proportion of these crayons is red?

7 The ratio of bats to owls in an area is 80 : 3.
How many bats are there if there are 18 owls?

8 Ava says that the ratio 24 : 16 : 30 is the
same as the ratio 3 : 2 : 4. Is she correct?
Explain your answer fully.

9 7 skirts cost £161 and 12 dresses cost £372.
How much more do 17 dresses cost than 19 skirts?

10 Some money is shared between Emma and Felix in the ratio 8 : 13.
How much money is shared in total if Felix gets £208?

Extension questions with proportion and ratio

1 Manu says that the ratio 25 kg : 500 g can be simplified to 500 : 1. Cerys does not agree.
Who is correct? Give full reasons for your answer.

2 Write these ratios in simplified form.

    (a) 6 m : 50 cm   (b) 2 kg : 100 g   (c) 1.5 km : 300 m

    (d) 2 cm : 5 mm   (e) 3.5 kg : 500 g   (f) 4 m : 20 cm : 2 m

3 Ishaan and Faith spend 75 minutes and 60 minutes respectively roller skating one morning. In the afternoon their ratio of times spent roller skating remains the same. How long does Faith roller skate for if Ishaan skates for 90 minutes?

4 Simplify the ratio 0.4 : 0.25 so that all the numbers are whole numbers.

5 Mason needs to use 250 g sugar to make 20 muffins.
How much sugar will he need to make 50 muffins?

6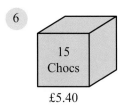

15 Chocs
£5.40

25 Chocs
£9.25

Which box of chocolates offers the best value? Explain your answer fully.

7 Write these ratios in simplified form.

(a) 0.7 : 0.3

(b) 0.05 : 0.6

(c) $\frac{1}{2} : 0.1$

(d) $\frac{1}{6} : \frac{1}{3}$

(e) $\frac{3}{5} : \frac{1}{10}$

(f) $\frac{5}{9} : \frac{2}{3}$

8 The ratio of apples to oranges in a grocers is 3 : 2. The ratio of apples to pears in the same grocers is 3 : 4. Tilly says that there are twice as many pears as oranges. Is she correct? Justify your answer.

9 Lily earns £1600 each month.
She pays her rent with $\frac{3}{8}$ of the money then uses 30% of the remaining money for her food. She splits the remaining money in the ratio 9 : 5 on entertainment and savings. Work out the difference between her rent and her savings each month.

10 The ratio of Tabi's height and Colin's height is 4 : 5 and the sum of their heights is 3.15 m. Two years later the ratio of their heights has changed to 5 : 6 and the sum of their heights is 3.3 m. By how much has Tabi grown during these two years?

240

✖ Spot the mistakes 7 ✖

Percentages, proportion, ratio

Work through each question below and *explain clearly* what mistakes have been made.
Beware – some questions are correctly done.

1 Increase £40 by 5%.

Solution: 5% of 40 = 40 ÷ 5 = 8
            Answer = 40 + 8 = £48

2 Some green paint is made by mixing blue and yellow in the ratio 3:5.
   Danielle says that $\frac{3}{5}$ of the paint mixture is blue.

3 Ron sells lollipops. His costs are 90p for each
   lollipop sold. He makes a profit of 90% on
   each lollipop he sells. How much profit does
   he make if he sells 164 lollipops?

Solution: profit = 90% of 90p
            10% of 90 = 9
            so 90% of 90 = 81p
            Total profit = 164 × 81p
                         = 13284p
                         = £132.84

```
    164
  ×  81
    164
  13120
  13284
```

4 Some sweets are shared between Ian, Anya and Vitali in the ratio 2:5:3.
   If Anya gets 40 sweets, how many sweets does Vitali get?

Solution: number of shares = 2 + 5 + 3 = 10 shares
            one share = 40 ÷ 10 = 4 sweets
            Vitali gets 3 shares = 3 × 4 = 12 sweets

5 Work out 2% of £12.

Solution: 2% of 12 = 0.2 × 12
                   = 2.4
                   = £2.40

6 Express the area of P as a percentage
   of the area of Q.

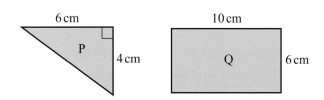

Answer: area P = $\dfrac{6 \times 4}{2}$ = 12 cm²

area Q = 10 × 6 = 60 cm²

12 is $\dfrac{1}{5}$ of 60 and $\dfrac{1}{5} = \dfrac{20}{100} = 20\%$

so area P is 20% of area Q.

7   Simplify the ratio 8 m : 40 cm.

Solution: 8 : 40 = 1 : 5

8   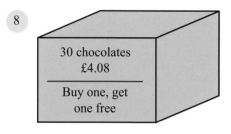      Jess needs to buy 90 chocolates as cheaply as possible.

30 chocolates
£4.08

Buy one, get
one free

45 chocolates
£5.49

Solution: 3 × 30 chocolates = 3 × 4.08 = £12.24
2 × 45 chocolates = 2 × 5.49 = £10.98
so Jess buys two boxes of 45 chocolates

9   Simplify the ratio $\dfrac{1}{2} : \dfrac{3}{4}$

Solution: Multiply both numbers by 4

$\dfrac{1}{2} \times 4 : \dfrac{3}{4} \times 4 = 2 : 3$

10   A father is 28 years old and his daughter is 4 years old.
Work out the ratio of their ages in two years time.

Solution: ratio of ages = 28 : 4
= 7 : 1
in 2 years time, ratio = 9 : 3
= 3 : 1

CHECK YOURSELF ON SECTIONS 4.1 and 4.2

1   Conversion of fractions, decimals and percentages

(a) Which is greater: $\frac{7}{20}$ or 0.4?

(b) Work out $\frac{3}{25}$ + 38%

Copy and complete this table.

	Fraction	Decimal	Percentage
(c)		0.08	
(d)	$\frac{4}{5}$		
(e)		0.9	
(f)			32%
(g)	$\frac{18}{25}$		

2   Recognising common percentages

(a) What percentage of the shape is shaded green?

(b) Before cooking, Roger finds that two-fifths of his vegetables are rotten.
What *percentage* of his vegetables are not rotten?

(c) Bev knocks over a bottle and loses two-thirds of her coke. What *percentage* of her coke does she still have?

3   Percentage increases and decreases

(a) A camera costs £300. It is reduced in price by 5%. What is the new price?

(b) Increase £720 by 12%.

4   Tackling problems involving proportion

(a) 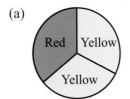 What proportion of this circle is red?

(b) 22 children are playing football. Nine of the children are in Year 7.
What proportion of the children are in Year 7?

(c) Find the cost of 7 toys if 9 toys cost £72.

5   Using ratios

(a) Write the ratio 12:32 in simplified form.

(b) During one week Urma and Terry eat 15 ice-creams in the ratio 3:2.
How many ice-creams does Urma eat?

(c) Janet buys gifts for her husband and son. She spends money in the ratio 3:7.
If she spends £56 on her son, how much does she spend in total on the gifts?

4.3 Constructing triangles

In section 4.3 you will learn how to:

- construct triangles with a protractor and ruler

- construct triangles with three sides given

A triangle is an extremely rigid structure. It is used extensively in the real world to support many objects such as the roof on your house or the brackets holding up your bookshelf.

Draw the triangle ABC full size and measure the length x.

(a) Draw a base line *longer than* 8.5 cm

(b) Put the centre of the protractor on
A and measure an angle 64°.
Draw line AP.

(c) Similarly draw line BQ at an
angle 40° to AB.

(d) The triangle is formed.
Measure $x = 5.6$ cm.

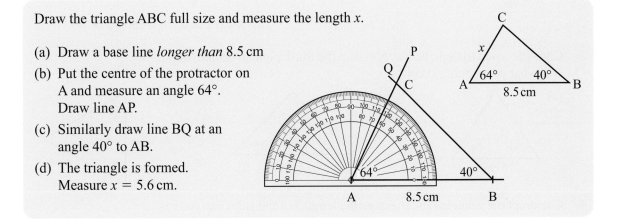

Exercise 1M

1 Measure the angles below to make sure you can still use a protractor accurately.

(a)

(b)

(c)

2 (a) Use a protractor and ruler to draw AB = 7 cm and CÂB = 50° as shown below.

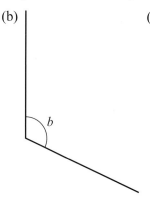

(b) Put the centre of the protractor on B and measure an angle of 50° as shown below.

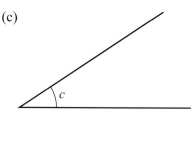

(c) Measure AĈB. It should be 80°.

3 Construct each triangle below. Measure the third angle in each triangle. Is it what you would expect?

(a)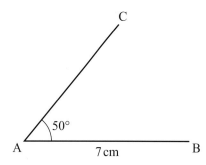

(b)

(c)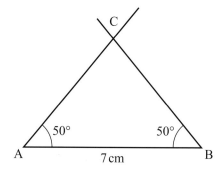

4 Construct the triangles and measure the lengths of the sides marked x.

(a)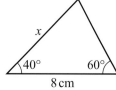

(b)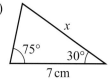

(c)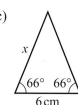

5   Construct triangle PQR where PR = 6.8 cm, RP̂Q = 72° and PR̂Q = 60°.
Measure the length of QR.

6   Emma walks 5 km due South from home then
12 km due East to her grandmother's house.
Construct the diagram opposite using a scale
of 1 cm to 1 km. How far is Emma's home
from her grandmother's house?

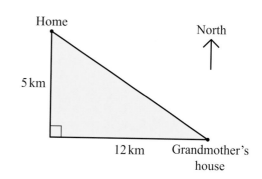

Triangles with three sides given

Draw triangle XYZ and measure XẐY.

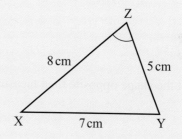

(a) Draw a base line longer than 7 cm and
     mark X and Y exactly 7 cm apart.

(b) Put the point of a pair of compasses on
     X and draw an arc of radius 8 cm.

(c) Put the point of the pair of compasses on
     Y and draw an arc of radius 5 cm.

(d) The arcs cross at the point Z so the triangle
     is formed.

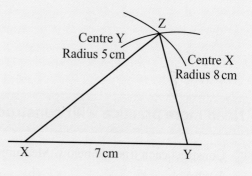

Measure XẐY = 60°

Exercise 2M

Use a ruler and a pair of compasses to construct the triangles in questions 1 to 4.
For each triangle, measure the angle x.

1   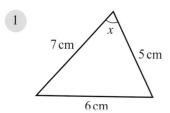

2   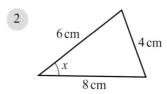

246

246

3

7.5 cm
6 cm
5.2 cm
x

4

9.5 cm
5 cm
7 cm
x

5 Construct triangle XYZ where XY = 6.7 cm, YZ = 8.2 cm and ZX = 7.9 cm. Measure XẐY.

6 Construct the shape opposite then measure angle x.

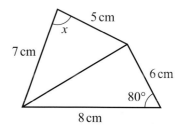

5 cm
x
7 cm
6 cm
80°
8 cm

7 Construct the shape opposite then measure angle x.

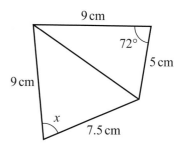

9 cm
72°
5 cm
9 cm
x
7.5 cm

Need more practice with constructing triangles?

1 Construct each triangle below. Measure the lengths of the sides marked x.

(a)

x
110°
40°
8 cm

(b)

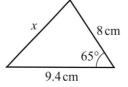

x
8 cm
65°
9.4 cm

(c)

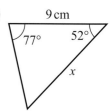

9 cm
77°
52°
x

2 Construct each triangle below. For each triangle, measure the angle x.

(a)

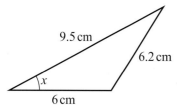

9.5 cm
6.2 cm
x
6 cm

(b)

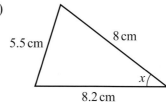

5.5 cm
8 cm
x
8.2 cm

3 Construct triangles with the angles given below. Measure the third angle in each triangle. Is it what you would expect?

(a) 65°, 65°   (b) 35°, 80°   (c) 50°, 75°

4 Construct this rectangle accurately using a ruler and protractor.

Measure the length of the diagonal of the rectangle.

5 cm
8 cm

Extension questions with constructing triangles

1 Construct the shape shown opposite. Measure the angle x.

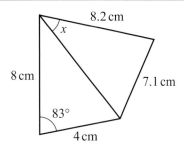

8.2 cm
x
8 cm
7.1 cm
83°
4 cm

2 Construct the rhombus shown below.

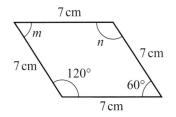

7 cm
m
n
7 cm
7 cm
120°
60°
7 cm

Measure the size of m and n.

3 Construct the parallelogram shown below.

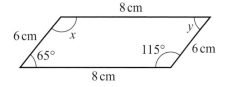

8 cm
6 cm
x
y
65°
115°
6 cm
8 cm

Measure the size of x and y.

4 Construct each shape below and measure the lengths of the sides marked x.

(a)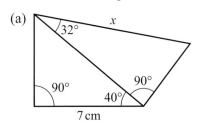

32°
x
90°
90°
40°
7 cm

(b)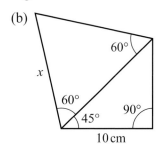

60°
x
60°
45°
90°
10 cm

5   Marie and Leo both construct a triangle ABC with sides 6 cm, 8 cm and 10 cm.
    Marie measures AB̂C and says the answer is 37°. Leo measures AB̂C and says the
    answer is 53°. Explain why this might have happened?

6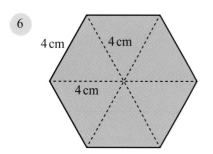
    4 cm   4 cm

    4 cm

    A regular hexagon is made from six
    equilateral triangles. Construct the hexagon
    shown opposite.

4.4 Two dimensional shapes

In section 4.4 you will review:

- recognising parallel, perpendicular, horizontal and vertical lines
- identifying different polygons, particularly types of quadrilaterals

Lines

- A straight line has infinite length.

  A *line segment* is part of a straight line and has finite length.

  A ———————— B   AB is a line segment

- Lines which are at right angles are *perpendicular* to each other.

  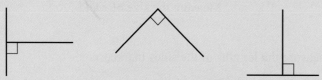

- A *horizontal* line is parallel to the horizon.

- A *vertical* line is perpendicular to the surface of the earth.

For each of the letters of the word 'LINES' use the following 'key' to indicate …

1. perpendicular lines

2. parallel vertical lines ⟶ ↓ ↓

3. parallel horizontal lines ⟶

… like this:-

Exercise 1M

Copy out the key given in the above example and the stencil of the alphabet below onto squared paper. Use the key to show on all the letters any:

(a) perpendicular lines   (b) parallel vertical lines   (c) parallel horizontal lines

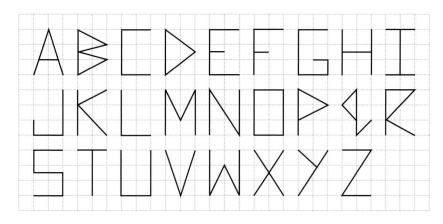

Exercise 2M

In questions ① to ③ write the sentence choosing the correct word.

1

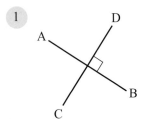

AB is (parallel/perpendicular) to CD.

250

2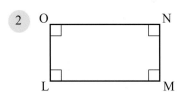

LM is (parallel/perpendicular) to MN.

ON is (parallel/perpendicular) to LM.

OL is (parallel/perpendicular) to MN.

3 Look at the diagram on the right.
Copy and complete.

CD is _____ to EF.

AB is _____ to CD.

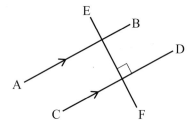

4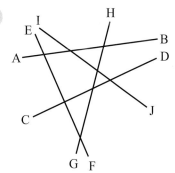

Which lines are perpendicular to each other?

5 Copy the diagram on the right.

(a) Draw a line through C which is perpendicular to AB.

(b) Draw a line through D which is parallel to AB.

(c) Draw a line through D which is perpendicular to the line AB.

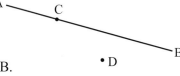

6 In the rectangle WXYZ, XY is perpendicular to WX.

(a) Which other line is perpendicular to WX?

(b) Which line is parallel to ZY?

7 Draw a polygon (shape with straight sides) which has exactly 3 pairs of perpendicular sides.

8 How many sides in this shape are parallel to side AB?

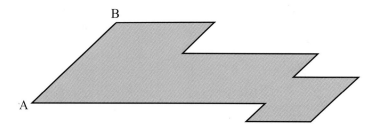

9   Use the sides of a ruler to draw a four-sided shape (quadrilateral) with two pairs of parallel sides. Mark the parallel sides with arrows.

10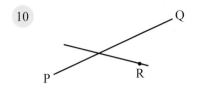
Copy the diagram on the left.
(a) Draw a line through R which is parallel to PQ.
(b) Draw a line through R which is perpendicular to PQ.

Triangles

scalene
3 different sides and 3 different angles.

right-angled
contains a right angle.

isosceles
2 equal sides and 2 equal angles.

equilateral
3 equal sides and 3 equal angles.

Quadrilaterals

A quadrilateral has four sides and four angles. Special types of quadrilateral

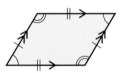

Square

Rectangle

Parallelogram

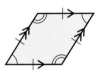

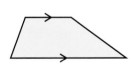

Rhombus

Trapezium

Kite

Polygons

A polygon is a shape with straight sides.

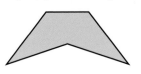

This is a five-sided polygon or pentagon.

252

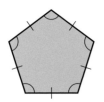

A *regular* polygon has all its sides and angles equal.

This is a *regular* pentagon.

Names of common polygons:

hexagon (6 sides),   heptagon (7 sides),   octagon (8 sides),

nonagon (9 sides),   decagon (10 sides).

Exercise 3M

1   For each of the following triangles state whether it is scalene, isosceles, equilateral or right-angled. (Lines of the same length are indicated by dashes and equal angles are marked.)

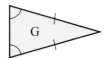

2   Mia says that the triangle shown opposite is isosceles. Is she correct? You must give a reason for your answer.

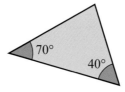

3   A quadrilateral has one pair of equal angles and no parallel sides. Which quadrilateral is it?

4   Which shape below is not a regular polygon?

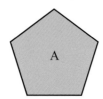

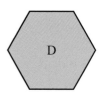

5   What changes must be made to a rhombus for it to become a square?

6 Explain clearly why both of these shapes are trapeziums.

7 Name any quadrilaterals which have one but not two pairs of equal angles.

8 Write down the name for each shape below. If the shape has a special name like 'parallelogram' or 'kite' write that name. If not, write 'quadrilateral', 'hexagon', 'regular pentagon' and so on.

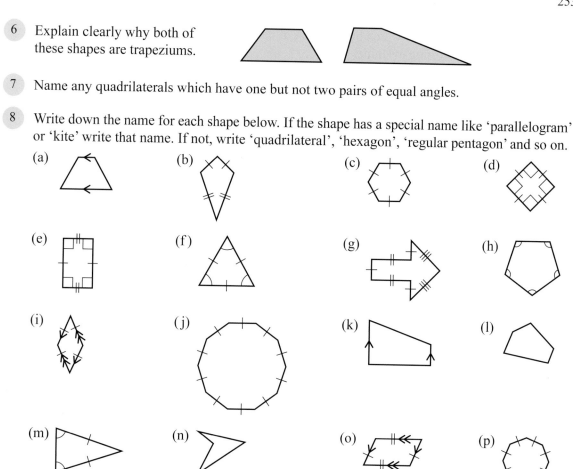

(a) (b) (c) (d)

(e) (f) (g) (h)

(i) (j) (k) (l)

(m) (n) (o) (p)

(q) (r) (s) (t)

Need more practice with two dimensional shapes?

1 A diagonal joins one corner (vertex) of a polygon to another corner.

Draw any rhombus. Write as many facts as possible about the diagonals of a rhombus.

2 Which quadrilaterals can be drawn by starting with the diagram opposite?

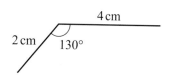

4 cm

2 cm   130°

3 Draw a hexagon which has exactly four obtuse angles.

4. Write down the letter for which bucket each of the 6 quadrilaterals will drop into when they pass through the sorting machine.

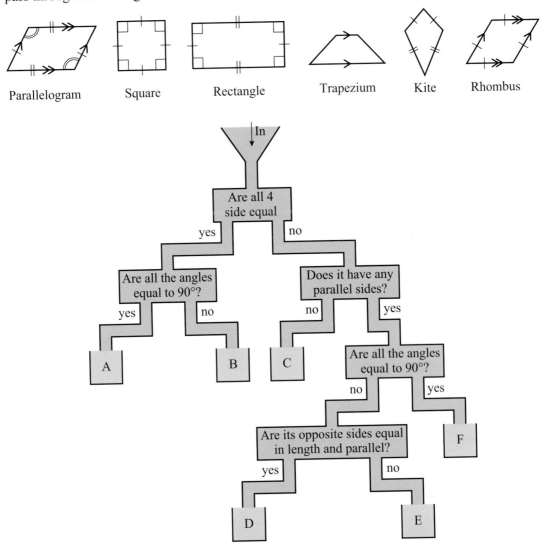

Parallelogram   Square   Rectangle   Trapezium   Kite   Rhombus

5. Copy the diagram of each quadrilateral in question 4. For each quadrilateral, write its name and describe the rules that make it that particular shape. Discuss these rules with a partner then as a class.

6. Is a parallelogram a type of rectangle?

7. Is a rectangle a type of parallelogram?

8. Callum says that all trapeziums have one line of symmetry only.
Is he correct? Justify your answer.

Extension questions with two dimensional shapes

Investigation – triangles and quadrilaterals

On a square grid of 9 dots it is possible to draw several different triangles with vertices on dots. A vertex (plural vertices) is where two lines meet. Look at the three examples below:

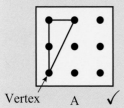 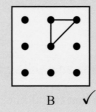 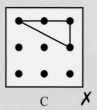

Vertex   A   ✓   B   ✓   C   ✗

A and B are different triangles but C is the same as A. If a triangle could be cut out and placed exactly over another triangle then the two triangles are the same. The two triangles are called *congruent*.

PART A
Copy A and B above and then draw as many different triangles as you can.
Check carefully that you have not repeated the same triangle.

PART B
On a grid of 9 dots it is also possible to draw several different *quadrilaterals*.

Copy the three shapes above and then draw as many other different quadrilaterals as possible. You are doing well if you can find 12 shapes but there are a few more!

Check carefully that you have not repeated the same quadrilateral. (Congruent shapes are not allowed.)

CHECK YOURSELF ON SECTIONS 4.3 AND 4.4

1   Constructing triangles with a protractor and ruler

Construct the triangle opposite.
Measure QR.

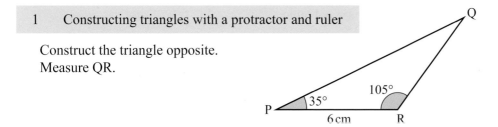

256

2   Constructing triangles with three sides given

Construct the triangle opposite.
Measure BÂC.

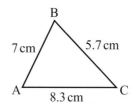

3   Recognising parallel, perpendicular, horizontal and vertical lines

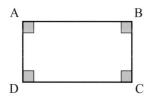

(a) Name a horizontal line.

(b) Name a side perpendicular to AD.

(c) Name a vertical line.

(d) Name a side parallel to AD.

4   Recognising different polygons, particularly types of quadrilaterals

(a)

Write down the correct name for this type of triangle.

(b) Write down the rules that make an isosceles triangle.

(c) Match each quadrilateral to the correct name:

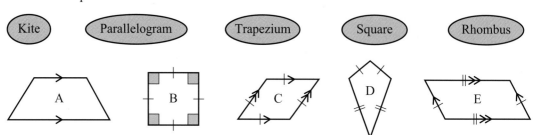

(d) Write down the rules that make a rhombus.

(e) Write down which shapes below are polygons.

         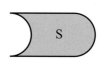

(f) How many sides has a decagon?

4.5 Translation

In section 4.5 you will learn about:

- translating shapes

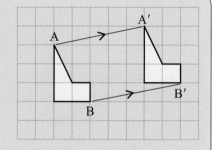

A **translation** is a transformation in which every point of the object moves the same distance in a parallel direction.

A translation can be described by two instructions, the move parallel to the *x*-axis and the move parallel to the *y*-axis.

In the example shown, the translation is 5 units to the right and 1 unit up.

We use a **translation vector**, not words.

A translation vector is a vertical bracket as shown below:

$\begin{pmatrix} 5 \\ 1 \end{pmatrix}$ The number at the *top* shows 5 units to the *right*.
The number at the *bottom* shows 1 unit *up*.

If the number at the top was −5 it would be 5 units to the *left*.
If the number at the bottom was −1 it would be 1 unit *down*.

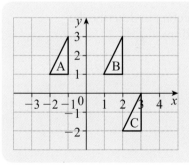

The translation of B to C is $\begin{pmatrix} 1 \\ -3 \end{pmatrix}$

The translation of C to A is $\begin{pmatrix} -4 \\ 3 \end{pmatrix}$

The translation of A to B is $\begin{pmatrix} 3 \\ 0 \end{pmatrix}$

Exercise 1M

1 Draw the triangle opposite on squared paper then translate it by the vector $\begin{pmatrix} 2 \\ -2 \end{pmatrix}$.

Label the new triangle P.

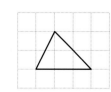

258

2

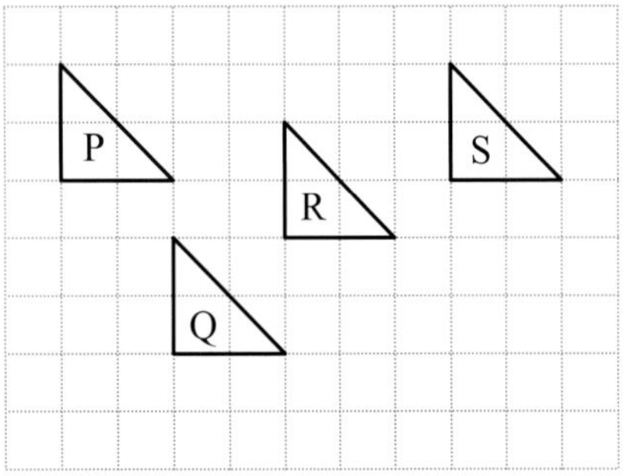

Use translation vectors to describe the following translations.

(a) P → Q

(b) Q → S

(c) R → P

(d) S → P

3 (a) Draw shape A as shown.

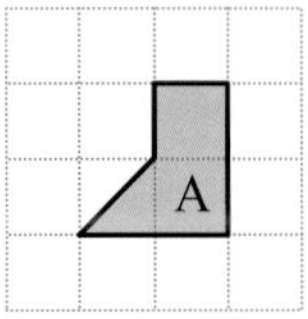

(b) Translate shape A by $\begin{pmatrix} 5 \\ 0 \end{pmatrix}$. Label the new shape B.

(c) Translate shape B by $\begin{pmatrix} 0 \\ -3 \end{pmatrix}$. Label the new shape C.

(d) Translate shape C by $\begin{pmatrix} -3 \\ -1 \end{pmatrix}$ and label the new shape D.

(e) Use a translation vector to describe the single translation which would move shape A onto shape D.

4

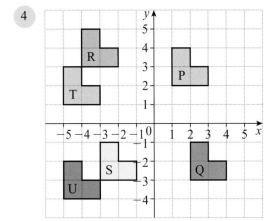

Use translation vectors to describe the following translations.

(a) P to R

(b) P to S

(c) S to Q

(d) T to Q

(e) Q to T

(f) R to U

(g) U to S

5 Shape A is translated to shape B with the translation vector $\begin{pmatrix} -5 \\ 3 \end{pmatrix}$.

Write down the translation vector which moves shape B to shape A.

6 What shape do you move to when you:

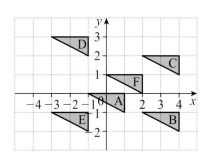

(a) translate shape A by $\begin{pmatrix} -2 \\ -1 \end{pmatrix}$?

(b) translate shape E by $\begin{pmatrix} 5 \\ 3 \end{pmatrix}$?

(c) translate shape D by $\begin{pmatrix} 3 \\ -2 \end{pmatrix}$?

(d) translate shape B by $\begin{pmatrix} -5 \\ 0 \end{pmatrix}$?

7 A computer controls a pen which starts at A opposite. Use translation vectors to describe the 8 translations required to draw the shape given.

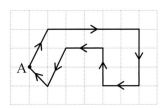

8 Shape P is translated to shape Q by $\begin{pmatrix} 3 \\ 2 \end{pmatrix}$ then shape Q is translated to shape R by $\begin{pmatrix} 2 \\ 6 \end{pmatrix}$.

Write down the translation vector which moves shape P to shape R.

4.6 Reflection

In section 4.6 you will:

- reflect shapes

A reflection is a transformation in which points are mapped to images by folding along a mirror line.

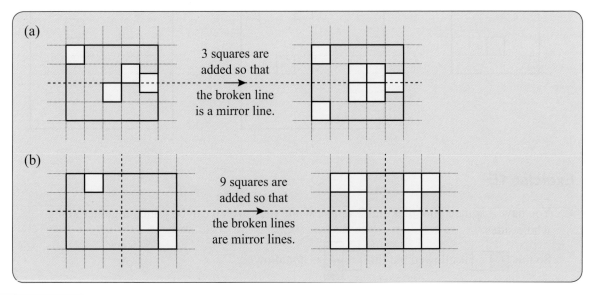

(a)

3 squares are added so that

the broken line is a mirror line.

(b)

9 squares are added so that

the broken lines are mirror lines.

260

Exercise 1M

Copy each diagram and, using a different colour, shade in as many squares as necessary so that the final pattern has mirror lines shown by the broken lines. For each question write down how many new squares were shaded in.

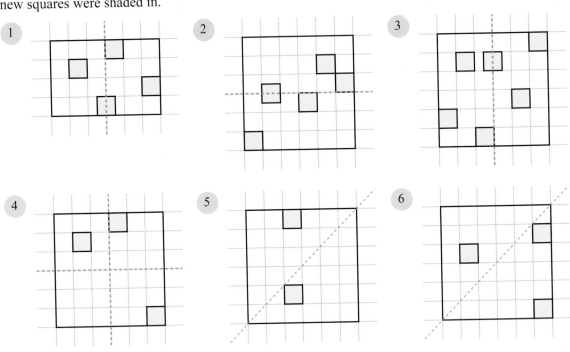

Be careful when the mirror line is a diagonal line. You can check your diagram by folding along the mirror line.

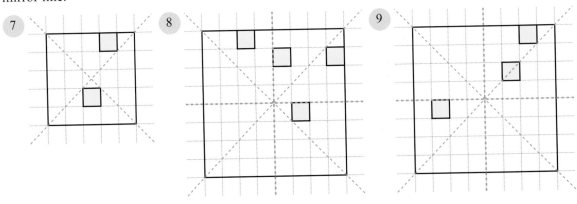

Exercise 1E

1   You have 3 square pink tiles and 2 square white tiles, which can be joined together along whole sides.

So this 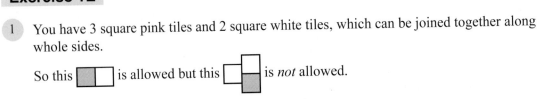 is allowed but this is *not* allowed.

Draw as many diagrams as possible with the 5 tiles joined together so that the diagram has line symmetry.

For example Fig. 1 and Fig. 2 have line symmetry but Fig. 3 does not have line symmetry so Fig. 3 is not acceptable.

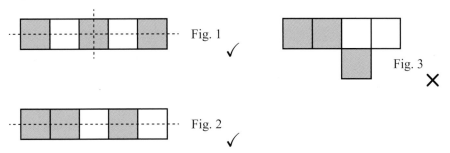

2   Now you have 2 pink tiles and 2 white tiles. Draw as many diagrams as possible with these tiles joined together so that the diagram has line symmetry.

3   Finally with 3 pink tiles and 3 white tiles draw as many diagrams as possible which have line symmetry.

Here is one diagram which has line symmetry.

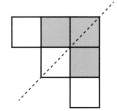

4   Shape A is a single square. | A   Shape B consists of four squares. | B

Draw three diagrams in which shapes A and B are joined together along a whole edge so that the final shape has line symmetry.

5   Shape C is a single square. | C   Shape D consists of five squares. | D

Draw four diagrams in which shapes C and D are joined together along a whole edge so that the final shape has line symmetry.

262

Using coordinates

Triangle A is reflected in the line $x = -1$
to give triangle B.
(Triangle B is the image of triangle A.)

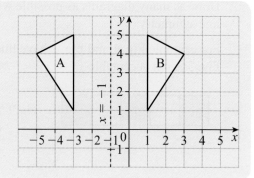

Exercise 2M

1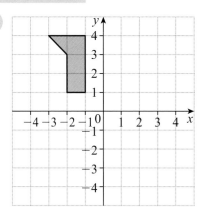

Copy the diagram.

(a) Reflect the shape in the y-axis.
Label the image A.

(b) Reflect the shape in the x-axis.
Label the image B.

2 Copy the diagram onto squared paper.

(a) Reflect shape A in the line $x = 3$.
Label the image B.

(b) Reflect shape A in the line $y = 1$.
Label the image C.

(c) Reflect shape A in the y-axis.
Label the image D.

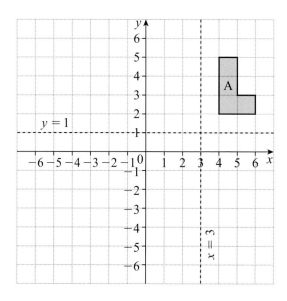

3

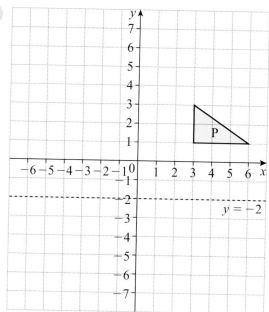

Copy the diagram onto squared paper.

(a) Reflect shape P in the line $y = -2$.
   Label the image Q.

(b) Draw the line $x = 1$.

(c) Reflect shape P in the line $x = 1$.
   Label the image R.

(d) Reflect shape P in the line $y = 3$.
   Label the image S.

4 (a) Draw x and y axes from -4 to 4.

(b) Draw a rectangle with vertices (corners) at $(-2, 1)$, $(-2, 4)$, $(-3, 4)$ and $(-3, 1)$.
   Label the rectangle P.

(c) Reflect rectangle P in the line $x = -1$. Label the image Q.

(d) Reflect rectangle Q in the line $x = -1$. What do you notice?
   Explain clearly why this has happened.

5 Write down the equation of the mirror line for the following reflections.

(a) A to B

(b) D to E

(c) F to E

(d) A to C

(e) C to D

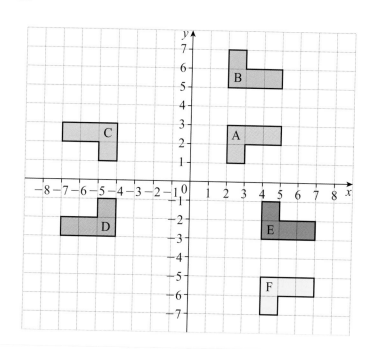

4.7 Rotation

In section 4.7 you will learn about:

- rotating shapes
- rotational symmetry

In these diagrams shape B has been rotated onto shape Y.

In the first diagram shape B is rotated 90° (1 right angle) anticlockwise around point P.

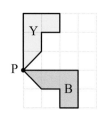

In the second diagram shape B is rotated 180° (2 right angles) around point Q.

Notice that for a 180° rotation it makes no difference whether you turn clockwise or anticlockwise.

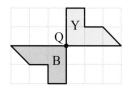

Exercise 1M

In questions 1 to 9 copy each diagram and then draw its new position after it has been turned. You can use tracing paper if you wish.

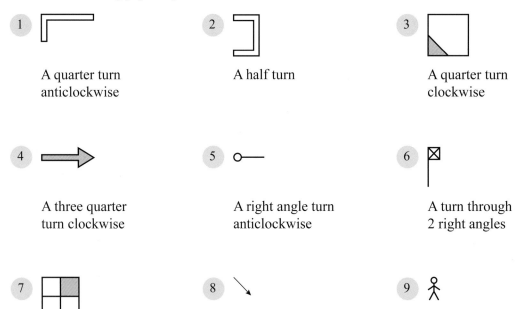

1 A quarter turn anticlockwise

2 A half turn

3 A quarter turn clockwise

4 A three quarter turn clockwise

5 A right angle turn anticlockwise

6 A turn through 2 right angles

7 A 90° turn anticlockwise

8 A 90° turn clockwise

9 One and a half turns clockwise

In questions ⑩ to ⑮ describe the rotation. Give the angle and the direction.

10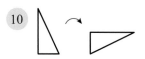

11

12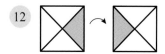

13

14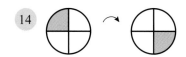

15

Rotate this shape 90° clockwise around the point A.

The point A is called the *centre of rotation*.

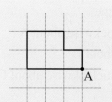

Here is the result.

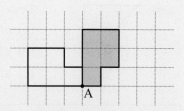

The shaded shape is called the *image*.

Exercise 2M

Use tracing paper if you wish.

1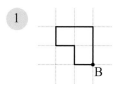

(a) Copy this shape on squared paper.

(b) Draw the image of the shape after a quarter turn clockwise around the point B.

In questions ② to ④ copy the shape on squared paper and then draw and shade its new position.

2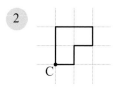

Half turn around the point C

3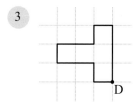

Quarter turn clockwise around the point D

4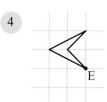

Turn 90° anticlockwise around the point E

266

5   The diagram shows shapes which have been
    rotated about the points A, B, C, D and E.

    Which shape do you get when you:
    (a) rotate shape R 90° clockwise about A
    (b) rotate shape R 90° clockwise about B
    (c) rotate shape Q 180° about C
    (d) rotate shape S 90° anticlockwise about D
    (e) rotate shape P 180° about E

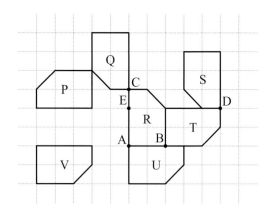

6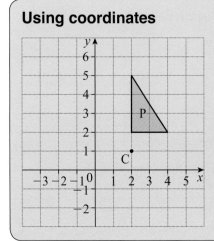
    Draw this shape on squared paper.
    Draw the image of the shape
    (a) after a 90° rotation clockwise about A
    (b) after a 180° rotation about B
    (c) after a 90° rotation anticlockwise about C

Using coordinates

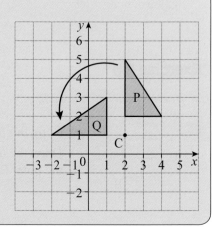

Triangle P is to be
rotated 90° anticlockwise
about the point C (2, 1).

Maybe use tracing paper.
Hold a pencil on point C
then turn the tracing
paper 90° anticlockwise.

Triangle Q is the image
of P.

Exercise 3M

Use tracing paper if you wish.

1   Copy the diagram opposite.
    (a) Rotate the shape 90° anticlockwise about (0, 0).
    (b) Write down the coordinates of the
         corner A in its new position.

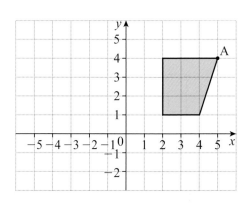

2 Copy the diagram opposite.

   (a) Rotate shape A 90° clockwise about (0, 0).
Label the image C.

   (b) Rotate shape B 90° anticlockwise about (0, 0).
Label the image D.

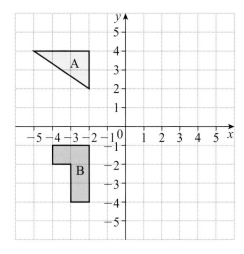

3 (a) Draw x and y axes from -5 to 5.

   (b) Draw a rectangle with vertices at $(1, -2)$, $(1, -4)$, $(5, -4)$ and $(5, -2)$.
Label this rectangle P.

   (c) Rotate P 90° anticlockwise about $(1, -1)$. Label the image Q.

   (d) Rotate Q 180° about $(0, -1)$. Label the image R.

4 Copy the diagram opposite.

   (a) Rotate ⊟ 90° anticlockwise
about $(6, -1)$.

   (b) Rotate ⊤ 90° anticlockwise
about $(11, 1)$.

   (c) Rotate Å 180° about $(8, 1)$.

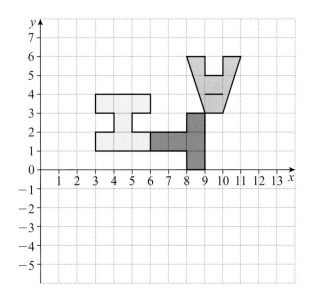

5 A shape is rotated 90° clockwise about the origin $(0, 0)$ then the new shape is rotated 180° about the origin.

This new shape is then rotated 90° anticlockwise about the origin.

Describe what has happened to the original shape to give the final image.

Rotational symmetry

The shape B fits onto itself three times when rotated through a complete turn. It has *rotational symmetry of order three*.

B

The shape C fits onto itself six times when rotated through a complete turn. It has rotational symmetry of order six.

C

Exercise 4M

For each diagram decide whether or not the shape has rotational symmetry.
For those diagrams that do have rotational symmetry state the order.

1.

2.

3.

4.

5.

6.

7.

8.

9.

10.

11.

12.

13.

14.

15.

16.

Exercise 4E

1 (a) If this umbrella was viewed from above would it have rotational symmetry?

(b) If so what is the order of rotational symmetry?

In questions 2 to 7 copy each diagram and complete it so that the final design has rotational symmetry of the order stated.

2

Order 4

3

Order 4

4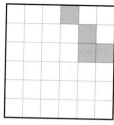

Order 4

5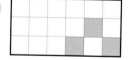

Order 2

6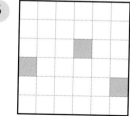

Order 4

7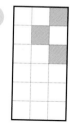

Order 2

8

This shape is made using coloured pencils.

If you ignore the different colours, what is the order of rotational symmetry of the shape?

270

Need more practice with translation, reflection and rotation?

1 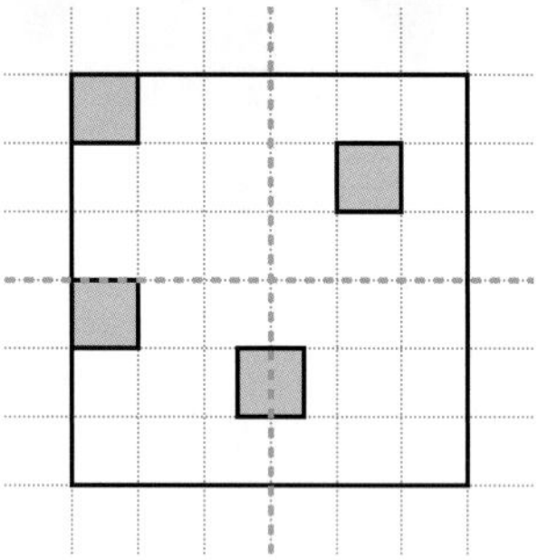　Copy this diagram and shade in as many squares as necessary so that the final pattern has mirror lines shown by the broken lines. Write down how many new squares were shaded in.

2　Do any of these letters have both line symmetry and rotational symmetry?

N Z E H T

3　Copy the shape shown opposite on squared paper.
Rotate the shape 90° clockwise about the point C.

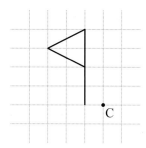

4 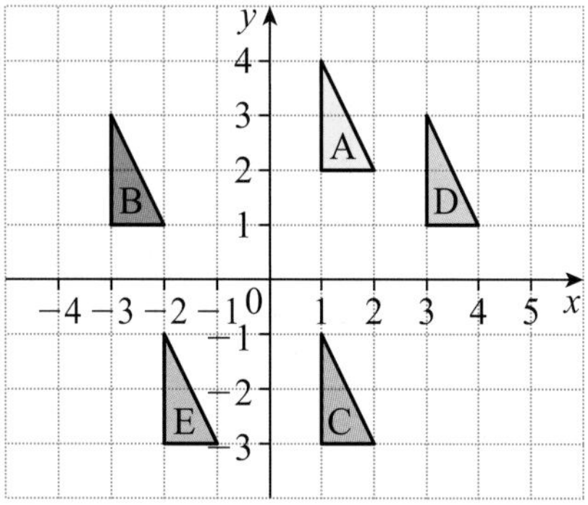　Use translation vectors to describe the following translations.
(a) A to B　　　(b) B to C
(c) C to E　　　(d) E to A
(e) D to C　　　(f) D to A

5　(a) Draw x and y axes from −5 to 5.
(b) Draw a rectangle with vertices at (2, 1), (2, 4), (4, 4) and (4, 1).
Label this rectangle A.

(c) Translate A by $\begin{pmatrix} -5 \\ 1 \end{pmatrix}$. Label the image B.

(d) Translate B by $\begin{pmatrix} 4 \\ -7 \end{pmatrix}$. Label the image C.

(e) Translate C by $\begin{pmatrix} -6 \\ 1 \end{pmatrix}$. Label the image D.

(f) Write down the translation vector which translates D to B.

6 Copy the diagram opposite.
  (a) Reflect the triangle in the line $y = 1$.
  (b) Reflect the triangle in the line $x = \frac{1}{2}$.
  (c) Draw the line $x = -3$ then reflect
      the triangle in the line $x = -3$.

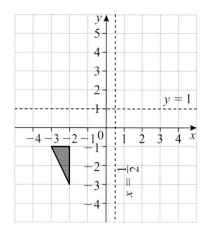

7 A shape is reflected in the line $x = 2$.
  The new shape is then reflected in the line $x = 2$.
  Describe the position of the final shape.

8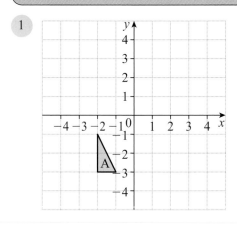

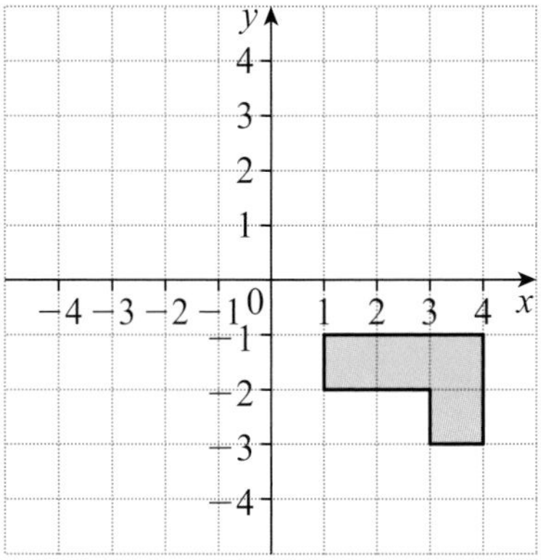

Copy the diagram opposite.
  (a) Rotate the shape 90°
      anticlockwise about (0, 0).
  (b) Rotate the shape 180°
      about (0, 0).

Extension questions with translation, reflection and rotation

1

Copy the diagram opposite.
  (a) Rotate triangle A 180° about (0, 0).
      Label the image B.
  (b) Reflect triangle B in the x-axis.
      Label the image C.
  (c) Triangle C can be reflected back
      onto triangle A. Describe the mirror
      line for this reflection.

2   Draw a quadrilateral with order of rotational symmetry 2.

3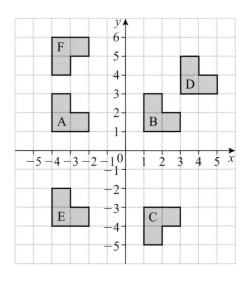

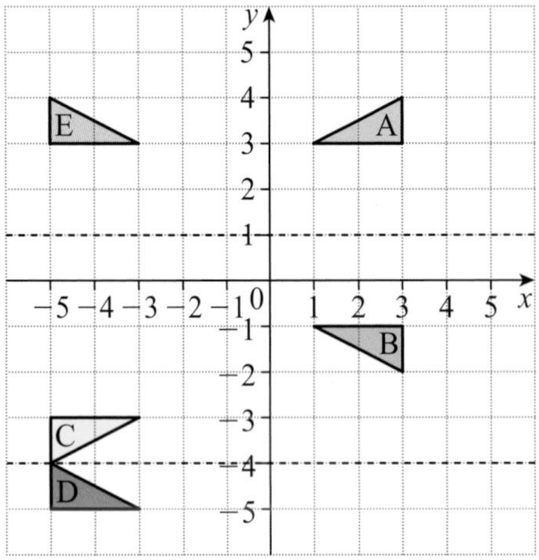

Write down the equation of the mirror line for the following reflections.

(a) A to B

(b) C to D

(c) E to A

4   A shape P is translated by $\begin{pmatrix} -5 \\ 3 \end{pmatrix}$ then the new shape is translated by $\begin{pmatrix} 2 \\ -1 \end{pmatrix}$.

The final shape is labelled Q.

Write down the translation vector which will translate shape Q back to shape P.

5   (a) Draw x and y axes from -6 to 6.
     (b) Draw a triangle with vertices at $(-6, -3)$, $(-3, -3)$, and $(-3, -4)$.
          Label the triangle A.
     (c) Reflect triangle A in the x-axis. Label the image B.
     (d) Reflect triangle B in the y-axis. Label the image C.
     (e) Reflect triangle C in the x-axis. Label the image D.
     (f) Triangle D can be reflected back to triangle A.
          Describe the mirror line for this reflection.

6   Describe fully each transformation below –
     either a translation or a reflection.

     (a) A to B

     (b) B to C

     (c) B to D

     (d) A to E

     (e) A to F

     (f) D to E

7 An L-shape is rotated 180° about (0, 0). Charlotte says that the image is not the same shape because it is upside down. Is she correct? Explain your answer fully.

8 (a) Draw x and y axes from -6 to 6.

(b) Draw a rectangle with vertices at $(1, -2)$, $(2, -2)$, $(2, -5)$ and $(1, -5)$. Label the rectangle A.

(c) Rotate A 180° about (0, 0). Label the image B.

(d) Translate B by $\begin{pmatrix} -3 \\ -1 \end{pmatrix}$. Label the image C.

(e) Reflect C in the line $x = -1$. Label the image D.

(f) Translate D by $\begin{pmatrix} 2 \\ -6 \end{pmatrix}$. Label the image E.

(g) Rectangle E is reflected onto rectangle A. Write down the equation of the mirror line.

The tile factory: an activity

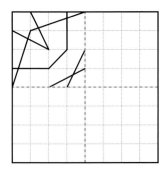

1 Copy this square and pattern onto the top left hand corner of a piece of A4 centimetre squared paper.

2 Lightly mark the reflection lines on the diagram as shown.

3 Use these lines to help you reflect the pattern across …

… and then down.

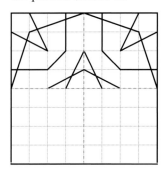

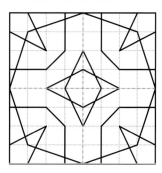

274

4　Repeat the process with the same tile so that your tile neatly covers the piece of paper →.

5　Now colour or shade in your work as neatly and symmetrically as you can.

 Spot the mistakes 8

Two dimensional shapes, transformations and constructing triangles

Work through each question below and *explain clearly* what mistakes have been made. Beware – some questions are correctly done.

1　Triangle A is to be reflected in the line $y = -1$. The solution is shown opposite.

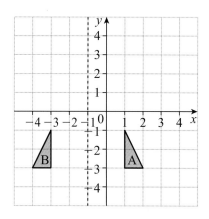

2　How many lines of symmetry does a rectangle have?

Answer: 4

3　The point P with coordinates $(2, -3)$ is reflected in the y-axis. Write down the new coordinates of point P.

Answer: $(2, 3)$

4　Shape A opposite is to be rotated 90° anticlockwise about the point C. The answer is shown opposite.

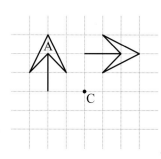

5   Shape P is translated by $\begin{pmatrix} 5 \\ -3 \end{pmatrix}$ to shape Q.

Shape Q is translated by $\begin{pmatrix} 4 \\ 1 \end{pmatrix}$ to shape R.

What translation vector will translate shape P to shape R?

Answer: $\begin{pmatrix} 5 \\ -3 \end{pmatrix} + \begin{pmatrix} 4 \\ 1 \end{pmatrix} = \begin{pmatrix} 9 \\ -2 \end{pmatrix}$

6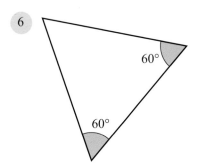

Is this an isosceles triangle?

Answer: Yes because there are two equal angles.

7   What is the order of rotational symmetry of a kite?

Answer: 2

8   (a) Translate triangle P by $\begin{pmatrix} 5 \\ -5 \end{pmatrix}$.
Label the image Q.

(b) Rotate Q 90° clockwise about (0, 0).
Label the image R.
The solution is shown opposite.

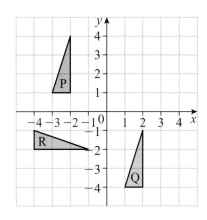

9

A triangle ABC is to be constructed with BC= 6 cm, $A\hat{B}C = 70°$ and $A\hat{C}B = 30°$.

The solution is shown opposite.

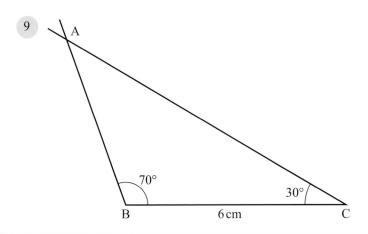

10 (a) Rotate shape A 90° clockwise about (0, 0).
        Label the image B.

    (b) Reflect B in the x-axis. Label the image C.

    The solution is shown opposite.

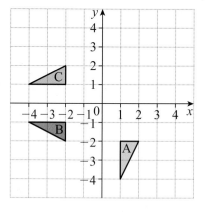

CHECK YOURSELF ON SECTIONS 4.5, 4.6 and 4.7

1   Translating shapes

    (a) Use translation vectors to describe each
        translation below:
        (i)   A to C
        (ii) C to D
        (iii) B to E

    (b) Draw the triangle A on squared paper.

        Translate triangle A by $\begin{pmatrix} 4 \\ 3 \end{pmatrix}$.

        Label the image F.

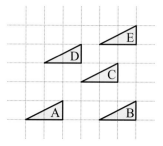

2   Reflecting shapes

    Copy the diagram opposite.

    (a) Reflect triangle A in the y-axis.
        Label the image B.

    (b) Reflect triangle A in the line $y = -1$.
        Label the image C.

    (c) Write down the mirror line for the reflection
        of triangle P onto triangle Q.

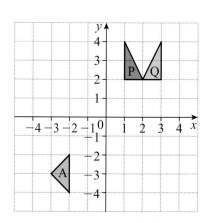

3   Rotating shapes

(a) Draw the shape opposite on squared paper.
Draw the new position of the shape after
it is rotated 90° anticlockwise about the
point B.

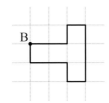

(b) Copy the diagram opposite.

(c) Rotate shape A 180° clockwise
about (0, 0). Label the image B.

(d) Rotate shape A 90° clockwise
about (0, 0). Label the image C.

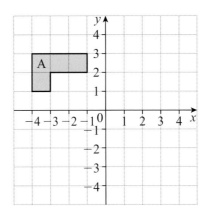

4   Rotational symmetry

State the order of rotational symmetry of each shape

(a)    (b)    (c)    (d)

(e) Draw the two patterns on the right and
shade in more squares so that the final
patterns have rotational symmetry
of order 2.

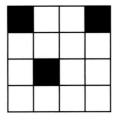   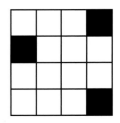

4.8 Applying mathematics 4

In section 4.8 you will apply maths in a variety
of situations.

1   A film starts at 18:35 and ends at 21:10. How many minutes did the film last for?

2 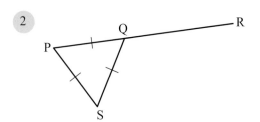 Triangle PQS is equilateral.
Work out the size of RQ̂S.
Give full reasons for your answer.

3 The ingredients for a chocolate cake cost £1.25 and the chef charges £1.10 to make each cake.
A shop sells the cakes at £11.99. Calculate the total profit made if 200 cakes are sold.

4 Jason spends $\frac{1}{3}$ of his money at the cinema and $\frac{2}{5}$ of his money on food.
What fraction of his money is left over after spending on the cinema and food?

5 Write down the ratio of the
triangle area to the rectangle area.
Give the ratio in its simplest form.

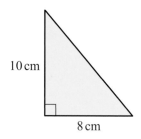 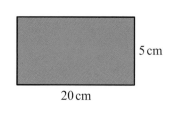

6 In a new office building there are 82 doors.
If each door is fastened by 3 hinges and if each hinge requires 6 screws,
what is the total number of screws required to fit all the doors?

7

| 65 | 72 | 73 | 51 | ? |

English   Maths   Science   History Geography

Amy takes 5 exams. Her percentage marks are shown above.
Her mean average mark for all five exams is 66%.
What was her mark for Geography?

8 Copy and complete this multiplication square.

×	3	7		
		35		20
			48	
	27			
			16	8

9   On a Saturday Dom spends 90 minutes playing
    a game and Morgan spends 70 minutes playing
    the same game. On the Sunday, Dom increases
    his playing time by 15% and Morgan spends
    45% more time playing the game.

    Who spends the longer time playing on the
    Sunday and what is the difference between
    their playing times?

10 A bag contains red balls and blue balls only.
    One ball is to be removed at random.
    The probability of removing a red ball is 0.1.
    How many blue balls are in the bag if there are 4 red balls to start with?

UNIT 4   MIXED REVIEW

Part one

1   The price of a computer game is £40 but it is increased by 5%. What is the new price?

2   Gwen and Tim are given £99 in the ratio 8:3. How much money does Tim get?

3   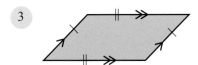   Name this shape.

4   In each of the following diagrams, mirror lines are shown as broken lines.
    Copy each diagram and complete the reflections.

    (a)   (b)   (c)

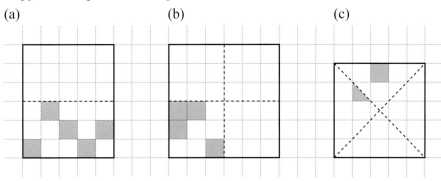

5 If you buy 3 tins of cat food for £2.16, how much would 5 tins cost?

6 If 76% of people wear a wristwatch, what percentage does not?

7 What is 70% as a fraction?

8 Three friends share a prize of £5000 in the ratio 2:3:5. How much was the largest share?

9 The price of a dress costing £45 was decreased by 10%.
Six months later the price was increased by 10%. Calculate the final price of the dress.

10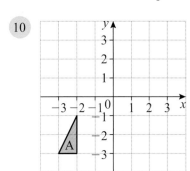

Copy the diagram opposite.

(a) Translate triangle A by $\binom{3}{4}$. Label the image B.

(b) Translate triangle B by $\binom{2}{-3}$. Label the image C.

(c) What translation vector will translate triangle C back to triangle A?

11 A laptop costs £450. In a sale the price is reduced by 20%.
What does the laptop now cost?

12 Use a protractor and ruler to construct this triangle.
Measure the side marked x.

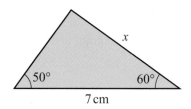

Part two

1 Which is larger? $\dfrac{7}{25}$ or   27%

2 A recipe uses 3 eggs and 2 apples for every cake. A chef has an order for several cakes.
He uses 24 eggs. How many apples does he use?

3 (a) Copy the diagram.

   (b) Rotate triangle A 90° clockwise around the
        point (0, 0). Label the image B.

   (c) Rotate triangle A 90° anticlockwise around the
        point (4, 3). Label the image C.

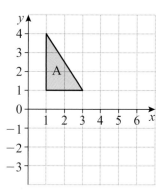

4 There are 30 children in a class. $\frac{4}{5}$ of the children bring a coat to school.

   Out of these children 75% of them also bring a hat. How many children bring a coat and a hat?

5 Work out (number of sides in a decagon – number of sides in a hexagon)^2.

6 Look at the diagram.

   (a) Write down the ratio
        shaded length : unshaded length.

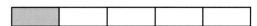

   (b) As a percentage, what proportion of the diagram is shaded?

7 In how many ways can you join the square X to shape Y along an edge
   so that the final shape has line symmetry?

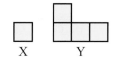

8 Draw a scalene triangle.

9 Use a ruler and compasses to construct the
   diagram opposite.
   Use a protractor to measure angles x and y.

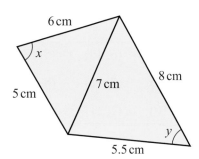

10 A rectangular window measures 24.3 cm by 35.7 cm.
    The area of a circular window is 80% of the area of the rectangular window.
    Find the ratio of the circular window area to the rectangular window area.
    Give the answer in its simplest form.

Puzzles and Problems 4

Coordinates puzzles

1 Draw a pair of axes with the values shown.

Plot the points below and join them up with a ruler in the order given.

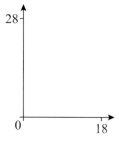

(10, 28)	(16, 28)	(18, 26)	(18, 24)	(16, 22)
$(14\frac{1}{2}, 20)$	(14, 18)	(14, 8)	(12, 6)	(12, 1)

ON THE SAME PICTURE plot the points below and join them up with a ruler in the order given.

DO NOT JOIN THE LAST POINT IN THE BOX ABOVE WITH THE FIRST POINT IN THE NEW BOX.

(5, 1)	(7, 3)	(7, 5)	(6, 6)	(5, 6)	(4, 7)	(6, 7)	(8, 7)	(10, 8)

ON THE SAME PICTURE plot the points below and join them up with a ruler in the order given

(4, 7)	(3, 8)	(4, 9)	(6, 9)

ON THE SAME PICTURE plot the points below and join them up with a ruler in the order given.

(4, 9)	(4, 10)	(5, 10)

ON THE SAME PICTURE plot the points below and join them up with a ruler in the order given.

(7, 12)	(6, 13)	(5, 13)	(4, 12)	(4, 11)	(5, 10)	(6, 10)
(7, 11)	(7, 12)	(8, 13)	(9, 13)	(10, 12)	(10, 11)	(9, 10)
(8, 10)	(7, 11)					

ON THE SAME PICTURE plot the points below and join them up with a ruler in the order given.

(10, 28)	(8, 26)	(7, 24)	$(6\frac{1}{2}, 22)$	(6, 20)	$(5\frac{1}{2}, 18)$	
(5, 16)	(5, 13)	$(5, 13\frac{1}{2})$	(7, 14)	(9, 14)	(12, 13)	(12, 6)

283

Draw a ⊕ around the points below, making  the circles touch like this

(7, 4)   (8, 4)   (9, 4)   (10, 4)   (11, 4)   (12, 4)

Draw a • at (6, 11) and a • at (9, 11)

2   Draw a pair of axes with the values shown.

Plot the points below and join them up with a ruler in the order given.

(4, 2)   (4, 4)   (2, 6)   (0, 6)   (−1, 4)   (−1, 2)   (0, 1)

(2, 1)   (4, 2)   (6, 2)   (6, 1)   (5, 1)

ON THE SAME PICTURE plot the points below and join them up with a ruler in the order given.

DO NOT JOIN THE LAST POINT IN THE BOX ABOVE WITH THE FIRST POINT IN THE NEW BOX.

(−3, 13)   (−3, 1)   (−2, 1)

ON THE SAME PICTURE plot the points below and join them up with a ruler in the order given.

(0, −4)   (−2, −3)   (−2, −1)   (−4, −1)   (−4, 1)   (−3, 1)

ON THE SAME PICTURE plot the points below and join them up with a ruler in the order given.

(3, −5)   (4, −5)   (5, −4)   (4, −3)   (4, −2)   (3, −2)

(−1, −1)   (−1, −2)   (1, −3) $(1, −1\frac{1}{2})$

ON THE SAME PICTURE plot the points below and join them up with a ruler in the order given.

(4, −3)   (1, −3)   (3, −3)   (3, −2)   (7, −2)   (7, 1)

(6, 1)   (7, 1)   (8, 2)   (8, 4)   (7, 6)

ON THE SAME PICTURE plot the points below and join them up with a ruler in the order given.

(−3, −1)   (−3, −6)   (−4, −6)   (6, −6)   (4, −6)   (4, −5)

16

−6

10

−6

ON THE SAME PICTURE plot the points below and join them up with a ruler in the order given.

(4, 4)	(5, 6)	(7, 6)	(7, 13)	(6, 14)	(6, 13)	(5, 14)	
(5, 13)	(4, 14)	(4, 13)	(3, 14)	(3, 13)	(2, 14)	$(1\frac{1}{2}, 13)$	$(\frac{1}{2}, 14)$
(0, 13)	(−1, 14)	(−1, 13)	(−2, 14)	(−2, 13)	$(-3\frac{1}{2}, 14)$	(−3, 13)	

Draw a • at (1, 4) and a • at (6, 4) Who am I? Colour me in?

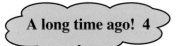

A long time ago! 4

Roman numerals

Many clock faces still use roman numerals like IV and XI. At the end of a film, the year in which the film was made is often given using roman numerals. MCMLXXX means 1980.

I	one	XI	eleven
II	two	XII	twelve
III	three	XX	twenty
IV	four (one before five)	XXX	thirty
V	five	XL	forty (ten before fifty)
VI	six	L	fifty
VII	seven	LX	sixty
VIII	eight	C	hundred
IX	nine (one before ten)	CM	nine hundred
X	ten	M	thousand

Note

When we reach 10 before 50, we write XL not XXXX. Your teacher may explain this more fully.

Exercise

1 Write down the value of each of the numbers written below in roman numerals.

(a) VII   (b) XIII   (c) XVI   (d) XXVII

(e) XVIII   (f) XIX   (g) XLV   (h) LXXII

(i) CCCXXVII   (j) XCIV   (k) MMVI   (l) CMXLIX

2 Write these numbers in roman numerals.

(a) 8   (b) 17   (c) 22

(d) 58   (e) 39   (f) 84

(g) 78   (h) 123   (i) 339

(j) 1265   (k) 1066   (l) 3194

3 Write this year in roman numerals.

4 Work out the questions below, giving your answers in roman numerals.

(a) VI + III   (b) IX + VIII   (c) XIII + XVII

(d) XL − VI   (e) LIII − XVIII   (f) C − XLVII

(g) LXXV + CCXXXVI   (h) V × II   (i) IV × IX

(j) CCCXII − CLXXIX   (k) VII × VI   (l) VII × XII

(m) XXIV ÷ III   (n) L ÷ X   (o) CXX ÷ XX

(p) XXXVI ÷ IX   (q) MCC ÷ XXX   (r) MCCV + CCXXVIII − XCIV

5 **RESEARCH:**

(a) In the ancient Greek number system, Δ was the symbol for 10. Find out the ancient Greek
    symbol for   (i) 100   and   (ii) 50.

(b) Find the ancient Egyptian symbols for   (i) 10   (ii) 100   and   (iii) 1000.

(c) Find out three more ancient Egyptian symbols and sketch them as carefully as you can.

(d) Can you find out why particular letters are used for certain roman numerals?
    For example, why is C used for 100?

Mental Arithmetic Practice 4

Here are two sets of mental arithmetic questions. Ideally a teacher will read out each question twice, with pupils books closed. Each test of 20 questions should take about 20 minutes.

Test 1

1. What is half of half of eighty?

2. How many twenty pence coins make three pounds?

3. What is the perimeter of a rectangular room twelve metres by six metres?

4. I am facing South-West and the wind is hitting me on my back. What direction is the wind coming from?

5. If six per cent of pupils of a school are absent, what percentage of pupils are present?

6. Write nought point seven as a fraction.

7. What is twenty-fifteen in twelve hour clock time?

8. Write the number six thousand two hundred and four in figures.

9. What number is twelve more than fifty-seven?

10. If pears cost eleven pence each, how many can I buy for one pound?

11. With three darts I score six, double five and treble five. What is my total score?

12. A film lasting one and a half hours starts at six twenty p.m. What time does the film finish?

13. If I buy a card for sixty-five pence and a stamp for thirty-two pence, how much change do I get from one pound?

14. What number is nine less than sixty-two?

15. How many degrees are there in one tenth of a right angle?

16. A fifth of my wages is taken in tax. What percentage have I got left?

17. How many grams are there in half a kilogram?

18. What four coins make forty pence?

19. One angle in an isosceles triangle is one hundred and twenty degrees. How large is each of the other two angles?

20. What number is one hundred times bigger than nought point six?

Test 2

1. How many sides has a pentagon?

2. What is nought point one as a percentage?

3. How much change from a ten pound note will I receive if I spend three pounds and ninety-nine pence?

4. What are eight thirties?

5. What number is nineteen more than twenty-six?

6. Write in figures the number two thousand and fifteen.

7. What is one quarter of eighty-eight?

8. What is the sum of sixty-three and twenty-nine?

9. How many sevens are there in sixty-three?

10. A DVD costs £9.50. How much change do you get from a £20 note?

11. What is fifty per cent of fifty pounds?

12 How many sides has an octagon?

13 I think of a number, double it and the answer is seven. What was the number I thought of?

14 What is four thousand four hundred and fifty-nine to the nearest hundred?

15 What is nought point two multiplied by one hundred?

16 Two angles of a triangle add up to one hundred and fifteen degrees. What size is the third angle?

17 Write noon in twenty-four hour clock time.

18 You are facing East and turn through three right angles clockwise. What direction are you now facing?

19 A thermometer in a room shows twenty-two degrees. The temperature outside the room is minus 8 degrees. What is the difference in temperature between inside and outside?

20 If you have four thousand and eleven pennies, how much do you have in pounds and pence?

UNIT 5

5.1 More algebra

In section 5.1 you will:

- review section 1 algebra
- solve equations
- multiply out single brackets

Review of section 1 algebra

$ab = a \times b$ $\qquad \dfrac{a}{b} = a \div b$ $\qquad a^2 = a \times a$

$5a + 4b + a - 2b = 6a + 2b$ (only like terms can be added or subtracted)

$m = 8 + 3n + nc$

Find m when $n = 5$ and $c = 7$
$m = 8 + (3 \times 5) + (5 \times 7)$

$m = 58$

Exercise 1M

1   Simplify the following expressions where possible.
   (a) $5y - 2y$ (b) $8m + 2$ (c) $7x - x$ (d) $5w - 3$

2   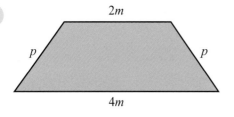   Write down an expression for the perimeter of this trapezium.

3   Simplify
   (a) $3 \times m \times n$ (b) $5 \times p \times 3 \times q$ (c) $2 \times m \times 3 \times m$

4　Which pair of expressions below are equal to each other?

$\boxed{2n + 1}$　　$\boxed{2n + n}$　　$\boxed{n \times n \times n}$　　$\boxed{3n}$　　$\boxed{n + 3}$

5　Simplify by collecting like terms.

(a) $7m + 3n - n + 4m$　　(b) $8x + 6y + 2x - 3y$　　(c) $4p + 5p + 3q - 2p$

6　$w = 25 - 4n$
Find w when $n = 5$

7　$a = 2(b - 6)$
Find a when $b = 10$

8　$c = 8(d + 3)$
Find c when $d = 6$

9　$y = x^2$
Find y when $x = 7$

10　Jack says that $2x - x$ is equal to 2. Is he correct? Explain your answer fully.

11　The average speed s of a sprinter is given by the formula

$$s = \frac{d}{t}$$

where d is the distance covered and t is the time taken.
Find the value of s when $d = 200$ and $t = 25$

12　The cost in pounds C for hiring a van is given by the formula $C = 3n + 65$ where n is the number of miles travelled.
Find C when $n = 60$

Exercise 2M

1　Simplify by collecting like terms.

(a) $6x + 3y - y - y$　　(b) $9m + 3 + 4m$　　(c) $8p + 6 + 2p - 1$

2　Simplify

(a) $8n \times 5p$　　(b) $6m \times 6m$　　(c) $3m \times 2n \times 3p$

3　
x
$3x$

(a) Write down an expression for the area of this rectangle.

(b) Find the value of the area of the rectangle when $x = 7$ cm.

4　I start with a number w, double it then subtract 18.
Write down an expression for what I now have.

5　$p = 2q + 5r$
Find p when $q = 6$ and $r = 7$

6　$f = gh$
Find f when $g = 9$ and $h = 8$

7 $m = \dfrac{n}{4}$

Find m when $n = 48$

8 $a = b(c - 7)$

Find a when $b = 10$ and $c = 15$

9 Imi says that the expression $\dfrac{n}{6}$ gives the same answer as $\dfrac{6}{n}$. Is she correct?

Give a reason for your answer.

10

2m

2m

5n

5n

The perimeter p of this shape is given by the formula

$$p = 4m + 10n$$

Find p when $m = 8$ and $n = 13$

11 Which expression below is the odd one out?

| $5a \times 4b$ | $10b \times 2a$ | $5b \times 4a$ | $16a \times b$ |

12 $V = IR$ is an electrical formula. Find the value of V when $I = 0.5$ and $R = 68$

Negative numbers can be substituted into formulas

$m = 6 - n$
Find m when $n = -2$

$m = 6 - (-2)$
$m = 6 + 2$
$m = 8$

$y = 3x + w$
Find y when $x = 4$ and $w = -8$

$y = (3 \times 4) + (-8)$
$y = 12 - 8$
$y = 4$

Exercise 2E

1 Work out
   (a) $7 + (-3)$ (b) $7 - (-3)$ (c) $7 \times (-3)$ (d) $-7 \times (-3)$
   (e) $-8 - (-2)$ (f) $-9 \div (-3)$ (g) $-6 - 2$

2 Copy and complete the following.
   (a) $x = -7 - (-4)$
       $x = -7 \; \square \; 4$
       $x = \square$
   (b) $y = -3 + (-10)$
       $y = -3 \; \square \; 10$
       $y = \square$

3 $a = 7 + b$
   Find a when $b = -5$

4 $w = 16 - p$
   Find w when $p = -3$

5 $m = 3n$
   Find m when $n = -9$

6 $h = 3g - 6$
   Find h when $g = -6$

7 $c = 2d + e$
   Find c when $d = -4$ and $e = -7$

8 $n = 5x - y$
   Find n when $x = -10$ and $y = -40$

9 $p = m^2$
   Find p when $m = -6$

10 $a = \dfrac{b}{7}$
    Find a when $b = -63$

11 $y = 3(8 - x)$
    Find y when $x = -2$

12 $p = -2(8 + q)$
    Find p when $q = -3$

13 $a = 2b + 2c$
    Find a when $b = -4$ and $c = -5$

14 $c = \dfrac{d}{-3}$
    Find c when $d = -36$

15 $y = mx + c$
    Find y when $m = 4$,
    $x = -6$ and $c = 3$

16 $p = uw - t$
    Find p when $u = 7$,
    $w = -2$ and $t = -8$

Solving equations

- Tom is thinking of a mystery number. He knows that if he doubles the number and then adds nine, the answer is twenty-three.

  He could write $\boxed{?}$ for the mystery number.

  So $2 \times \boxed{?} + 9 = 23$

  This is an *equation*. It contains an '$=$' sign.

  There is one unknown number shown by the question mark.

- People prefer to use *letters* to stand for unknowns when they write equations. Tom's equation would be

  $2 \times n + 9 = 23$ where n is the mystery number.

  or $2n + 9 = 23$

  What is Tom's mystery number?

- Equations are like weighing scales which are balanced. The scales remain balanced if the same weight is added or taken away from both sides.

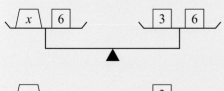

On the left pan is an unknown weight x plus a 6 kg weight. On the right pan there is a 6 kg weight and a 3 kg weight.

If the two 6 kg weights are taken from each pan, the scales are still balanced so the weight x is 3 kg.

Exercise 3M

Find the weight x by removing weights from both pans. Weights are in kg.

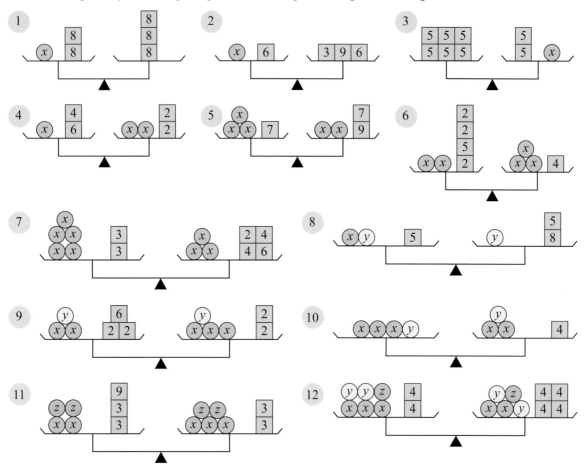

Rules for solving equations

Equations can be solved in the same way as the weighing scale problems were solved.

The main rule is

> Do the same thing to both sides

If you need to, you may:

    add the same thing to both sides

    subtract the same thing from both sides

    multiply both sides by the same thing

    divide both sides by the same thing

Solve the equations. The circles show what is done to both sides of the equation.

(a) $x + 4 = 16$

$\boxed{-4}\ \boxed{-4}$

$x = 12$

(b) $x - 5 = 14$

$\boxed{+5}\ \boxed{+5}$

$x = 19$

(c) $3x = 18$

$\boxed{\div 3}\ \boxed{\div 3}$

$x = 6$

(d) $\dfrac{x}{2} = 6$

$\boxed{\times 2}\ \boxed{\times 2}$

$x = 12$

Exercise 4M

Solve the equations below.

1 $x + 5 = 12$

2 $x + 6 = 19$

3 $x - 4 = 8$

4 $x - 9 = 8$

5 $3 + x = 11$

6 $7 + x = 17$

7 $5 = x + 3$

8 $6 = x - 2$

9 $2 = x - 6$

10 $3 + x = 3$

11 $x - 14 = 10$

12 $17 = 5 + x$

Questions 13 to 27 involve multiplication and division.

13 $7n = 21$

14 $4n = 12$

15 $5n = 45$

16 $10 = 2n$

17 $8 = 8n$

18 $2n = 1$

19 $4n = 100$

20 $6n = 0$

21 $\dfrac{n}{3} = 2$

22 $\dfrac{n}{5} = 4$

23 $70 = 7n$

24 $2n = 1000$

25 $\dfrac{n}{8} = 3$

26 $\dfrac{n}{4} = 1$

27 $10 = \dfrac{n}{2}$

Exercise 5M

Solve the equations below to find the value of a.

1 $a - 17 = 21$

2 $4a = 32$

3 $9 + a = 60$

4 $5 = a + 5$

5 $63 = 9a$

6 $15a = 45$

7 $a + 36 = 120$

8 $a - \dfrac{1}{3} = \dfrac{2}{3}$

9 $3a = 1$

10 $65 = a - 25$

11 $140 = a - 20$

12 $4a = 412$

13 $109 = a - 206$

14 $\dfrac{a}{3} = 9$

15 $\dfrac{a}{5} = 100$

16 $0 = 15a$

17 $a + 14 = 14$

18 $\dfrac{a}{10} = 6$

19 $8 = \dfrac{a}{2}$

20 $63 = a + 24$

21 $320 = 4a$

22 $3 = 12a$

23 $71 = a - 56$

24 $20 = \dfrac{a}{6}$

Equations with two operations

(a) $6n - 5 = 19$

$\quad\quad (+5)\ (+5)$

$\quad\quad 6n = 24$

$\quad\quad (\div 6)\ (\div 6)$

$\quad\quad n = 4$

Check: $6 \times 4 - 5 = 19$

(b) $3n + 4 = 31$

$\quad\quad (-4)\ (-4)$

$\quad\quad 3n = 27$

$\quad\quad (\div 3)\ (\div 3)$

$\quad\quad n = 9$

Check: $3 \times 9 + 4 = 31$

Exercise 6M

Solve the equations below. Check by substituting the answer back in the equation.

1 $4n - 1 = 11$

2 $2n + 3 = 17$

3 $6n - 9 = 15$

4 $5n + 6 = 16$

5 $4n - 9 = 11$

6 $2n - 10 = 8$

7 $3n + 7 = 37$

8 $9n + 4 = 13$

9 $7n - 6 = 15$

10 $7n - 10 = 25$

11 $4n - 7 = 73$

12 $3n + 8 = 26$

In questions 13 to 24 solve the equations to find x.

13 $7x + 2 = 30$

14 $5x - 9 = 31$

15 $6x - 40 = 20$

16 $8x + 3 = 59$

17 $2 + 4x = 30$

18 $19 + 3x = 19$

19 $12 + 6x = 42$

20 $10x - 13 = 27$

21 $7x - 40 = 100$

22 $2x - 38 = 62$

23 $7 + 2x = 19$

24 $2x + 6 = 7$

Using equations to solve problems

Tina is thinking of a number. She tells us that when she trebles it and adds 8, the answer is 23. What number is Tina thinking of ?

Let n be the number Tina is thinking of.

She tell us that $\qquad$ $3n + 8 = 23$

Subtract 8 from both sides: $\qquad$ $3n = 15$

Divide both sides by 3: $\qquad$ $n = \dfrac{15}{3} = 5$

So Tina is thinking of the number 5.

Exercise 6E

In questions ① to ⑦ I am thinking of a number.

Write down an equation then solve it to find the number.

① I multiply the number by 4 and then add 9.
The answer is 17.

② I multiply the number by 6 and then add 2.
The answer is 50.

③ I multiply the number by 9 and then subtract 5.
The answer is 22.

④ I double the number and then add 17.
The answer is 37.

⑤ I multiply the number by 5 and then subtract 11.
The answer is 24.

⑥ I treble the number and then subtract 13. The answer is 2.

⑦ I multiply the number by 4 and then add 15. The answer is 135.

⑧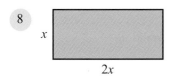

The length of a rectangle is twice its width.
An expression for its perimeter is

$$x + 2x + x + 2x$$

If the actual value of the perimeter is 48 cm,
make an equation and find the value of x.

⑨ The length of a rectangle is four times its width. If the perimeter of the rectangle is 50 cm, find its width. [Hint: Let the width be x.]

10　The length of a rectangle is 5 cm more
than its width as shown opposite.
If the perimeter of the rectangle is 38 cm,
find its width.

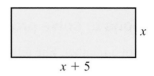

11　For each triangle, write down an equation then solve it to find x.
(Remember: the angles in a triangle add up to 180°)

(a)

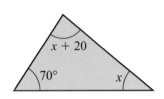

(b)

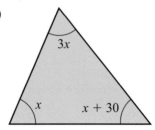

12　The angles of a triangle are A, B and C. Angle B is three times as big as angle A.
Angle C is 45° bigger than angle A. Find the size of angle A.
(Hint: let the size of angle A be $x°$)

13　Uncle Ben is x years old and Auntie Janet is 7 years older.
The sum of their ages is 91. Find Uncle Ben's age.

Mixed equations

Solve the equations where the 'n' terms are on the right hand side.

(a) $7 = 5n - 8$
  (+8) (+8)
  $15 = 5n$
  (÷5) (÷5)
  $3 = n$

(b) $11 = 3 + 2n$
  (−3) (−3)
  $8 = 2n$
  (÷2) (÷2)
  $4 = n$

Exercise 7M

Solve the equations below. Check by substituting the answer back in the equation.

1　$37 = 4n + 1$

2　$7 = 2n - 5$

3　$7 = 20n - 13$

4　$33 = 2n + 9$

5　$3n + 16 = 25$

6　$55 = 15 + 8n$

7　$16 = 16 + 3n$

8　$19 = 2n - 11$

9　$59 = 4n + 3$

In questions ⑩ to ㉑ find the value of the letter in each question.

⑩ $6t - 9 = 45$

⑪ $50 = 7y + 8$

⑫ $11 = 3 + 8c$

⑬ $3x + 10 = 85$

⑭ $0 = 4m - 36$

⑮ $16 + 2p = 106$

⑯ $7 + 5n = 62$

⑰ $8w - 25 = 47$

⑱ $10a - 15 = 205$

⑲ $3y - 70 = 260$

⑳ $156 = 26 + 2q$

㉑ $540 = 3x - 63$

Multiply out single brackets

$6(4 + 3) = 6(7) = 6 \times 7 = 42$

We also get the correct answer if the number outside the brackets multiplies each number inside the brackets.

$6(4 + 3) = 6 \times 4 + 6 \times 3 = 24 + 18 = 42$

(a) Multiply out $3(a + b)$

$3(a + b) = 3 \times a + 3 \times b = 3a + 3b$

(b) Multiply out $6(n - 3)$

$6(n - 3) = 6 \times n - 6 \times 3 = 6n - 18$

Exercise 8M

① Multiply out the brackets and match up with the correct answer.

Question		Answer	
(a)	$5(n + 2)$	A	$6n + 18$
(b)	$3(4 - 2n)$	B	$5n + 2$
(c)	$6(n + 3)$	C	$10n + 15$
(d)	$2(4n - 1)$	D	$6n + 3$
(e)	$5(2n + 3)$	E	$5n + 10$
		F	$8n - 2$
		G	$8n - 1$
		H	$12 - 6n$

② Helina says that $4(3x - 1)$ equals $12x - 1$.
Aaron says that $4(3x - 1)$ equals $12x - 4$.
Explain clearly who is correct and why.

Multiply out the brackets in questions ③ to ㉓ .

③ $2(x + 3)$ ④ $6(x + 4)$ ⑤ $3(x + 9)$

⑥ $5(x + 8)$ ⑦ $4(x - 7)$ ⑧ $2(x - 8)$

⑨ $9(x - 4)$ ⑩ $6(x - 8)$ ⑪ $4(x + y)$

⑫ $7(a + b)$ ⑬ $3(m - n)$ ⑭ $5(2x + 3)$

⑮ $6(4x - 7)$ ⑯ $4(2a + b)$ ⑰ $9(m + 2n)$

⑱ $4(x + 3y)$ ⑲ $2(4m + n)$ ⑳ $7(5x - 3)$

㉑ $8(3 - x)$ ㉒ $6(4 - 2x)$ ㉓ $5(3a + 5b)$

㉔   Josh says that an expression for the area of the
     rectangle opposite is $(21m - 14)\,\text{cm}^2$.
     Rachel says he is not correct.
     Explain clearly who is correct.

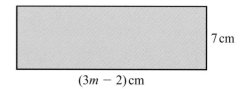

7 cm

$(3m - 2)\,\text{cm}$

'Expand' means 'multiply out'.

(a) Expand $m(n + y)$ (b) Expand $w(w - 3)$

$m(n + y) = m \times n + m \times y$ $w(w - 3) = w \times w - 3 \times w$
$\qquad\quad = mn + my$ $\qquad\quad = w^2 - 3w$

Exercise 9M

Expand

① $p(q + r)$ ② $m(n - p)$ ③ $a(b + c)$

④ $a(b - e)$ ⑤ $x(y + 3)$ ⑥ $m(n - 6)$

⑦ $x(y - 9)$ ⑧ $p(q - 5)$ ⑨ $a(c + 7)$

⑩ $d(e + 8)$ ⑪ $a(a + 4)$ ⑫ $m(m - 6)$

⑬ $p(p - 2)$ ⑭ $x(x + 9)$ ⑮ $a(7 - a)$

⑯ $x(2 + y)$ ⑰ $5(2a + 3)$ ⑱ $9(3m - 2)$

⑲ $6(4x - 1)$ ⑳ $4(8n + 7)$ ㉑ $b(4 - b)$

22 Carly writes that $n(5 - 3n) = 5n - 3n = 2n$. Explain clearly why this is not correct.

23

$2n$ | P | $3n+1$

$3n$ | Q | $n+2$

$4n$ | R | $2n-3$

(a) Write down the area of each shape with no brackets.

(b) Which shape has the largest area when $n = 4$?
Explain your answer clearly.

24 Ian earns £$(m + 25)$ each week.

(a) Write down an expression for how much he earns in n weeks.

(b) Simplify your answer to part (a).

(c) How much money does Ian receive if $m = 230$ and $n = 6$?

Need more practice with algebra?

Solve the equations below.

1 $8x = 56$

2 $76 = x + 39$

3 $\dfrac{x}{4} = 8$

4 $63 = 7x$

5 $7 = \dfrac{x}{8}$

6 $48 = x - 16$

7 $5x - 7 = 23$

8 $9x + 4 = 58$

9 $10x + 3 = 43$

10 $3x - 6 = 27$

11 $6x + 20 = 74$

12 $4x - 10 = 34$

13 Tilly says that the expression $6m \times 4n$ is the same as the expression $2n \times 12m$.
Is she correct? Explain your answer fully.

14 There are 4 people in a boat in a
rowing race.

(a) Write down an expression for how
many people are in n boats.

(b) How many people are in 12 boats?

15 Which expression below is the odd one out?

$5x + 3y - y + 2x$ $7y + 3x - 4y + 4x$ $9x + y + y - 2x$

16 $4(2m + 9) = 8m + 36$. Is this correct or not? Explain your answer fully.

17 $y = mx + c$
Find y when $m = 6$, $x = 3$ and $c = 12$.

18 $P = 3(2n - 1)$
Find P when $n = 7$.

19 Expand (multiply out)

(a) $3(n + 6)$ (b) $5(4n + 6)$ (c) $n(n + 4)$

(d) $m(2m - 3)$ (e) $a(b + 4)$ (f) $y(2x - y)$

Extension questions with algebra

1 Ayden and Emily are trying to solve the equation $\dfrac{n}{2} = 6$.

Ayden says the answer is $n = 12$ and Emily says that the answer is $n = 3$.
Who is correct and explain what mistake the other person has made.

2 Simplify these expressions.

(a) $5n \times 6 \times 2m$ (b) $4m \times 7n \times 3$ (c) $7m \times 2n \times 2n$

3 Write down an equation involving x
for the triangle opposite then find
the value of x.

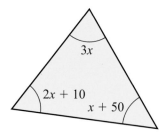

$3x$

$2x + 10$

$x + 50$

4 Solve the equations below.

(a) $3n = 1$ (b) $2n = 15$ (c) $3n + 7 = 9$

(d) $5n - 3 = 13$ (e) $6n - 1 = 4$ (f) $2n + 3 = 20$

5 Jon says that $8m + 6m - 4$ is equal to $10m$.
Is he correct? Explain your answer fully.

6
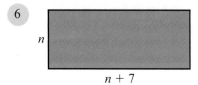

n

$n + 7$

The length of a rectangle is 7 cm more
than its width. The perimeter of the
rectangle is 50 cm.
Form an equation in terms of n then work
out the width of the rectangle.

7 $m = 6 - n$
Find m when $n = -5$.

8   $y = 3x + c$
    Find y when $x = -2$ and $c = -6$.

9   Write down an expression for the area of
    the triangle opposite. Give the answer
    in simplified form.

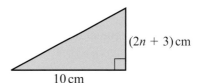

$(2n + 3)$ cm

10 cm

10 For each expression below,
    expand the brackets then collect the like terms.
    (a) $4(x + 3) + 2(x + 5)$ (b) $7(x + 4) + 4(x + 2)$
    (c) $7(2x + 5) + 3(x + 4)$ (d) $6(3x + 4) + 5(2x + 1)$
    (e) $9(2x + 3) + 6(4x + 7)$ (f) $3(4x + 9) + 2(9x + 5)$
    (g) $3(4x + 2) + 2(2x - 1)$ (h) $8(5x + 3) + 6(4x - 3)$

5.2 Interpreting graphs

In section 5.2 you will:

- read and draw line graphs in real life situations

- interpret travel graphs

Exercise 1M

1   This graph converts miles into
    kilometres.

    (a) Convert 20 miles into km

    (b) Convert 64 km into miles

    (c) Sharon's journey to work is
         10 miles. How far is that
         in kilometres?

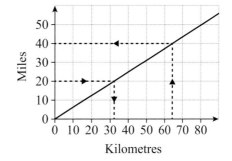

2   This graph converts rupees into pounds.
    The rupee is the currency in India.

    (a) Convert into pounds
         (i)   280 rupees   (ii)   110 rupees
         (iii) 250 rupees   (iv)   360 rupees

    (b) Convert into rupees
         (i)   £5.00   (ii)   £2.40
         (iii) £4.20   (iv)   £0.80

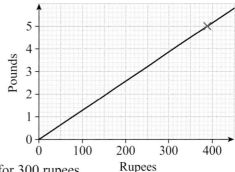

    (c) On holiday in India, Jason bought fish and chips for 300 rupees.
         How much did the meal cost in pounds?

3   Jerome was not well one day.
    The graph shows his temperature
    between 07.00 and 13.00 one day.

    (a) What was his temperature at
        (i) 8.00   (ii) 10.30

    (b) At what time was his temperature
        highest?

    (c) At what two times was his
        temperature 38.5°C?

    (d) Between which two times did his
        temperature rise most quickly?

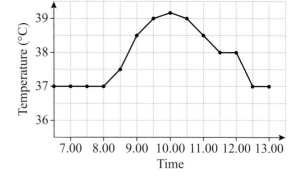

4   The graph shows the cost of making calls
    to two directory enquiry numbers.

    (a) How much does it cost for a
        50 second call to 118500?

    (b) Using 118118, for how long can you
        call for 55p?

    (c) At what length of call do both numbers
        cost the same?

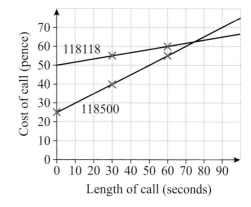

5   The cost of hiring a tank for filming depends on the duration of the hire.

    (a) How much does it cost to hire the tank for
        (i) 1 day   (ii) $5\frac{1}{2}$ days   (iii) 3 days?

    (b) What is the minimum hire charge?

Exercise 2M

1   Draw a graph to convert kilograms into pounds.
    Draw a line through the point where 3 kg is equivalent
    to 6.6 pounds. Use a scale of 1 cm to 1 pound across the
    page and 2 cm to 1 kg up the page.
    Use your graph to convert

    (a) 1.2 kg into pounds

    (b) 2 pounds into kg

    (c) *Explain* how you would use this graph to convert
        8 kg into pounds.

    (d) *Explain* how you would use this graph to convert 20 pounds into kg.

    (e) Which is greater – 10 kg or 23 pounds? Give a reason for your answer.

2   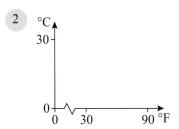 Draw a graph to convert temperatures from °F to °C.
    Draw a line through the points 50°F = 10°C
                                  and 86°F = 30°C.

    Use the graph to convert:

    (a) 77°F into °C   (b) 15°C into °F

3   A mobile phone company charges £10 a month rental plus
    20p per minute for calls.

Minutes of calls	0	20	40	60	80
Cost in £	10	14	18	22	26

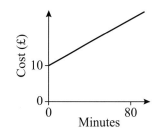

    (a) Draw a graph to show this information.

    (b) Use your graph to find the total cost of making
        65 minutes of calls.

Travel graphs

- This graph shows the details of a cycle ride that
  Jim took starting from his home.

    (a) In the first hour Jim went 30 km so his speed
        was 30 km/h.

    (b) He stopped for $\frac{1}{2}$ hour at a place 30 km from
        his home.

    (c) From 09.30 until 11.00 he cycled back home.
        We know that he cycled back home because
        the distance from his home at 11.00 is 0 km.

    (d) The speed at which he cycled home was 20 km/h.

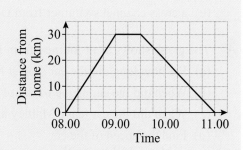

Exercise 3M

1. The graph shows a car journey from A to C via B.
   (a) How far is it from A to C?
   (b) For how long does the car stop at B?
   (c) When is the car half way between B and C?
   (d) What is the speed of the car
       (i) between A and B?
       (ii) between B and C?

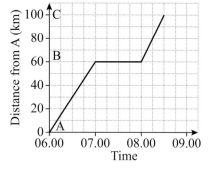

2. The graph shows the motion of a train as it accelerates away from Troon.
   (a) How far from Troon is the train at 08.45?
   (b) When is the train half way between R and S?
   (c) Find the speed of the train
       (i) from R to S
       (ii) from Q to R
   (d) How long does it take the train to travel 100 km?

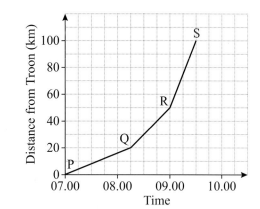

3. The diagram shows the travel graphs of five objects. Which graph shows:
   (a) a car ferry from Dover to Calais
   (b) a hovercraft from Dover to Calais
   (c) a car ferry from Calais to Dover
   (d) a buoy outside Dover harbour
   (e) a cross channel swimmer from Dover?

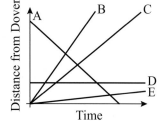

4. The graph shows a car journey from Lemsford.
   (a) For how long did the car stop at Mabley?
   (b) When did the car arrive back at Lemsford?
   (c) When did the car leave Mabley after stopping?
   (d) Find the speed of the car
       (i) from Mabley to Nixon
       (ii) from Nixon back to Lemsford.

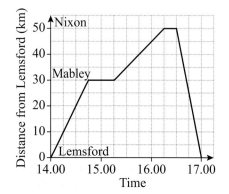

Need more practice with interpreting graphs?

1   A car went on a five hour journey starting at 12.00 with a full tank of petrol. The volume of petrol in the tank was measured after every hour; the results are shown below.

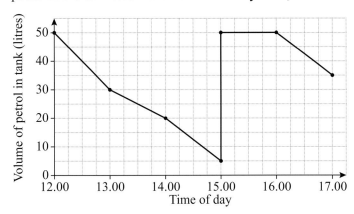

(a) How much petrol was in the tank at 13.00?

(b) At what time was there 5 litres in the tank?

(c) How much petrol was used in the first hour of the journey?

(d) What happened at 15.00?

(e) What do you think happened between 15.00 and 16.00?

(f) How much petrol was used between 12.00 and 17.00?

2   Draw a graph to convert gallons into litres.
Draw a line as shown opposite through the point where 1 gallon is equivalent to 4.5 litres.
Use the graph to convert

(a) 0.8 gallon into litres

(b) 2 litres into gallons

(c) 22.5 litres into gallons

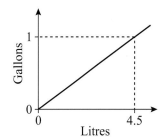

3   The graph shows a cyclist's journey from home to a friend's house.

(a) Between what times does the cyclist stop for a rest?

(b) How far does the cyclist travel between the 2 rest periods?

(c) How far has the cyclist travelled by 1 pm?

(d) Find the speed of the cyclist between home and the first rest period at 11 am.

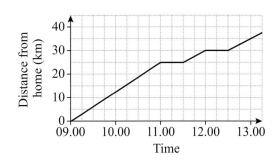

4 A man climbing a mountain measures his height above sea level after every 30 minutes; the results are shown on the graph.

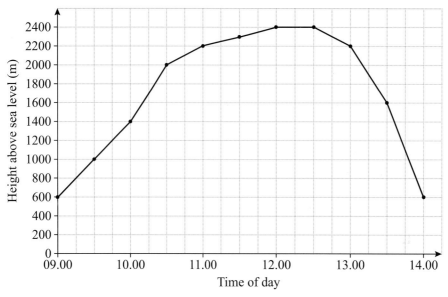

(a) At what height was he at 10.00?
(b) At what height was he at 13.30?
(c) Estimate his height above sea level at 09.45.
(d) At what two times was he 2200 m above sea level?
(e) How high was the mountain? (He got to the top!)
(f) How long did he rest at the summit?
(g) How long did he take to reach the summit?

Extension questions with interpreting graphs

1 At 17.00 Lisa leaves her home and cycles at 20 km/h for 1 hour. She stops for $\frac{1}{4}$ hour and then continues her journey at a speed of 40 km/h for the next $\frac{1}{2}$ hour. She then stops for $\frac{3}{4}$ hour. Finally she returns home at a speed of 40 km/h.
   (a) Copy the graph shown opposite and complete a travel graph to show Lisa's whole journey.
   (b) When did she arrive home?

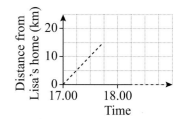

2 Declan leaves home at 13.00 on his horse and rides at a speed of 20 km/h for one hour. Declan and his horse then rest for 45 minutes and afterwards continue their journey at a speed of 15 km/h for another one hour. At what time do they finish the journey?

3 At 12.00 Amar leaves home and drives at a speed of 30 km/h. At 12.30 he increases his speed to 50 km/h and continues to his destination which is 65 km from home. He stops for $\frac{1}{2}$ hour and then returns home at a speed of 65 km/h.

(a) Draw a travel graph for Amar's journey. Use the same scale as in question $\boxed{1}$.

(b) At what time does Amar arrive home?

4 As Mrs Sadler leaves home in her car at 13.00 she encounters heavy traffic and travels at only 20 km/h for the first $\frac{1}{2}$ hour. In the second half hour she increases her speed to 30 km/h and after that she travels along the main road at 50 km/h for 1 hour.

She stops at her destination for $\frac{1}{2}$ hour and then returns home at a steady speed of 50 km/h.

Draw a graph to find out when she returns home. Use the same scale as in question $\boxed{1}$.

✗ Spot the mistakes 9 ✗

Algebra and interpreting graphs

Work through each question below and *explain clearly* what mistakes have been made. Beware – some questions are correctly done.

1 Solve $5x - 1 = 3$

Answer: $5x - 1 = 3$
$$5x = 2$$
$$x = \frac{2}{5}$$

2 Conan uses the conversion graph opposite to work out how many dollars are equivalent to £3. His answer is $2.80

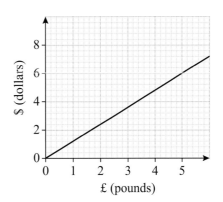

3 Simplify $5xy + 6y - 2xy + yx - y$
Answer: $3xy + 6y + yx$

4 Expand $3(2n + 5)$
Answer: $6n + 5$

5   Work out the actual value of each
angle in the triangle opposite.

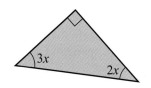

Answer: $3x + 2x + 90 = 180$

$$5x + 90 = 180$$

$$5x = 270$$

$$x = \frac{270}{5} = 54$$

Actual angles: $3x = 3 \times 54° = 162°$ and $2x = 2 \times 54° = 108°$
and the right angle $= 90°$

6   I think of a number, multiply it by 7 then subtract 3.
The answer is 2. What number did I think of?

Solution: Let the number be n.

$$7n - 3 = 2$$

$$7n = 5$$

$$n = \tfrac{5}{7}$$

so the number is $\tfrac{5}{7}$

7   Faith is three times older than Pete. If Faith is n years old, write down an expression
for Pete's age.

Answer: Pete is $3n$ years old.

8   Megan drives from her
home to make a hospital
visit. The travel graph
opposite shows her
journey. What was her
speed during the first
half an hour of her
journey?

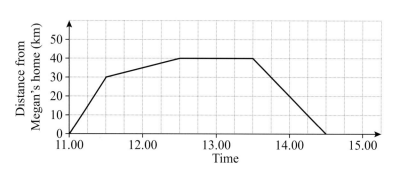

Answer: Megan travels 30 km in 30 minutes so her speed is 60 km/h.

9   Find the value of P when $n = 3$ if $P = \dfrac{2n + 5}{4}$

Answer: $P = \dfrac{23 + 5}{4} = \dfrac{28}{4} = 7$

10   Find the value of y when $m = -2$ and $x = -3$ if $y = 6(3m - x)$

Answer: $y = 6(3 \times -2 - -3)$

$$y = 6(-6 + 3)$$

$$y = 6(-9) = 6 \times -9 = -54$$

CHECK YOURSELF ON SECTIONS 5.1 AND 5.2

1 Review of section 1 algebra

Simplify the expressions.

(a) $3a + 7c + a$

(b) $2 \times a \times b$

(c) $3m - n + 5m + 3n$

(d) $\dfrac{x^2}{x}$

(e) $\dfrac{10c}{5}$

(f) $2a + 4a + ab$

(g) $s = 3u - 6$

Find s when $u = 5$

(h) $h = 4(2a - b)$

Find h when $a = 8$ and $b = 9$

2 Solving equations

Solve

(a) $x - 9 = 17$

(b) $\dfrac{m}{6} = 5$

(c) $3n - 7 = 23$

(d) $54 = 7a + 5$

3 Multiplying out single brackets

Expand (multiply out)

(a) $5(x + 7)$

(b) $n(p - 3)$

(c) $x(x + 8)$

4 Reading and drawing line graphs in real life situations

This line graph shows the average daily temperature in Sweden.

(a) What was the temperature in June?

(b) In which month was the temperature 7°C?

(c) In which two months was the temperature 3°C?

(d) Between which two months was there the largest increase in temperature?

(e) What was the range of temperature over the year?

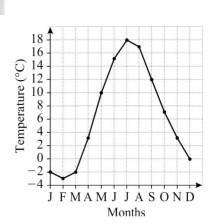

5   Interpreting travel graphs

Trevor travels 100 km from home.
The travel graph opposite shows his journey.

(a) Trevor stops at 10.00. For how long does he stop?

(b) When is Trevor 90 km from home?

(c) What is Trevor's speed
    (i) between 09.00 and 10.00?
    (ii) between 10.30 and 11.00?

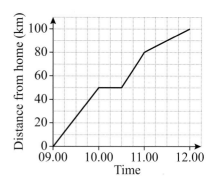

5.3 Number review

In section 5.3 you will review:

- multiples, factors, prime numbers, H.C.F. and L.C.M.
- fractions, decimals and percentages
- long multiplication and division
- adding, subtracting, multiplying and dividing decimals
- using percentages and fractions of
- using ratios

Multiples, factors and prime numbers

The first six *multiples* of 5 are   5, 10, 15, 20, 25, 30

The factors of 8 are   1, 2, 4, 8

The first five prime numbers are   2, 3, 5, 7, 11

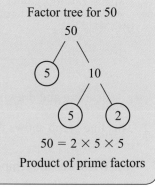

Factor tree for 50

$50 = 2 \times 5 \times 5$

Product of prime factors

Exercise 1M

1   In the diagram on the next page the factors of the numbers from 1 to 25 are to be shaded in.

For example:

4 has factors 1, 2 and 4 so shade in those factor boxes above the number 4.

5 has factors 1 and 5 so shade in those factor boxes above the number 5.

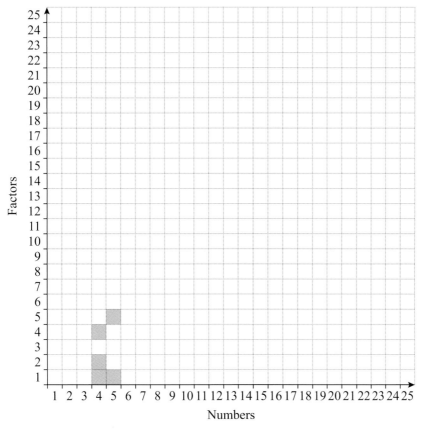

Copy and complete your chart for all the numbers.

Count up how many boxes you have shaded and write down the answer.

2   Write down the odd one out
    (a) Multiples of 9:   18, 27, 54, 83, 99
    (b) Multiples of 8:   18, 32, 40, 64
    (c) Multiples of 7:   7, 35, 56, 69

3   Write down the first eight prime numbers in order of size.

4   Write down two prime numbers whose sum is a prime number.

5   Write down the 1-digit numbers that have three factors.

6
    20   65   2
      30   5
    1   Write down the numbers in the hoop which are
                     (a) factors of 10
                     (b) multiples of 10

7   Find three numbers that are multiples of both 2 and 3.

8   Write down the smallest prime number which is greater than 30.

Exercise 2M

1. (a) Write down the first six multiples of 4.
   (b) Write down the first six multiples of 5.
   (c) Write down the lowest common multiple
       (L.C.M.) of 4 and 5.

   > Reminder:
   > The L.C.M. is
   > the lowest number
   > which is in both lists.

2. Find the L.C.M. of 3 and 5

3. The table shows the factors and common factors of 12 and 18

Number	Factors	Common factors
12	1, 2, 3, 4, 6, 12	}1, 2, 3, 6
18	1, 2, 3, 6, 9, 18	

   Write down the highest common factor (H.C.F.) of 12 and 18.

   > The H.C.F. is
   > the highest number
   > which is in both lists.

4. Find the H.C.F. of
   (a) 9 and 12   (b) 24 and 36   (c) 12 and 16

5. Why is this factor tree for 180 not correct?

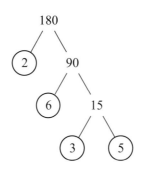

$$180 = 2 \times 3 \times 5 \times 6$$

6. Copy and complete this factor tree.

7. Write the following numbers as products of their prime factors by drawing factor trees first.
   (a) 50   (b) 108   (c) 150   (d) 180

8. Part of a factor tree is shown opposite.
   Write down the number which has this factor tree.

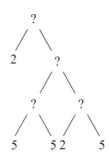

Fractions, decimals, percentages

Exercise 3M

1   Find the missing number to make these fractions equivalent.

(a) $\dfrac{3}{4} = \dfrac{\square}{12}$

(b) $\dfrac{4}{7} = \dfrac{\square}{35}$

(c) $\dfrac{6}{10} = \dfrac{\square}{5}$

(d) $\dfrac{3}{8} = \dfrac{\square}{24}$

(e) $\dfrac{3}{8} = \dfrac{9}{\square}$

(f) $\dfrac{4}{5} = \dfrac{12}{\square}$

(g) $\dfrac{8}{9} = \dfrac{16}{\square}$

(h) $\dfrac{1}{3} = \dfrac{5}{\square}$

2   Copy and use the two diagrams opposite to explain why $\dfrac{2}{3} + \dfrac{1}{4} = \dfrac{11}{12}$

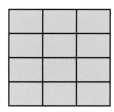 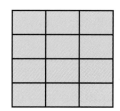

3   Work out

(a) $\dfrac{2}{5} + \dfrac{1}{4}$

(b) $\dfrac{1}{5} + \dfrac{1}{2}$

(c) $\dfrac{5}{6} - \dfrac{1}{2}$

(d) $\dfrac{2}{5} + \dfrac{1}{7}$

4   Convert these fractions into decimals.

(a) $\dfrac{3}{10}$

(b) $\dfrac{1}{4}$

(c) $\dfrac{3}{5}$

(d) $\dfrac{3}{4}$

(e) $\dfrac{9}{100}$

(f) $\dfrac{27}{100}$

(g) $\dfrac{35}{70}$

(h) $\dfrac{3}{12}$

(i) $\dfrac{24}{200}$

(j) $\dfrac{4}{25}$

5   Copy and complete

(a) $\dfrac{1}{5} = \dfrac{20}{100} = \square\,\%$

(b) $\dfrac{3}{20} = \dfrac{15}{100} = \square\,\%$

(c) $\dfrac{1}{25} = \dfrac{4}{100} = \square\,\%$

(d) $\dfrac{9}{20} = \dfrac{}{100} = \square\,\%$

(e) $\dfrac{11}{50} = \dfrac{}{100} = \square\,\%$

(f) $\dfrac{11}{25} = \dfrac{}{100} = \square\,\%$

6   In different tests Isabel got $\dfrac{7}{10}$ and Dani got $\dfrac{15}{25}$.

Who got the higher percentage and by how much?

7   Lily writes the following on a whiteboard.

$$\dfrac{9}{10} - \dfrac{5}{8} = \dfrac{36}{40} - \dfrac{25}{40} = \dfrac{11}{40}$$

Is Lily correct? If not, explain the mistake she has made.

8 Write down each fraction with its equivalent percentage.

(a) $\dfrac{1}{3}$ 　　(b) $\dfrac{2}{5}$ 　　(c) $\dfrac{3}{4}$ 　　(d) $\dfrac{3}{100}$ 　　(e) $\dfrac{2}{3}$

9 Which of the following calculations does not equal $\dfrac{5}{24}$?

You must fully justify your answer.

$\dfrac{5}{6} \times \dfrac{4}{16}$ 　　　 $\dfrac{5}{8} \times \dfrac{2}{6}$ 　　　 $\dfrac{1}{4} \times \dfrac{4}{6}$ 　　　 $\dfrac{3}{6} \times \dfrac{5}{12}$

10 Write the following in order of size, smallest first

(a) $\dfrac{3}{4}$, 60%, 0.7 　　　　(b) 5%, $\dfrac{1}{50}$, 0.03 　　　　(c) $\dfrac{3}{9}$, 0.3, 23%

Long multiplication and division

Exercise 4M

Work out

1 27×23 　　2 72×48 　　3 125×19 　　4 214×36

5 Copy and complete.

(a) $\boxed{} \div 25 = 15$ 　　(b) $\boxed{} \div 33 = 17$ 　　(c) $\boxed{} \div 27 = 42$

6 Work out

(a) $784 \div 14$ 　　(b) $544 \div 32$ 　　(c) $806 \div 31$ 　　(d) $1035 \div 23$

7 There are 47 seats on a coach.
How many coaches will be needed to transport 206 people to a concert?

8 A ferris wheel rotates one whole circle
every 96 seconds. How many complete
circles will the wheel manage if it turns
steadily for 4 hours
(4 hours = $4 \times 60 \times 60 = 14\,400$ seconds)?

9   There are twenty-two balls in a set of snooker balls.
Each ball weighs 154 grams.
Calculate the total weight of the set of snooker balls.

10   Chocolates are packed eighteen to a box.
How many boxes are needed for 648 chocolates?

Calculations involving decimals

Exercise 5M

1   Work out.

(a) $4 + 5.2$ (b) $6.1 + 18.7$ (c) $9.54 - 7$ (d) $0.74 + 3.4$

(e) $0.65 + 0.888$ (f) $11 - 3.2$ (g) $4.2 + 7.4 + 6$ (h) $32.7 - 19$

2   Copy and complete

(a)
```
   6 . □ 4
 + □ . 7 □
 ─────────
   8 . 2 7
```

(b)
```
   4 . 7 □
 + 4 . □ 5
 ─────────
   □ . 1 0
```

(c)
```
   6 . □ 7 2
 + □ . 2 □ 9
 ───────────
   8 . 0 9 □
```

3   Answer true or false: $0.8 \times 100 = 8000 \div 10$

4   Copy and complete

(a) $0.72 \times \square = 7.2$ (b) $\square \times 100 = 170$ (c) $10 \times \square = 16$

(d) $100 \times \square = 85.4$ (e) $3.2 \times \square = 3.2$ (f) $\square \times 100 = 2$

5   What is the total weight of 7 eggs if each egg weighs 8.2 grams?

6   What five different coins make £1.77?

7   What number when multiplied by 7 gives an answer of 16.8?

8   Work out

(a) 8.23×4 (b) $3.12 \div 4$ (c) $6.2 \div 5$ (d) 0.85×4

(e) $31.8 \div 6$ (f) 7×1.23 (g) $9.94 \div 7$ (h) 6×8.02

(i) 0.9×0.4 (j) 0.08×0.3 (k) 0.007×0.02 (l) 0.08×1.6

9   Five people share the cost of a meal which costs £42.
How much does each person pay?

10 Copy and complete the cross number.

Clues across
1. $5.7 \div 3$
3. 0.8×3
5. $(17 - 8) \times 2$
6. $44.8 \div 8$
7. $4.9 + 3.5$
8. $16.7 - 9.8$
10. $(10 \times 10) - (10 \times 1)$
11. $46.4 + 47.6$

Clues down
1. $203 - 86$
2. $7 \times 2 \times 7$
3. $(1000 \div 4) + 4$
4. $7 \times 7 - 3$
7. $44.5 \div 5$
8. $3 \times 2 \times 5 \times 2$
9. 11×0.4

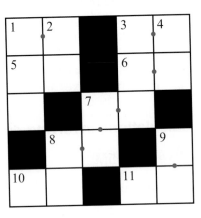

Using percentages and fractions of

Exercise 6M

1 Work out

(a) $\frac{1}{3}$ of 69

(b) $\frac{2}{3}$ of 69

(c) $\frac{1}{5}$ of 80

(d) $\frac{4}{5}$ of 80

2 Copy and complete

(a) $\frac{1}{\Box}$ of $35 = 5$

(b) $\frac{1}{\Box}$ of $121 = 11$

(c) $\frac{1}{\Box}$ of $74 = 37$

(d) $\frac{2}{5}$ of $45 = \Box$

(e) $\frac{2}{\Box}$ of $12 = 8$

(f) $\frac{1}{\Box}$ of $3000 = 30$

3 There are four hundred and fifty mushrooms in a garden and $\frac{1}{50}$ of them are poisonous. How many of the mushrooms are poisonous?

4 In one week 400 people took their driving test and three fifths of them passed. How many people passed the test that week?

5 Harvey earns £1300 each month. He is given a 5% pay rise. How much does Harvey now earn each month?

6 Answer true or false

(a) 25% of $60 = 15$

(b) $33\frac{1}{3}\%$ of $60 = 20$

(c) 10% of $9000 = 90$

(d) 1% of $5000 = 50$

(e) 20% of $45 = 8$

(f) 2% of $200 = 4$

7. Rowena buys a car for £12 500. One year later the car has lost 12% of its value. How much is the car worth one year later?

8. Which is greater: 5% of 800 or 18% of 300? Explain why you chose your answer.

9. A piece of wood is 85.6 cm long. A quarter of the wood is cut off. How long is the remaining piece of wood?

10. A factory produces forty-five thousand clocks every week and, when tested, two per cent of them are not accurate. How many inaccurate clocks are made each week?

11. Kanu invests £3500 and five years later this money has increased by $\frac{2}{7}$.

    Ellie invests £4000 and five years later this money has increased by 11%.

    Who has more money after five years and by how much?

12. Work out (5% of £30) + (4% of £200) + (11% of £1200)

Using ratios

Exercise 7M

1. 7 sweaters cost £273 and 9 jackets cost £567. Which cost more – 11 jackets or 17 sweaters and by how much more?

2. Write these ratios in simplified form.
   (a) $21:49$
   (b) $8:32:12$
   (c) $20:15:35$
   (d) $2\,kg:400\,g$
   (e) $6\,cm:4\,mm$
   (f) $0.6:0.3$

3. Blue, yellow and green paint are mixed in the ratio $5:7:2$. If 20 litres of blue paint are used, how much yellow and green paint is used in total?

4. £3600 is shared between Josiah and Mira in the ratio $5:4$. How much money does Mira get?

5. Tins of biscuits are sold in 3 sizes as shown opposite. Which size is the best value? Show all your working out.

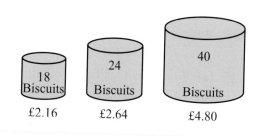

18 Biscuits £2.16

24 Biscuits £2.64

40 Biscuits £4.80

6   The ratio of the lengths of the sides
of the two squares shown is $1:6$.
Work out the area of the larger square.

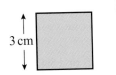

3 cm

Area = ?

7   A will of £48 000 is split between Joel and his sister in the ratio $3:5$.
Joel then splits his money between himself and his children in the ratio $4:5$.
How much money do his children get?

8   In a pattern the ratio of red squares to blue squares is $5:7$.
What fraction of the red and blue squares are blue?

9   The ratio of dark chocolates to milk chocolates in a box is $3:7$.
How many more milk chocolates are there than dark chocolates if
a box contains 40 chocolates?

10

300g shortcrust pastry

210g flour
90g butter

A chef needs to make 900 g of shortcrust
pastry using the recipe shown opposite.
The chef has 400 g of flour in the kitchen.
How much more flour is needed to make the pastry?

Need more practice with number work?

1   Write down the odd one out.
      (a) Factors of 24:   2, 3, 8, 24, 48   (b) Factors of 50:   2, 5, 10, 20, 25
      (c) Multiples of 11:   22, 66, 88, 111   (d) Multiples of 15:   1, 15, 30, 45

2   Cancel down each fraction to its lowest terms

      (a) $\dfrac{8}{10}$ (b) $\dfrac{9}{12}$ (c) $\dfrac{15}{25}$ (d) $\dfrac{7}{28}$ (e) $\dfrac{28}{36}$

      (f) $\dfrac{45}{50}$ (g) $\dfrac{30}{70}$ (h) $\dfrac{56}{64}$ (i) $\dfrac{27}{63}$ (j) $\dfrac{18}{72}$

3   What is the smallest number with two factors?

4   (a) Write down the first seven multiples of 3
      (b) Write down the first seven multiples of 7
      (c) Write down the L.C.M. of 3 and 7

5   On average Lian checks her
    phone 37 times each day.
    How many times does she
    check her phone during the
    month of July?

6   Reduce £250 by 3%.

7   I started with 0.756 and then added a number. The answer was 0.777.
    What number did I add?

8   Change these percentages into fractions (cancel down where possible).
    (a) 30%   (b) 75%   (c) 12%   (d) 35%   (e) 4%

9   £700 is shared between Carl, Amy and Justin in the ratio 3 : 5 : 2.
    How much more money does Amy get than Justin?

10 Copy and complete

    (a)   6 . ☐ 9   (b)   ☐ . 7 ☐   (c)   7 . 4 8
          − ☐ . 3 ☐   − 3 . ☐ 6   − 6 . ☐ ☐
          ─────────   ─────────   ─────────
            5 . 5 7   5 . 4 7   ☐ . 7 0

11 What number when divided by five gives an answer of 3.2?

12 Write down which fractions are
    greater than the percentage.

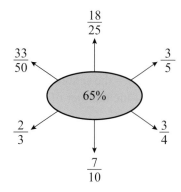

$\frac{18}{25}$

$\frac{33}{50}$ $\frac{3}{5}$

65%

$\frac{2}{3}$ $\frac{3}{4}$

$\frac{7}{10}$

13 Copy and complete
    (a) $\frac{1}{4}$ = ☐ %   (b) $\frac{2}{5}$ = ☐ %   (c) $\frac{1}{3}$ = ☐ %   (d) $\frac{1}{50}$ = ☐ %

14 Simplify the ratio $28 : 42 : 21$

15 Copy and complete.

(a)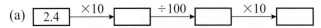
2.4 → ×10 → ☐ → ÷100 → ☐ → ×10 → ☐

(b) 0.43 → ×100 → ☐ → ÷1000 → ☐ → ×100 → ☐

(c) 1.4 → ×5 → ☐ → ×3 → ☐ → ÷10 → ☐

Extension questions with number work

1   11   21   31   51   71   81

Which of the numbers above are prime numbers?

2   (a) Copy the diagram shown.

(b) Shade in red the section which contains
    factors of 22

(c) Shade in green the section which contains
    multiples of 7

(d) Shade in blue the section which contains
    multiples of 3

(e) Shade in orange the section which contains
    prime numbers

(f) Shade in any colour of your choice the
    section which contains factors of 4.

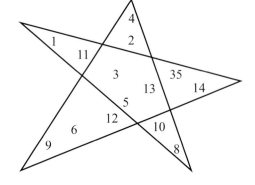

3   The number of students in a school is 1200. In a nearby college there are 1250 students.
    The number of students in the school increases by 11% in the following year and the number
    of students in the college increases by 6%.
    Which has more students now – the school or the college?
    Write down the difference in the number of students.

4   Copy and complete the factor tree
    opposite then express 140 as the
    product of its prime factors.

140
70

5   Find the remainder when 276 is divided by 11.

6 Write in order of size, smallest first.

(a) 20%, $\frac{1}{4}$, 0.15   (b) $\frac{3}{5}$, 52%, 0.05   (c) 0.7, $\frac{2}{3}$, 66%

7 Work out the perimeter of the triangle
   shown opposite.

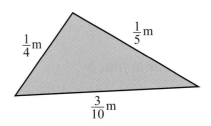

8 Change these percentages into decimals.
   (a) 42%   (b) 67%   (c) 9%   (d) 7%   (e) 94%

9 Copy and complete the table

	Fraction	Decimal	Percentage
(a)			40%
(b)		0.15	
(c)	$\frac{3}{25}$		
(d)			16%
(e)		0.04	

10 Find the difference between the answers to $\frac{3}{5} \times \frac{2}{3}$ and $\frac{5}{10} \times \frac{2}{3}$.

11 20% of a number is 8. What is the number?

12 The colours of a flag are red, green and yellow in the ratio $5:3:4$.
    What fraction of the flag is red?

13 Work out 22% of $\frac{2}{3}$ of 480.

14 Work out 0.784×4.3

15 Jacob is paid a work bonus of £6500. He spends 40% of this on a holiday and saves $\frac{5}{6}$ of the
    remaining money. He uses the left over money to buy presents and clothes in the ratio $9:4$.
    How much money does he spend on clothes.

5.4 Rounding numbers

In section 5.4 you will:

- review rounding off to decimal places
- calculate using estimates

Round to one decimal place

- Using a calculator to work out $25 \div 9$, the answer is 2.777777.

On a number line we can see that the answer is nearer to 2.8 than to 2.7. We will *round off* the answer to 2.8 correct to 1 *decimal place*.

Leave just 1 digit after the decimal point when rounding off to 1 decimal place.

- Using a calculator to work out 11% of 21.23, the answer is 2.3353.

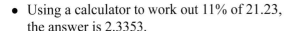

On a number line we can see that the answer is nearer to 2.3 than to 2.4. So the answer is 2.3, correct to 1 decimal place (1 d.p. for short).

- Suppose the calculator shows 1.75. This number is exactly half way between 1.7 and 1.8. Do we round up or not?

The rule for rounding off to l decimal place is:

> If the figure in the 2nd decimal place is 5 or more, round up.
> Otherwise do not.

$$3.7538 = 3.8 \text{ to 1 d.p.}$$
↑

$$14.287 \ = 14.3 \text{ to 1 d.p.}$$
↑

$$17.9582 = 18.0 \text{ to 1 d.p. (We need the zero!)}$$
↑

7.96 rounded to the nearest whole number is 8

7.96 rounded to 1 decimal place is 8.0 [The zero is needed.]

Exercise 1M

1 Round these numbers to 1 decimal place.

    (a) 2.41   (b) 8.94   (c) 4.65   (d) 12.47   (e) 16.35

2 Write down any number greater than 40 which has been rounded off to 1 decimal place.

3 Write the following numbers correct to 1 decimal place.

    (a) 18.7864   (b) 3.55   (c) 17.0946   (d) 0.7624

    (e) 5.421   (f) 11.27   (g) 10.252   (h) 7.084

4 Work out these answers on a calculator and then round the answer to one decimal place.

    (a) $65 \div 7$ (b) 85×0.7 (c) $8.64 \div 11.014$ (d) 8×16.22

    (e) 1.4×0.97 (f) $82 \div 7$ (g) $113 \div 5$ (h) $0.6 \div 0.022$

5 Measure the lines below and give the lengths in cm correct to one decimal place.

    (a) —————————————————————————

    (b) —————————

    (c) ————————————————————————————

    (d) ————————————————————

    (e) ——————————————————————————————————

6 Measure the dimensions of the rectangles below.

    (a) Write down the length and width in cm, correct to one decimal place.

    (b) Work out the area of each rectangle and give the answer in cm²,
        correct to one decimal place.

    (i) 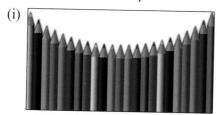   (ii)

7 Mel rounds off 14.973 to one decimal place and writes the answer 15.
    Explain clearly why this is not correct.

324

> **Rounding to 2 decimal places** – leave 2 digits after the decimal point when rounding off.
> If the figure in the 3rd decimal place is 5 or more, round up. Otherwise do not.
>
> 2.6382 = 2.64 to 2 d.p.　　　　5.7326 = 5.73 to 2 d.p.
> 　↑　　　　　　　　　　　　　　↑
> round up　　　　　　　　round down

Exercise 2M

1 Round these numbers to 2 decimal places.

(a) 1.924　　　(b) 4.065　　　(c) 9.997　　　(d) 65.374　　　(e) 14.043

2 Work out the following on a calculator and write the answers correct to 2 decimal places.

(a) $11 \div 7$　　　(b) $213 \div 11$　　　(c) $1.4 \div 6$　　　(d) $29 \div 13$

(e) 1.3×0.95　　　(f) 1.23×3.71　　　(g) $97 \div 1.3$　　　(h) 0.95×8.3

3 Work out the area of each shape opposite and round each answer to 2 decimal places.

3.68 cm 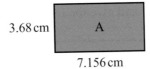 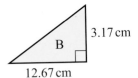 3.17 cm

7.156 cm　　　12.67 cm

4 Round the following numbers to the accuracy indicated.

(a) 6.1723 (1 d.p.)　　　(b) 14.6958 (2 d.p.)　　　(c) 0.010102 (2 d.p.)

(d) 712.816 (1 d.p.)　　　(e) 3.9084 (2 d.p.)　　　(f) 24.65298 (1 d.p.)

5 Write down the smallest number that would be rounded up to 8.2 to 1 decimal place.

6 Write down the smallest number that would be rounded up to 11.67 to 2 decimal places.

7 Use a calculator to work out $\dfrac{3.8^2 + 1.6943}{2.6 - 2.198}$, giving your answer to 2 decimal places.

Calculating with estimates, checking results

- Hazim worked out 38.2×10.78 and wrote down 41.1796. He can check his answer by working with estimates.

  Instead of 38.2 use 40, instead of 10.78 use 10.

  　　So $40 \times 10 = 400$.

  Clearly Hazim's answer is wrong. He put the decimal point in the wrong place.

- Here are three more calculations with estimates.

  (a) 27.2×51.7

  $\approx 30 \times 50$

  ≈ 1500

  (b) $78.9 \div 1.923$

  $\approx 80 \div 2$

  ≈ 40

  (c) 12% of £411.55

  $\approx 10\%$ of £400

  $\approx £40$

  [The symbol $\approx$ means 'approximately equal to']

Exercise 3M

Do not use a calculator. Decide, by estimating, which of the three answers is closest to the exact answer. Write the calculation and the approximate answer for each question (use $\approx$).

	Calculation	A	B	C
1.	102.6×9.7	90	500	1000
2.	7.14×11.21	30	70	300
3.	1.07×59.2	6	60	200
4.	2.21×97.8	200	90	20
5.	8.95×42.1	200	400	4000
6.	4.87×6.18	15	10	30
7.	789×12.3	8000	4000	800
8.	978×9.83	1 million	100 000	10 000
9.	1.11×28.7	20	30	60
10.	9.8×82463	8 million	1 million	800 000
11.	$307.4 \div 1.97$	50	100	150
12.	$81.2 \div 0.99$	8	0.8	80
13.	$6121 \div 102.4$	60	300	600
14.	$59.71 \div 3.14$	10	20	180
15.	$1072 \div 987.2$	0.2	1	10
16.	$614 - 297.4$	300	100	3000
17.	$0.104 + 0.511$	0.06	0.1	0.6
18.	$8216.1 + 1.44$	800	4000	8000
19.	51% of £8018.95	£40	£400	£4000
20.	9% of £205.49	£10	£20	£200

Exercise 4M

1 A 'Pritt Stick' costs £1.99.

(a) Without a calculator, estimate the cost of twelve Pritt Sticks.

(b) Find the exact cost of twelve Pritt Sticks.

2 A box of drawing pins costs £3.85.

Estimate the cost of 20 boxes of drawing pins.

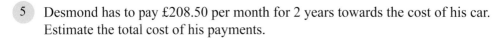

3 A painting measures 12.2 cm by 9.7 cm.
  (a) Without a calculator, estimate the area of the painting.
  (b) Use a calculator to work out the exact area of the painting.

4 A newspaper was sold at £2.95 per copy.
Estimate the total cost of 47 copies.

5 Desmond has to pay £208.50 per month for 2 years towards the cost of his car.
Estimate the total cost of his payments.

6 Two hundred and six people share the cost of hiring a train.
Roughly how much does each person pay if the total cost was £61 990?

7 A footballer is paid £79 200 per week. Estimate how much the footballer is paid in a year.

8 Emily earns £41 123 each year. She is given a 4.8% pay increase.
Estimate how much extra she will earn after the pay increase.

In questions **9** and **10** there are six calculations and six answers.

Write down each calculation and insert the correct answer from the list given. Use estimation.

9 (a) 6.9×7.1 (b) $9.8 \div 5$ (c) 21×10.2
  (d) $0.13 + 15.2$ (e) $3114 \div 30$ (f) 4.03×1.9

| Answers: | 1.96 | 15.33 | 48.99 | 103.8 | 7.657 | 214.2 |

10 (a) $103.2 \div 5$ (b) 7.2×7.3 (c) 4.1×49
  (d) $3.57 \div 3$ (e) $36.52 \div 4$ (f) $1.4 \div 10$

| Answers: | 52.56 | 1.19 | 9.13 | 200.9 | 20.64 | 0.14 |

Need more practice with rounding numbers?

1 Round each number:
  (a) to the nearest whole number,
  (b) to one decimal place
    (i) 8.41   (ii) 0.782   (iii) 7.92   (iv) 4.95

2 Answer 'true' or 'false' when the numbers are rounded to the nearest whole number.

(a) $7.7 \rightarrow 8$ (b) $3.4 \rightarrow 3$ (c) $11.5 \rightarrow 12$ (d) $9.6 \rightarrow 9$

(e) $11.1 \rightarrow 11$ (f) $6.5 \rightarrow 6$ (g) $0.7 \rightarrow 1$ (h) $27.5 \rightarrow 28$

3 Work out the following using a calculator and then round the answer to the *nearest hundred*.

(a) 67.5×841 (b) 173×11.4 (c) $25\,000 \div 241$

(d) $6781.4 + 374$ (e) $784 \div 0.92$ (f) $9801 - 416.2$

(g) 18.6×18.7 (h) $501\,000 \div 6751$ (i) $\sqrt{623\,000}$

4 Write the following numbers correct to 1 decimal place.

(a) 7.68 (b) 14.15 (c) 28.0817 (d) 0.516

(e) 6.349 (f) 15.17 (g) 12.186 (h) 6.087

5 2962 seedlings were planted in 153 tubs. Estimate how many seedlings were planted in each tub.

6 A TV costs £297. Estimate the total cost of 62 TV's.

7 $0.01998 = 0.0$ (to 1 decimal place) True or false?

8 How long is this rod to:

(a) the nearest cm   (b) the nearest 10 cm   (c) the nearest metre

160   161   162   163 164 cm

Extension questions with rounding numbers

1 Answer 'true' or 'false' when the numbers are rounded to 2 decimal places.

(a) $7.167 \rightarrow 7.16$ (b) $3.015 \rightarrow 3.02$ (c) $12.6328 \rightarrow 12.63$

(d) $0.1951 \rightarrow 0.19$ (e) $48.7046 \rightarrow 48.70$ (f) $39.8447 \rightarrow 39.85$

2 Carter says that 21.08×0.997 is approximately equal to 20. Explain fully whether he is correct or not.

3 Which number below does not round off to 4.78 when given to 2 decimal places?

| 4.776 | 4.777 | 4.7749 | 4.77501 |

4 Write the following numbers correct to 3 decimal places.

(a) 0.1752   (b) 0.8319   (c) 17.46448   (d) 5.64137

(e) 3.0655   (f) 38.17382   (g) 86.82749   (h) 6.93153

5 Calculate the area of the trapezium opposite.
Give the answer to 1 decimal place.

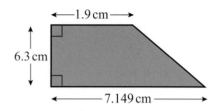

6 Write down each calculation and insert the correct answer from the list given.
Use estimation. *Do not use a calculator.*

(a) $20.16 \div 4$ (b) 39% of 60.2   (c) 4.3×4.1

(d) 9.02^2 (e) $160.8 \div 20$ (f) $19.698 \div 0.49$

Answers: 17.63   40.2   81.3604   8.04   23.478   5.04

7 Round off 2.9999999 to 4 decimal places.

8 Work out the following on a calculator and give the answer to the accuracy indicated.

(a) $\dfrac{2^2 - 0.07}{3.6^2}$ (2 d.p.)   (b) $\dfrac{6}{0.6} + 1.7319$ (3 d.p.)   (c) $(7.6 - 2.18)^2$ (2 d.p.)

CHECK YOURSELF ON SECTIONS 5.3 AND 5.4

1   Number review

(a) Draw a factor tree then express 180 as a product of its prime factors.

(b) A box contains 12 eggs. How many boxes are needed for 400 eggs?

(c) Work out $\frac{3}{4} - \frac{1}{3}$

(d) Some sweets are shared between Jason, Ariana, and Mariah in the ratio $7:4:8$.
How many sweets does Jason get if Ariana gets 32 sweets?

(e) A piece of wood is 0.6 m long. It is cut into 4 equal pieces.
How long is each piece of wood?

(f) $\dfrac{5}{\square} \times \dfrac{3}{4} = \dfrac{15}{28}$ Copy and fill in the empty box.

(g) Harry is awake for 16 hours each day. He goes to school for $\frac{3}{8}$ of this time. He plays sport for 15% of the remaining time. How much time does he spend playing sport each day?

2 Round off to decimal places

Write the following numbers to the accuracy indicated.

(a) 5.67 (1 d.p.)   (b) 0.1793 (2 d.p.)   (c) 0.77 (1 d.p.)

(d) 17.8372 (2 d.p.)   (e) 0.19338 (3 d.p.)   (f) 5.4072 (1 d.p.)

3 Calculating using estimates

Decide, by estimating, which of the three answers is closest to the exact answer.

(a) 81.5×2.24 [1500   150   40]

(b) 0.97×38.4 [40   4   0.4]

(c) $98.1 \div 11.7$ [1   1000   10]

(d) A tin of blackcurrants cost 95p. Estimate the cost of 63 tins.

5.5 Probability 2

In section 5.5 you will review:

- finding the probability of an event

Equally likely outcomes

(a) When you roll a fair dice there are six *equally likely outcomes*.
You can get a 1, 2, 3, 4, 5 or 6

The probability of rolling a 4 is $\frac{1}{6}$

(b) On this spinner there are five equal sections and two of these are blue.

The probability of spinning blue is $\frac{2}{5}$

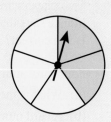

Exercise 1M

1   What is the probability of spinning a shaded section on each of these spinners?

(a) 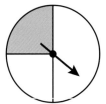   (b) 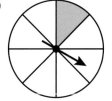   (c) 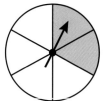   (d)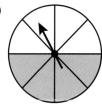

2   The cards below are placed in a bag and then one card is selected at random.

| 1 | 2 | 3 | 4 | 5 | 6 | 7 | 8 | 9 |

Find the probability of selecting

(a) the number 4   (b) an even number   (c) a number less than 5

3

red

yellow   blue

Hamish says that the probability of spinning yellow on this spinner is $\frac{1}{3}$.

Is Hamish correct? Explain your answer fully.

4   Cards with the letters of the word O C T O P U S are placed in a bag.
One letter is selected at random.

Find the probability of selecting

(a) a T   (b) an O

5   Bags A and B contain red and yellow balls as shown.
Gary wants to get a yellow ball.

From which bag does he have the better chance of
selecting a yellow ball? Explain your answer fully.

A   B

6   Two players are both 20 metres from a golf hole.
Maisie says that each player has the same probability of putting their ball in the hole.
Is she correct? Explain your answer fully.

7   Four cards numbered 1, 2, 3, 4 are placed face down. One card is chosen at random.

(a) What is the probability of selecting an even number?

(b) A card numbered 5 is added to the cards above. What is now the probability of selecting
an even number?

8

These balls are placed in a bag and then one ball is
selected at random. There are two purple balls, two red, and some
other colours. What is the probability of selecting

(a) a purple ball

(b) a purple ball or a red ball?

9   There are 16 pens in a box. All of them are black. Steve chooses one of the pens at random.
What is the probability that the pen is   (a) black   (b) red?

10 A bag contains green and yellow beads only. The total number of beads is 29.
Kelly says that the probability of removing a green bead is $\frac{1}{6}$. Ed says that the probability of removing a green bead is $\frac{1}{5}$. Explain clearly why both Kelly and Ed must be wrong.

A pack of playing cards, without jokers, contains 52 cards.
There is ace, king, queen, jack, 10, 9, 8, 7, 6, 5, 4, 3, 2 of four suits.
The suits are ...

Spades   Hearts   Diamonds   Clubs

A pack of cards is shuffled and then one card is chosen at random.

(a) The probability that it is a king of hearts is $\frac{1}{52}$

(b) The probability that it is an ace is $\frac{4}{52}\left(=\frac{1}{13}\right)$

(c) The probability that it is a spade is $\frac{13}{52}\left(=\frac{1}{4}\right)$

Exercise 2M

1 One card is picked at random from a pack of 52.
Find the probability that it is

(a) a queen   (b) the king of diamonds   (c) a spade

2 A small pack of twenty cards consists of the ace, king, queen,
jack and 10 of spades, hearts, diamonds and clubs.
One card is selected at random. Find the probability of selecting

(a) the ace of hearts   (b) a king   (c) a '10'

(d) a black card   (e) a heart

3 One card is selected at random from the cards shown.
What is the probability of selecting

(a) a red card

(b) a 5

(c) a card of the 'club' suit?

4   If Jake throws a 1 or a 4 on his next throw of a dice when playing
    'Snakes and Ladders' he will climb up a ladder on the board.
    What is the probability that he will *miss* a ladder on his next throw?

5   On a British lions rugby tour, the nationality of each player is shown in the table below.

Nationality	Number of players
English	10
Irish	8
Scottish	2
Welsh	12

A player is chosen at random for an interview.
Which nationality has a probability $\frac{3}{8}$ of being chosen?
Justify your answer.

6   A box contains 11 balls: 3 green, 2 yellow, 4 red and 2 blue.

    (a) Find the probability of selecting
        (i) a blue ball   (ii) a green ball

    (b) The 3 green balls are replaced by 3 blue balls.
        Find the probability of selecting
        (i) a blue ball   (ii) a yellow ball

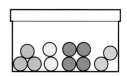

7   Debbie, Alan and Nicky were asked to toss a fair coin 16 times.
    Here are the results they wrote down.

    Debbie   H T H T H T H T H T H T H T H T
    Alan   H H T H T T H T T T H H T H H T
    Nicky   H H H H H H H H T T T T T T T T

    One of the three did the experiment properly while the other two just made up results.
    Explain what you think each person did.

8   Here are two spinners. Say whether the following statements are true or false.
    Explain why in each case.

    (a) 'Sarah is more likely to spin a 6 than Ben.'

    (b) 'Sarah and Ben are equally likely to spin an
        even number.'

    (c) 'If Sarah spins her spinner six times, she is bound
        to get at least one 6.'

Sarah's spinner   Ben's spinner

9   The probability of Carl not doing his maths homework is 0.2.
    What is the probability that Carl will do his maths homework?

Need more practice with probability?

1 A bag contains 3 black balls, 2 green balls, 1 white ball and 5 orange balls.
Find the probability of selecting

(a) a black ball   (b) an orange ball   (c) a white ball

2 A bag contains the balls shown. One ball is taken out at random.
Find the probability that it is

(a) yellow   (b) blue   (c) red

One more blue ball and one more red ball are added to the bag.

(d) Find the new probability of selecting a yellow ball from the bag.

3 These cards are shuffled and turned over. One card is picked at random.
What is the probability of picking

(a) the number 6

(b) the number 4

(c) the number 8?

| 2 | 5 | 6 | 8 | 8 |

4 A raffle has tickets numbered from 1 to 150. Maggie has ticket number 37.
What is the probability that Maggie wins the raffle?

5 Chun tosses a coin 100 times. The coin lands on tails 17 times.
Do you think this is a fair coin? Give a reason for your answer.

6 Children in France count up to five using their fingers and thumb as shown.
Michelle displays one number at random.
Find the probability that she shows

(a) the number three

(b) an even number.

(c) How do *you* count from 1 to 5 using your fingers?

7 A fair dice is rolled. What is the probability of rolling

(a) a 5

(b) an even number

(c) a number greater than 7?

8  There are 54 white cubes and 1 red cube in the pile shown.
The cubes are jumbled up in a box and then one cube is selected
at random.
What is the probability of selecting the red cube?

9   The numbers 1 to 10 are written on 10 cards. If I randomly remove one card, am I more likely to take a square number or a prime number? You must give full reasons for your answer.

10 One card is selected at random from a full pack of 52 playing cards.
    Find the probability of selecting

    (a) a heart   (b) a red card   (c) a '2'

    (d) any king, queen or jack   (e) the ace of spades

Extension questions with probability

In questions 1 to 4 a bag contains a certain number of red balls and a certain number of white balls. The tally charts show the number of times a ball was selected from the bag and then replaced. Look at the results and say what you think was in the bag each time.

1
2 balls in the bag
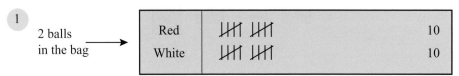

2
3 balls in the bag

3
3 balls in the bag

4
4 balls in the bag
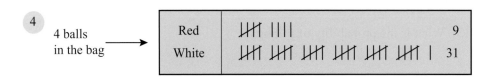

5   A bag contains 9 balls, all of which are black or white.
    Jane selects a ball and then replaces it. She repeats this several times.
    Here are her results (B = black, W = white):

    B   W   B   W   B   B   B   W   B   B   W   B   B   W   B
    B   B   W   W   B   B   B   B   W   B   W   B   B   W   B

    How many balls of each colour do you think there were in the bag?

6 Cards with numbers 1, 2, 3, 4, 5, 6, 7, 8, 9, 10 are shuffled and then placed face down in a line. The cards are then turned over one at a time from the left. In this example the first card is a '4'.

Find the probability that the next card turned over will be

(a) 7   (b) a number higher than 4

7 Suppose the second card is a 1.

Find the probability that the next card will be

(a) the 6   (b) an even number   (c) higher than 1

8 Suppose the first three cards are | 4 | 1 | 8 | ...

Find the probability that the next card will be

(a) less than 8   (b) the 4   (c) an odd number

9 Three friends Alf, Ben and Curtis sit next to each other on a bench.

(a) Make a list of all the different ways in which they can sit. (Use A = Alf, B = Ben and C = Curtis).

Find the probability that

(b) Alf sits in the middle

(c) Alf sits next to Curtis

(d) Ben sits at one end of the bench

10 Two coins are tossed together. Find the probability of getting exactly two heads by listing all the possible outcomes.

✖ Spot the mistakes 10 ✖

Number, work and probability

Work through each question and explain clearly what mistakes have been made.
Beware – some questions are correctly done.

1   Some money is shared between Russell, Anton and Tara in the ratio $7:2:5$. Tara gets £420. How much does Russell get?

Solution: Total number of shares $= 7 + 2 + 5 = 14$
              1 share $= 420 \div 14 = 30$
              Russell gets 7 shares $= 7 \times 30 = £210$

2   Work out $\dfrac{3}{5} \times \dfrac{2}{3}$

Answer: $\dfrac{3}{5} \times \dfrac{2}{3} = \dfrac{9}{15} \times \dfrac{10}{15} = \dfrac{90}{225} = \dfrac{2}{5}$

3   4302 books are packed into boxes. Each box contains 18 books.
How many boxes are needed for all the books?

Solution: 2 4 1 r. 4
           18$\overline{)43^70^22}$ so 242 boxes needed.

4   Use a factor tree to express 324 as the product of its prime factors.

Answer:

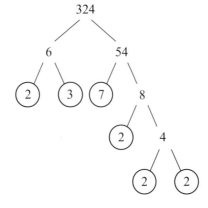

$$324 = 2 \times 2 \times 2 \times 2 \times 3 \times 7$$

5   What is the probability of Tessa beating Chun at a game of badminton?
Answer: 0.5 because Tessa is one of two players involved in the game.

6   A model ship costs £25.
Its price is reduced by 20% for a sale.
After the sale it has not sold and its
price is increased by 20%.
What does the model ship now cost?

Answer: It costs the original price of
£25 because the price was decreased
by 20% then increased by 20%.

7 A bag contains only red and blue balls. If one ball is randomly removed from the bag, the probability of it being red is $\frac{3}{7}$.

To start with there are 8 blue balls in the bag.
How many red balls are in the bag to start with?

Solution: probability of a blue ball $= \frac{4}{7} = \frac{8}{14}$

so there are 14 balls in the bag to start with.

There must be $14 - 8 = 6$ red balls in the bag.

8 In a class, two thirds of the students have dark hair and two sevenths of the students have blond hair. What fraction of the class have dark hair or blond hair?

Answer: $\dfrac{2}{3} + \dfrac{2}{7} = \dfrac{2+2}{21} = \dfrac{4}{21}$

so $\dfrac{4}{21}$ of the class have dark hair or blond hair.

9 Wire costs £0.85 per metre. How much does 0.4 m of wire cost?

Answer: 0.85×0.4

$$\begin{array}{r} 85 \\ \times\ \ 4 \\ \hline 340 \\ \hline {}_{2} \end{array}$$

$= £3.40$

10 The ratio of side a to side b is $1 : 4$.
Work out the length of b in metres
if the length of a is 62 cm.

a
b

Answer: length of $b = 4 \times 62 = 248$ cm

CHECK YOURSELF ON SECTION 5.5

1   Finding the probability of an event

(a) A bag contains red (r), blue (b)
and green (g) balls.

Write down the probability of selecting
(i) a red ball   (ii) a green ball

(b) There are eight balls in a different bag.
The probability of taking a white ball from the bag is 0.5
A white ball is taken from the bag and put on one side.
What is the probability of taking a white ball from the bag now?

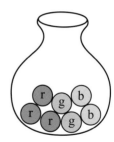

5.6 Applying mathematics 5

In section 5.6 you will apply maths in a variety
of situations.

1   Nia has saved £3240 and Ken has saved £2020.
    Ken earns more money and increases his savings by 35%.
    Nia, meanwhile, spends $\frac{3}{20}$ of her savings.
    Who now has more money and by how much?

2   Copy each calculation and find the missing numbers.

(a)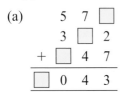

(b)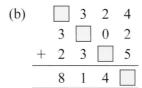

3   Form an equation to find the value of n
    then work out the actual value of the
    area of the rectangle opposite.
    All lengths are given in cm.

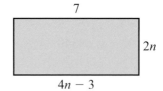

4   A box has a mass of 230 g when empty.
    When it is full of sugar the total mass is 650 g.
    What is its mass when it is half full?

5   The Colisseum had 2680 windows when it was built.
    The local window cleaner charged a quarter
    of a denarius per window and cleaned all the
    windows once a week.

    (a) What was his total income in 3 weeks?

    (b) Where is the Colisseum?

6   Triangle ABC is isosceles.

    Work out the value of BĈD,
    giving reasons for your answer.

7 The finish times (in seconds) in two track races are shown below.

Race 1						
Runner	A	B	C	D	E	F
Time	48.17	49.02	48.3	49	48.69	48.1

Race 2						
Runner	P	Q	R	S	T	U
Time	49.27	48.14	48	48.43	48.07	49.1

Find the difference between the finish times of the two runners who each finished in 3rd place in Race 1 and Race 2.

8 There are 208 people at a football competition. How many teams of six can be formed? How many people will be left over?

9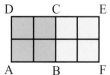

4 m

2 cm

2 cm

3 m

A

6 m

6 cm

B

4 cm

Work out the ratio of area A to area B. Give the answer in its simplest form.

10 Square ABCD can be moved onto square BCEF by either a translation or a reflection.

(a) Describe the translation using a vector.

(b) What is the mirror line for the reflection?

D   C   E

A   B   F

UNIT 5   MIXED REVIEW

Part one

1 Trisha, Stella and Vikky have lunch together and agree to share the cost equally. If lunch costs £24.99, how much should each pay?

2 Simplify the following expressions.
(a) $5n + 3 + 2n - 1$ (b) $6m + 2n - 2m + 7n$
(c) $3a + 7c - 3a + 5$ (d) $10n + 3 + 10n + 13$

3 An advert for toothpaste used a photo of a model's teeth. Sales of the toothpaste rose from 25 815 per week to 31 880. How many extra tubes were sold?

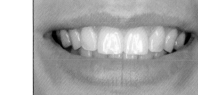

4 A rowing machine costs £360 plus 10% delivery charge. How much extra do you pay for the delivery charge?

5 Look at this group of numbers…

    10, 19, 25, 30, 21

(a) Which of the numbers is a multiple of both 3 and 5?
(b) Which of the numbers is a prime number?
(c) Which of the numbers is a square number?
(d) Which number is a factor of another number in the group?

6 If $y = 3x - c$, find the value of y when $x = 3$ and $c = -8$.

7 Solve   (a) $\dfrac{x}{4} = 6$ (b) $5x + 6 = 51$ (c) $58 = 3x - 8$

8 Use a calculator to work out the following and give your answers correct to 1 decimal place.
(a) $8.62 - \dfrac{1.71}{0.55}$ (b) $\dfrac{8.02 - 6.3}{1.3 + 4.6}$ (c) $\dfrac{5.6}{1.71} - 1.08$

9
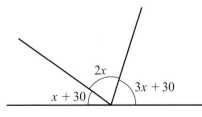

(a) Form an equation and find the value of x.
(b) Write down the actual size of each of the three angles.

(angle labels: $2x$, $x + 30$, $3x + 30$)

10 During one season the probability of Hatton United winning a game is $\frac{11}{20}$ and the probability of a draw is $\frac{7}{20}$. What is the probability that Hatton United will lose a game?

11 Two books cost £13.50 in total. One book is one-and-a-half times the price of the other.
How much does each book cost?

12 The temperature in a centrally heated house is recorded every hour from 12.00 till 24.00;
the results are shown below.

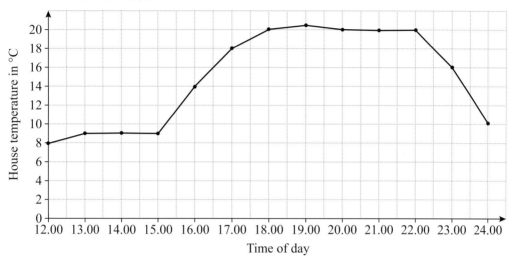

(a) What was the temperature at 20.00?
(b) Estimate the temperature at 16.30.
(c) Estimate the two times when the temperature was 18°C.
(d) When do you think the central heating was switched on?
(e) When do you think the central heating was switched off?

13

Crash dummies do have feelings!
Just before being 'tested' a dummy's
heart rate increased from 60 beats per
minute by 75%.
What is the raised heart rate?

14 Write down these calculations and find the missing digits.

(a)
```
    5 . □ 5
  + 3 . 7 □
  ─────────
    9 . 0 9
```

(b)
```
    7 . □ 8
  - 3 . 8 □
  ─────────
    □ . 1 5
```

(c)
```
    □ 3 . □
  + 2 □ . 3
  ─────────
    7 0 . 0
```

15 Bag A contains blue balls and yellow balls. If one ball is randomly removed, the probability of
taking a blue ball is $\frac{5}{8}$.

Bag B contains 3 blue balls and 1 yellow ball. If I remove one ball from each bag, which one
am I more likely to take a yellow ball from?

You must fully explain your answer.

Part two

1 Here are some number cards.

(a) Use two cards to make a fraction which is equal to $\frac{1}{3} = \frac{\square}{\square}$

(b) Use three of the cards to make the smallest possible fraction $= \dfrac{\square}{\square\square}$

2 Numbers are missing on four of these calculator buttons.
Copy the diagram and write in numbers to make the answer 30.

3 Expand (multiply out)

(a) $4(n + 3)$ (b) $m(4 - n)$ (c) $n(4n + 7)$

4 A normal pack of 52 playing cards (without jokers) is divided into two piles.

Pile A has all the picture cards (kings, queens, jacks)

Pile B has the rest of the pack.

Find the probability of selecting

(a) any 'three' from pile B

(b) the king of hearts from pile A

(c) any red seven from pile B.

5 Solve   (a) $3n = 18$ (b) $4n - 9 = 11$ (c) $7 = \dfrac{n}{8}$

6 Work out the total cost. You may use a calculator.

      13 kg of sand at 57p per kg.

      2 tape measures at £4.20 each

      2000 screws at 80p per hundred

      250 g of varnish at £6.60 per kg.

7   The graph converts Australian dollars
    into pounds.
    (a) Convert 84 dollars into pounds.
    (b) Convert 100 dollars into pounds.
    (c) Convert 20 pounds into dollars.
    (d) Convert 16 pounds into dollars.
    (e) A boomerang costs 140 dollars.
        How much does it cost in pounds?

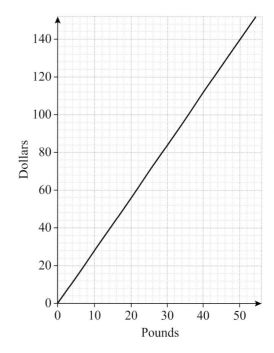

8   Look at the following numbers… 2, 3, 8, 9, 11, 15
    (a) How many numbers are odd?
    (b) How many numbers are even?
    (c) Write down the prime numbers.
    (d) Write down the number that is a multiple of five.
    (e) Write down the numbers that are factors of twenty-four.
    (f) Write down the number that is a square number.

9   Express as a ratio the answer for box A to the answer for box B.
    Give the answer in its simplest form.

    | A | 95% of 20 |

    | B | Decrease £80 by 5% |

10 Work out

    (a) $\dfrac{1}{4} + \dfrac{2}{5}$ (b) $\dfrac{5}{8} - \dfrac{3}{10}$ (c) $\dfrac{7}{10} \times \dfrac{5}{9}$

11 Find the highest common factor (H.C.F.) of 48 and 72.

12 Copy and complete

    (a) $3.25 + \square = 5$ (b) $100 \times \square = 3.7$

    (c) $\square - 0.23 = 2.5$ (d) $(\square + 1.2) \times 10 = 25$

13 A balloon seller has 150 balloons.
$\frac{1}{5}$ of the balloons are yellow.
The balloon seller sells 2 yellow balloons.
If a balloon is now taken randomly from
the balloon seller, what is the probability
that it will be a yellow balloon?

14 The star shape is made from four triangles
like the one shown.
(a) Calculate the area of the star shape.
(b) Calculate the perimeter of the star shape.
(c) Describe the symmetry of the star shape.

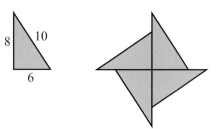

15 Copy and complete by filling in the boxes.
You can use any of the numbers 1, 2, 3, 4, 5 but you cannot use a number more than once.

(a) $\square + \square - \square = 7$

(b) $(\square + \square) \div \square = 3$

(c) $(\square + \square) \div (\square - \square) = 1\frac{1}{2}$

(d) $(\square + \square + \square) \times \square = 33$

Puzzles and Problems 5

Cross numbers

Make four copies of the pattern below and complete the puzzles using the clues given. To avoid confusion it is better not to write the small reference numbers 1–18 on your patterns.

1		2		3			4
				5			
	6		7			8	
9					10		
		11					12
				13	14		
15	16				17		
			18				

Part A

Across

1. Days in a year

3. $6524 - 4018$

5. 20% of 400

6. $43\,328 \div 8$

8. 82.74 to the nearest whole number

9. $126 \div 7$

10. $4^2 + 5^2$

11. $164 + 57 + 8$

13. Half of a half of 104

15. $10^3 + 10^2 + 1$

17. $4 \times (58 + 6 \times 7)$

18. Next in the sequence 8, 16, 32, 64

Down

1. 6^2

2. 7×72

4. $285 + 338$

7. $8^2 \times 3$

8. $269 + 270 + 271$

9. $5 \times 5 \times 5 \times 10 + 1$

11. $2 \times 3 \times 5 \times 7$

12. 967×9

14. $1000 - 352$

16. Two fifths of 45

346

Part B

Across

1. 3.25 m in cm

3. $4567 - 123$

5. Area of a square of side 7 cm

6. $50^2 + 555$

8. Total of the numbers on a dice

9. One fifth of 475

10. Find n, if $n - 23 = 37$

11. Angle sum of a triangle

13. Next in the sequence 3, 7, 15, 31

15. $100 \times 100 - 100$

17. $5^4 - 5$

18. Find n, if $\dfrac{n}{85} = 10$

Down

1. $2 \times 2 \times 2 \times 2 \times 2$

2. 1% of 50 000

4. $41 + 10 \times 41$

7. $4116 \div 7$

8. 9×23

9. $10\,001 - 2$

11. $11^2 - 5^2 + 2^2$

12. 3.3 km in metres

14. Angle sum of a quadrilateral

16. $10^2 - 1^2$

Part C

Across

1. Next square number after 100

3. $15 + 200 \times 7$

5. Minutes between 1.55 p.m. and 2.50 p.m.

6. $7416 - 4533$

8. $\frac{4}{5}$ as a percentage

9. Smallest two digit prime number

10. $1^1 + 2^2 + 3^3$

11. $180 - 65 \div 5$

13. Factor of 60

15. 6874 to the nearest 100

17. Find n, if $n \div 11 = 11$

18. Number of 2p coins in £10

Down

1. Half of a third of 66

2. Perimeter of a square of side 27 cm

4. Next in the sequence 70, 140, 280

7. Double 125 plus treble 202

8. $30^2 - 2^6 - 3^2$

9. William the Conqueror

11. Maximum score with three darts

12. $\frac{3}{7}$ of 3528

14. 17×30

16. Multiple of 8

Part D

Design your own crossnumber puzzle. Start with the answers and then write clues to the puzzle. Try to make your clues as varied and interesting as possible.

The Königsberg Problem

In the 18th century, the city of Königsberg (in Prussia) was split into parts by the River Pregel. There were seven bridges. The people of Königsberg tried to walk across all seven bridges without crossing the same bridge twice.

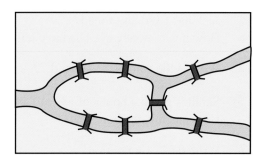

Exercise

1 Sketch the diagram above to show the river and the bridges. Use a pencil to show how you could walk across each bridge without crossing the same bridge twice.
   If you make a mistake, rub out the pencil and try again.
   If you find a way, show somebody else then show your teacher.

2 Make up a map of a city which has more than seven bridges. Get somebody else to copy your map and try to show you how to walk across each bridge without crossing the same bridge twice.

3 **RESEARCH:**

A famous mathematician, Leonhard Euler, examined the Königsberg problem.

(a) Find out when Euler lived.

(b) Find out what Euler said about the Königsberg problem.

(c) Königsberg is now called Kaliningrad and is in Russia. Find out how many of the seven bridges still exist.

(d) Discuss as a class your main findings about the Königsberg problem.

348

Mental Arithmetic Practice 5

There are two sets of mental arithmetic questions in this section. Ideally a teacher will read out each question twice, with pupils' books closed. Each test of 20 questions should take about 20 minutes.

Test 1

1. Jack has £330 and spends £295 How much money does he have left?

2. What is the sum of 73, 42 and 7?

3. Sarah is given a bonus of 5% of £440. How much is the bonus?

4. Write 0.07 as a fraction.

5. How many halves make up six whole ones?

6. What is eight squared?

7. What is the probability of getting an even number if you throw one dice?

8. A triangle has three equal sides. What is its special name?

9. Subtract 0.3 from 5.

10. Write down three factors of 6.

11. Penny leaves Norwich at 1:40 p.m. and gets to Cambridge at 3:15 p.m. How long did the journey take?

12. A rectangle of length 10 cm has an area of 35 cm². What is the width of the rectangle?

13. What is 300 multiplied by 8?

14. Write down a prime number between 15 and 20.

15. What is the mean average of 9, 6 and 15?

16. If $n = 4$, which is larger: $3n$ or n^2?

17. £420 is shared equally between seven people. How much does each person get?

18. What is three-fifths of 40?

19. 39° and 52° are added together. Is the answer acute or obtuse?

20. I think of a number. If I treble it and subtract 6, the answer is 21. What number did I think of?

Test 2

1. What is 54 divided by 9?

2. Work out $301 - 102$.

3. Round off three hundred and seventy-six to the nearest ten.

4. Find 25% of 880.

5. 38% of children at Wallis School travel by bus and 49% walk. The remainder travel by car. What percentage of the children travel by car?

6. What number is one less than two thousand?

7. What is the difference between six squared and two squared?

8. Write 20% as a fraction.

9. Don buys a book for £5.99 and a drink costing 50p. How much change does he get from a £10 note?

10. Hannah walks for 200 minutes and Ben walks for three hours ten minutes. Who walks for the longest time and by how much?

11. What is 400 divided by 20?

12 What is the product of 3, 4 and 5?

13 A triangle has two angles of 40° and 65°. What is the size of the third angle?

14 What is the median of 1, 2, 3, 4 and 5.

15 What is $4 - (-4)$?

16 There are 12 beads in a bag. Seven of the beads are red. I take out one bead from the bag. What is the probability that the bead is red?

17 How many lines of symmetry does a rectangle have?

18 What is half of 370?

19 How many fifty pence coins make £100.50?

20 How many seconds in one hour?

UNIT 6

6.1 Metric and imperial units

In section 6.1 you will:

- convert metric units
- convert between metric and imperial units
- read scales
- change units for some problems

Metric units

Length	Mass	Volume
1 cm = 10 mm	1 kg = 1000 g	1 millilitre (ml) = 1 cm^3
1 m = 100 cm	1 tonne = 1000 kg	1 litre = 1000 ml
1 km = 1000 m		

Converting metric units

Divide or multiply by 10, 100, 1000 and so on.

(a) 1.6 m = 160 cm   (b) 4300 g = 4.3 kg   (c) 59 litres = 59 000 ml

$\times 100$ $\div 1000$ $\times 1000$

Exercise 1M

1 Write each mass in grams.

   (a) 8 kg   (b) 1.8 kg   (c) 0.2 kg   (d) 0.035 kg

2 Write each mass in kg.

   (a) 7 tonnes   (b) 20 tonnes   (c) 6500 g   (d) 400 g

3 Percy the pig weighs 38 kg.

How many grams does Percy weigh?

4 A chef uses 240 g and 135 g of flour when making two cakes. He now has 0.6 kg of flour remaining. How much flour did he have before he made the cakes?

5 Copy and complete

(a) 2.4 kg = ☐ g   (b) 6 tonnes = ☐ kg   (c) 0.2 m = ☐ cm

(d) 500 g = ☐ kg   (e) 7 litres = ☐ ml   (f) 62 litres = ☐ ml

(g) 8.4 kg = ☐ g   (h) 2500 ml = ☐ litres   (i) 46 mm = ☐ cm

(j) 6.3 m = ☐ cm   (k) 0.85 kg = ☐ g   (l) 300 g = ☐ kg

6 A bag of cotswold stone weighs 25 kg. A lorry transports 85 bags.
What is the total weight of the bags? Give the answer in tonnes.

7 Write down the difference between each pair of measurements below.
(a) 7.4 litres and 7275 ml   (b) 60 g and 0.083 kg
(c) 62 litres and 6180 ml   (d) 3.7 m and 278 cm

8 Alec suggests that an adult lion
weighs around 190 g.
Comment on his answer.

9 A long stick of rock measures 2.5 m. It is cut into sticks which measure 18 cm.
How many 18 cm sticks will there be?

Converting between metric and imperial units

We still use imperial units. Imperial measurements were made by using appropriately sized bits of human being. The inch was measured using the thumb (we still sometimes say 'rule of thumb' when we mean rough measurement), the foot by using the foot.

1 foot ≈ 30 cm   1 kg ≈ 2.2 pounds

8 km ≈ 5 miles   1 gallon ≈ 4.5 litres

'≈' means 'is approximately equal to'

Divide or multiply by the appropriate number shown above.

(a) 3 feet ≈ 90 cm   (b) 11 pounds ≈ 5 kg   (c) 3 gallons ≈ 13.5 litres

× 30   ÷ 2.2   × 4.5

Exercise 2M

1   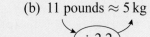   Danny puts 8 gallons of petrol into his car. *Roughly* how many litres of petrol did Danny put into his car?

Copy and complete questions 2 to 13

2   4 kg ≈ ☐ pounds   3   5 feet ≈ ☐ cm   4   10 gallons ≈ ☐ litres

5   120 cm ≈ ☐ feet   6   18 litres ≈ ☐ gallons   7   16 km ≈ ☐ miles

8   30 miles ≈ ☐ km   9   6 gallons ≈ ☐ litres   10 25 miles ≈ ☐ km

11 44 pounds ≈ ☐ kg   12 80 km ≈ ☐ miles   13 3 m ≈ ☐ feet

14 Phil has cycled 24 km from his house. His total journey will be 19 miles. How many *more* miles does he have to cycle?

15 The maximum height limit for children on a bouncy castle is 4 feet.
Julie is 130 cm tall. Is Julie inside the limit? Justify your answer.

16 Luke uses 9 gallons of water to wash his car. Jenny uses 40 litres of water to wash her car. Who uses more water?

17 The distance from Calais to Paris is about 240 km. About how many miles is this?

18 A restaurant needs 9 kg of potatoes for one evening. It has 20 pounds of potatoes. Will the restaurant have enough potatoes?

19 A helicopter can fly up to 500 miles from its base. How far is this in km?

20 Which shape opposite has the longer perimeter and by how much?

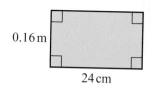
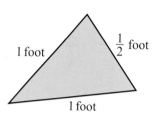

Reading scales

Exercise 3M

For each of the scales work out:

(a) the measurement indicated by each of the arrows.

(b) the difference between the two arrows.

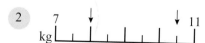

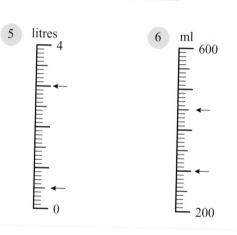
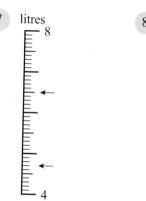

9 200 ↓   ↓ 1000
   g

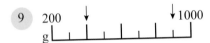

10 0   ↓   ↓ 4
   kg

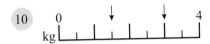

11 kg
    ↓ 4   ↓ 5

12 cm
        ↓   6   ↓ 7

13 litres
    ⌐ 4

14 ml
    ⌐ 400

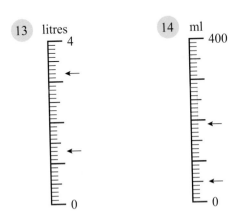

15 Read the measurement shown by the arrow on each dial.

(a)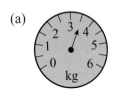

(b)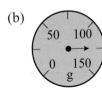

(c)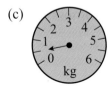

(d)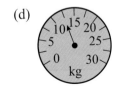

16 Here are scales for changing:

A kilograms and pounds,
B litres and gallons.

In this question give your answers to the
nearest whole number.

(a) About how many kilograms are
    there in 5 pounds?

(b) About how many litres are there in
    2.2 gallons?

(c) About how many pounds are there in
    1.8 kilograms?

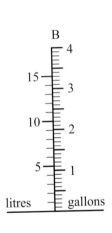

Changing units

When a problem has quantities measured in different units the first thing you must do is change some of the units so that all quantities are in the same units.

- Find the area (in cm²) of the rectangular table top shown.

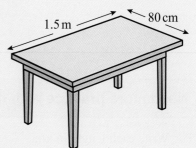

  Write 1.5 m as 150 cm.

  Area of table $= 150 \times 80$
  $= 12\,000 \text{ cm}^2.$

Exercise 4M

1 Work out
    (a) 3 m + 45 cm (in cm)   (b) 0.2 kg + 600 g (in g)   (c) 5 km + 326 m (in m)
    (d) 4 cm + 8 mm (in cm)   (e) 2.3 kg − 735 g (in kg)   (f) 6 cm − 5 mm (in mm)

2 Polly buys 3 bags of sugar weighing 0.6 kg each, a tube of toothpaste weighing 225 g and 12 packets of crisps each weighing 25 g. Find the total weight of these items in kg.

3 Find the perimeter of this triangle in cm.

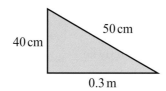

4 An urn containing 45 litres of water is used to fill cups of capacity 150 ml. How many cups can be filled?

5 Find the area of each shape in cm².

    (a)

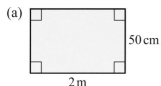

    (b)

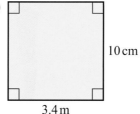

    (c)

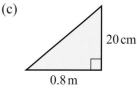

6 A large lump of 'playdoh' weighing 2.1 kg is cut up into 300 identical pieces. Find the weight of each piece in g.

7   A postage stamp measures 22 mm by 2 cm.
    Calculate the area of the stamp in cm².

Need more practice with metric and imperial units?

1   Write each length in km.
    (a) 2000 m   (b) 4600 m   (c) 750 m   (d) 300 000 m

2   Write each mass in kg.
    (a) 950 g   (b) 25 tonnes   (c) 20 g

3   A company uses 1.36 tonnes of gravel during a job. How many kilograms of gravel remain if
    the company started with 3 tonnes?

4   Copy and complete
    (a) 600 g = ☐ kg   (b) 3.5 km = ☐ m   (c) 40 mm = ☐ cm

    (d) 70 cm = ☐ m   (e) 4 litres = ☐ ml   (f) 5.6 tonnes = ☐ kg

    (g) 2.8 m = ☐ cm   (h) 0.09 kg = ☐ g

5   Carson is 6 feet tall.
    Molly is slightly shorter at 174 cm.
    How much taller is Carson?

6   A cake requires 175 g of mixed fruit. How many kilograms of mixed fruit are
    needed to make 12 cakes?

7   Work out
    (a) 5 litres + 700 ml (in ml)   (b) 0.6 m + 31 cm (in m)   (c) 4 tonnes − 300 kg (in kg)
    (d) 9 kg − 100 g (in g)   (e) 14 g + 0.6 kg (in g)   (f) 35 mm + 4.5 cm (in cm)

8   A rectangle measures 35 cm by 2 m. Penny says the area is 70 cm^2.
    Explain what mistake she has made.

9   Petrol costs £1.40 per litre. How much will 4 gallons of petrol cost?

10 Find the perimeter of
    this rectangle.

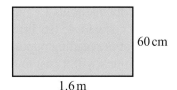

60 cm

1.6 m

Extension questions with metric and imperial units

1   The perimeter of a farm is about 36 km.
    What is the approximate perimeter of the farm in miles?

2   Harvey weighs 110 pounds. During one month he loses 4 kg on a diet.
    How much does he now weigh?

3   Write down the measurements below in order of size, starting with the smallest.

    | 0.87 ℓ | 1250 mℓ | 1.1 ℓ | 489 mℓ | 1.542 ℓ | 410 mℓ |

4   Elena has 375 m of a 3 km race still to run. Bella has run 2.12 km of the race.
    How far ahead of Bella is Elena?

5   Work out the perimeter
    of this shape.

2.3 m

60 cm

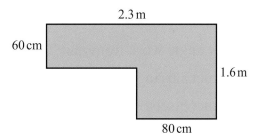

1.6 m

80 cm

6   Put these amounts in order starting with the largest.

    0.55 m, $\frac{2}{3}$ foot, 16 cm, 2 feet, 50 cm

7   Which is larger: 64 km or 40 miles?

8   When full, the large jar opposite contains
    0.6 litres of liquid and the smaller jar
    contains 450 ml.
    45 full large jars are emptied into the smaller jars.
    How many smaller jars are filled up?

9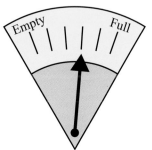

A petrol tank holds 15 gallons when full.
Petrol costs £1.45 per litre.
Look at the reading opposite.
How much will it cost to fill up the
petrol tank completely?

10 Work out the area of
    this trapezium.

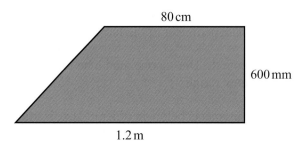

6.2 Angles and constructions

In section 6.2 you will:

- review angle work from unit 2

- construct a triangle with three sides given

- construct bisectors

Review of angle work

Exercise 1M

1   Use a protractor to draw the following angles accurately.
    (a) 65°   (b) 110°   (c) 170°   (d) 300°   (e) 73°   (f) 285°

2

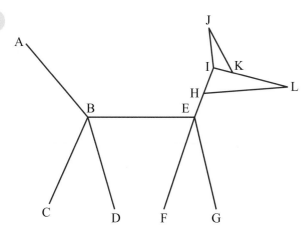

Write down true or false
for each statement below.

(a) AB̂C is acute.

(b) FÊG is acute.

(c) BÊH is obtuse.

(d) AB̂E is obtuse.

(e) HL̂K is acute.

(f) IĴK is obtuse.

3 Which angles stated in question ① are *reflex*?

4 Find the angles marked with letters.

(a)

(b)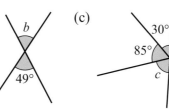

(c)

(d)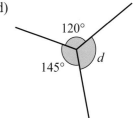

5 Find the angles marked with letters.

(a)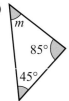

(b)

(c)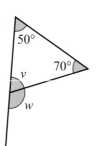

(d)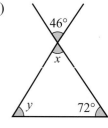

6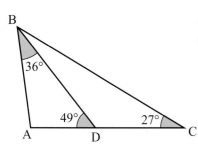

(a) Find the size of BD̂C.

(b) Find the size of DB̂C.

360

Exercise 1E

Find the angles marked with letters.

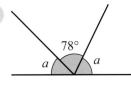

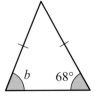

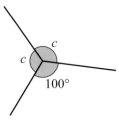

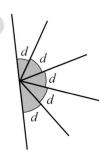

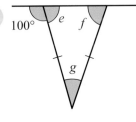

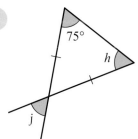

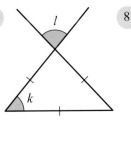

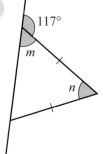

9   If you add together two acute angles, will the answer always be an obtuse angle?
Give a reason for your answer.

10   If you add together two obtuse angles, will the answer always be a reflex angle?
Explain your answer.

11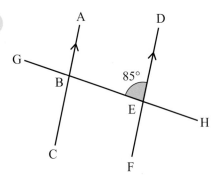

Work out the values of

(a) DÊH   (b) CB̂E   (c) AB̂G

12 Work out the values of

(a) QP̂R   (b) QR̂S   (c) QR̂P

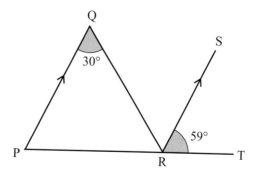

13

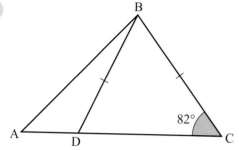

Find the size of AD̂B

Constructing a triangle with three sides given

Draw triangle XYZ and measure XẐY.

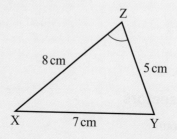

(a) Draw a base line longer than 7 cm and mark X and Y exactly 7 cm apart.

(b) Put the point of a pair of compasses on X and draw an arc of radius 8 cm.

(c) Put the point of the pair of compasses on Y and draw an arc of radius 5 cm.

(d) The arcs cross at the point Z so the triangle is formed.

Measure XẐY = 60°

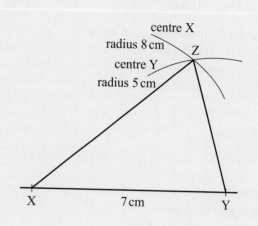

Exercise 2M

Use a ruler and a pair of compasses to construct the triangles in questions ① to ⑥.
For each triangle, measure the angle *x*.

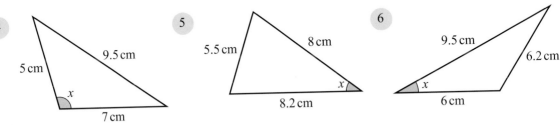

① ② 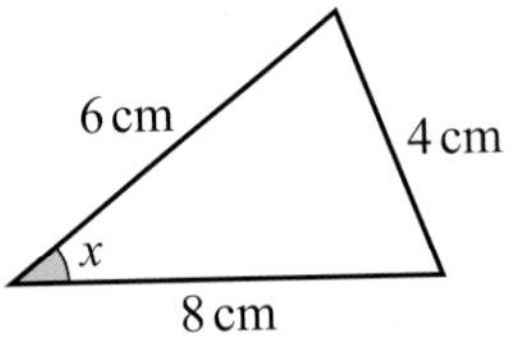 ③

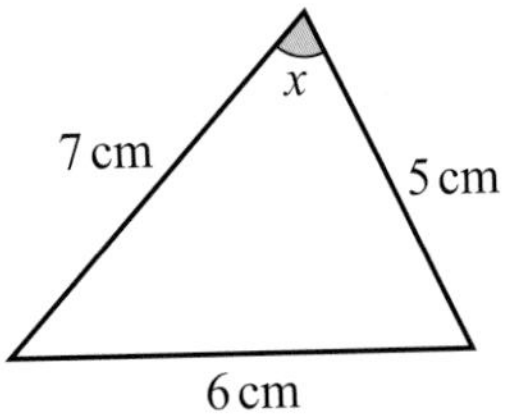

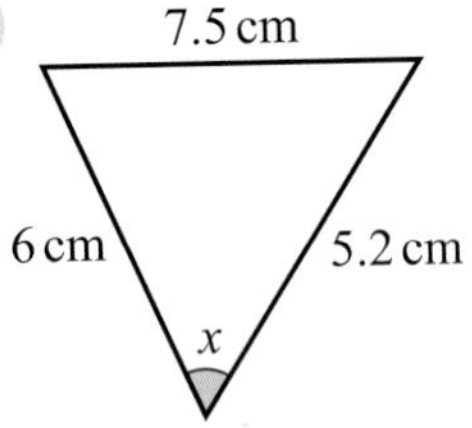

④ ⑤ ⑥

⑦ Construct this shape and measure the angle *x*.

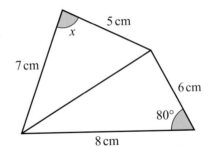

Constructing bisectors

Perpendicular bisector
Draw a line AB 8 cm long.

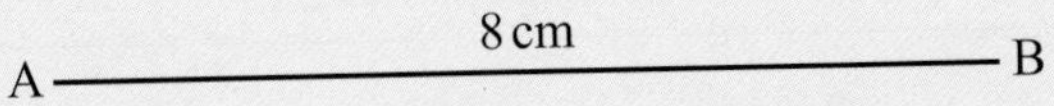

Set the pair of compasses to more
than 4 cm (half the line AB).
Put the compass point on A
and draw an arc as shown.

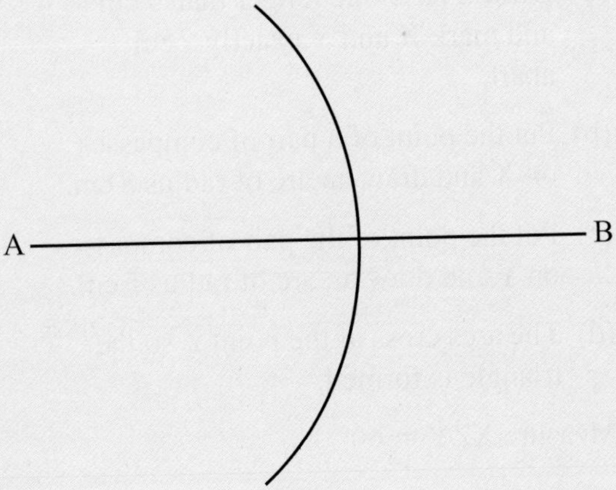

A ——————————————— B

A ——————————————— B

Put the compass point on B
(*Do not let the compass slip.*)
Draw another arc as shown.

Draw a broken line as shown.

This broken line cuts line AB in half (*bisects*) and is at right angles to line AB (*perpendicular*).

The broken line is called the *perpendicular bisector* of line AB.

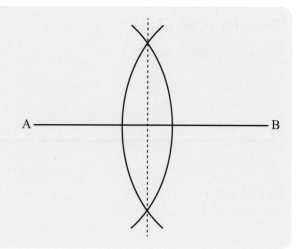

Exercise 3M

1　Draw a horizontal line AB of length 8 cm. Construct the perpendicular bisector of AB.

2　Draw a vertical line CD of length 6 cm. Construct the perpendicular bisector of CD.

3　Draw a vertical line EF of length 5 cm. Construct the perpendicular bisector of EF.

4　(a) Use a pencil, ruler and a pair of compasses *only* to *construct* the triangle ABC shown opposite.

　　(b) *Construct* the perpendicular bisector of line AB.

　　(c) *Construct* the perpendicular bisector of line AC.

　　If done accurately, your two lines from (b) and (c) should cross exactly on the line BC.

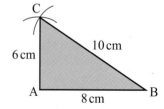

5　Draw *any* triangle KLM and construct

　　(a) the perpendicular bisector of KM

　　(b) the perpendicular bisector of KL. Mark the point of intersection X.

Take a pair of compasses and, with centre at X and radius KX, draw a circle through the points K, L and M. This is the *circumcircle of triangle KLM.*

Repeat the construction for another triangle of different shape.

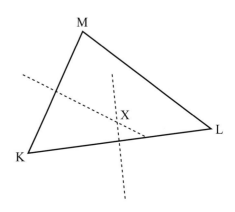

364

Bisector of an angle

Draw any angle as shown.

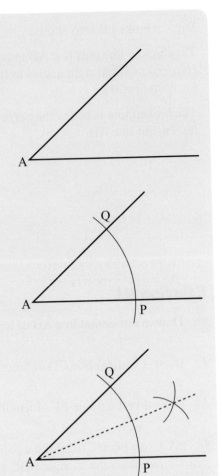

Put the compass point on A
and draw an arc as shown.

Put the compass point on P
and draw an arc as shown.
Put the compass point on Q
and draw an arc as shown.

Draw a broken line as shown.

This broken line cuts the angle in half (*bisects*).

This broken line is called the *angle bisector*.

Exercise 4M

1 Draw an angle of 60°. Construct the bisector of the angle (use a protractor to measure the angles to check that you have drawn the angle bisector accurately).

2 Draw an angle of 40°. Construct the bisector of the angle.

3 Draw an angle of 130°. Construct the bisector of the angle.

4 Draw an angle of 50°. Construct the bisector of the angle.

5 Draw any triangle ABC and then construct the bisectors of angles A, B and C. If done accurately the three bisectors should all pass through one point.

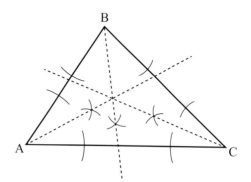

6 Draw any triangle ABC and construct the bisectors of angles B and C to meet at point Y.

With centre at Y draw a circle which just touches the sides of the triangle. This is the *inscribed circle of the triangle*.

Repeat the construction for a different triangle.

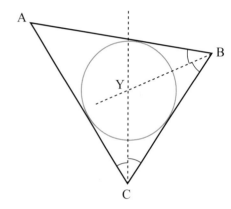

Need more practice with angles and constructions?

Find the angles marked with letters.

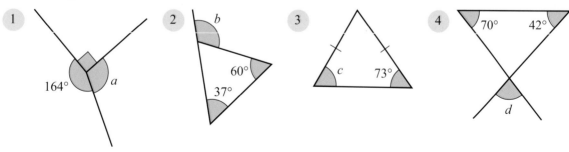

5 Draw any line and construct its perpendicular bisector.

6 An obtuse angle is subtracted from a reflex angle to give an acute angle. Suggest a value for each of these angles.

7   Use a ruler and compasses only
    to construct the triangle shown
    opposite.

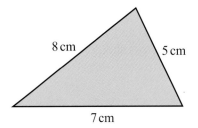

8 cm   5 cm

7 cm

8   (a) Construct a triangle with sides 6 cm, 5.5 cm and 6.5 cm.

    (b) Construct the perpendicular bisector of each side.

    (c) Comment on the point where the three perpendicular bisectors intersect each other.

9   Work out the value of BÂC opposite.
    Give full reasons for your answer.

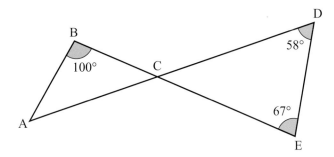

10 Use a protractor to draw an angle of 70° then construct the angle bisector.
    Check each angle is 35°.

Extension questions with angles and constructions

Find the angles marked with letters.

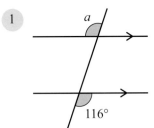

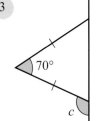

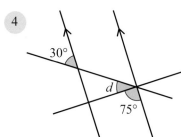

5   An isosceles triangle has an angle of 40° in it. What are the possible values of the other two
    angles? Could there be a different set of answers? If so, give their values.

6 (a) Construct triangle PQR shown opposite.

   (b) Construct the angle bisector of QP̂R.

   (c) Use a protractor to measure one of the smaller
        angles made in part (b).

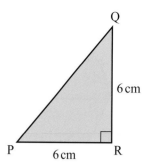

7 Construct triangle XYZ where XY = 6.7 cm, YZ = 8.2 cm and ZX = 7.9 cm.
   Measure XẐY.

8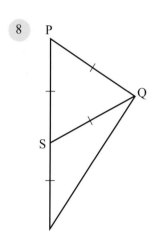

   Find the size of SR̂Q.

9 Use the diagram opposite to explain
   why the angles in a quadrilateral add
   up to 360°.

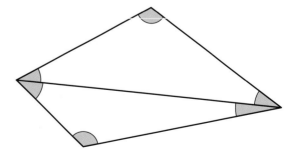

10 Draw accurately the diagrams below.

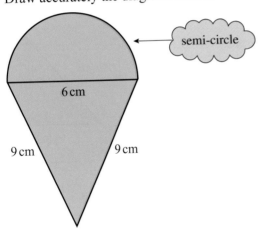

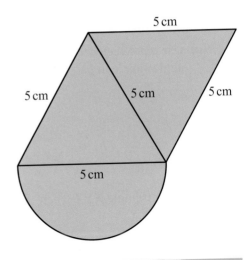

CHECK YOURSELF ON SECTIONS 6.1 AND 6.2

1   Converting metric units

Copy and complete:

(a) 7 km = ☐ m   (b) 0.4 m = ☐ cm   (c) 7500 ml = ☐ litres   (d) 4.8 kg = ☐ g

2   Converting between metric and imperial units

Copy and complete:

(a) 3 kg ≈ ☐ pounds   (b) 8 gallons ≈ ☐ litres   (c) 40 miles ≈ ☐ km

(d) Ed is 5 feet tall. Mo is 1.75 m tall. How many cm is Mo taller than Ed?

3   Reading scales

For each scale below write down the measurement indicated by the arrow.

(a)

(b) litres

(c)

4 Changing units for some problems

(a) What is the sum of 5.8 kg and 340 g (in g)?

(b) 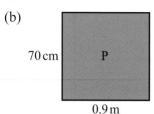 Which rectangle has the larger area and by how much?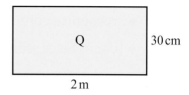

5 Review of angle work from unit 2

Find the angles marked with letters.

(a)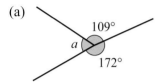

(b)

(c)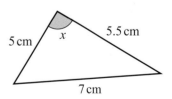

6 Constructing a triangle with three sides given

Construct this triangle with a ruler and compasses only. Use a protractor to measure the angle x.

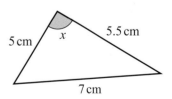

7 Constructing bisectors

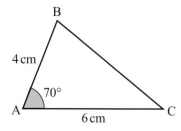

Use a ruler and protractor to draw this triangle accurately. Construct the perpendicular bisector of AC and the angle bisector of angle A. Mark with a P the point where the two bisectors meet. Measure and write down the length of AP.

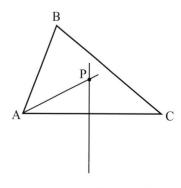

6.3 Three dimensional objects

In section 6.3 you will review how to:

- recognise common solid objects

- count faces, edges and vertices

- make shapes with nets

Common solid objects

Prisms

A *prism* has the same cross section throughout its length.

Here is a triangular prism.

If you cut through the prism parallel to its end (the face marked A in the diagram) you produce a shape exactly the same as A (marked A').

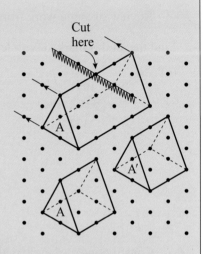

Faces, edges and vertices

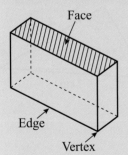

Many three-dimensional shapes have faces, edges and vertices. 'Vertices' is the plural of 'vertex'.

The *faces* of the cuboid are the flat surfaces on the shape. A cuboid has 6 faces.

The *edges* of the cuboid are the lines where the faces meet. A cuboid has 12 edges.

The *vertices* are where the edges meet at a point. A cuboid has 8 vertices (corners).

You should *learn* the names below.

Cube

Cuboid

Cylinder

Triangular prism

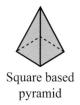
Square based
pyramid

Sphere

Cone

Hexagonal prism

Exercise 1M

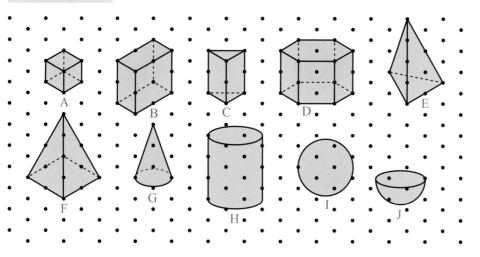

1 Write down the letters of all the objects above that are prisms and write next to the letter the name of the object.

2 Write down the letters of all the objects that are not prisms and write next to the letter the name of the object.

3 (a) For objects A to F, state the number of faces, edges and vertices.
Write your answers in a table with columns for 'shape', 'faces', 'edges' and 'vertices'.
(b) Try to find a connection between the number of faces, edges and vertices which applies to all the objects A to F.

4 Draw 3 pictures of a cube and label them A, B, C.
On A, colour in a pair of edges which are parallel.
On B, colour in a pair of edges which are perpendicular.
On C, colour in a pair of edges which are neither parallel nor intersect each other.

5 These diagrams show different solids when viewed from directly above. Describe what each solid could be. [There may be more than one correct response but you only have to give one.]

6   Sit back to back with a partner. Look at one of the models below but don't tell your partner
    which one. Tell your partner how to make the model. Now swap over. With practice you can
    design harder models of your own.

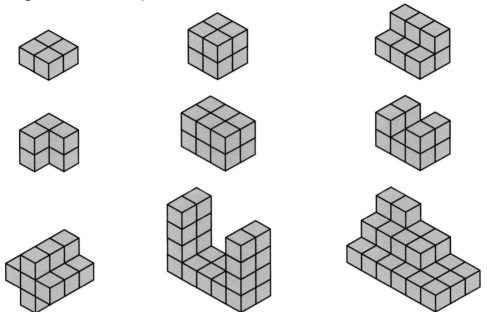

Nets for making shapes

- If the cube shown was made of cardboard, and you cut along some
  of the edges and laid it out flat, you would have a *net* of the cube.

  There is more than one net of a cube as you will see in the
  exercise which follows.

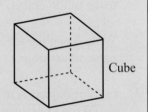

Cube

- To make a cube from card you need to produce the net shown
  below complete with the added 'tabs' for glueing purposes.

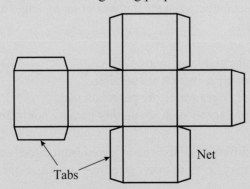

Tabs

Net

- In this section you will make several interesting 3D objects. You will need a pencil, ruler,
  scissors and either glue (Pritt Stick) or Sellotape.

Exercise 2M

1 Here are several nets which may or may not make cubes. Draw the nets on squared paper, cut them out and fold them to see which ones do make cubes.

(a)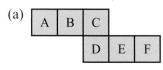

(b)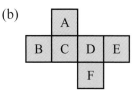

(c)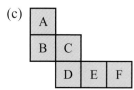

(d)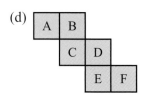

(e)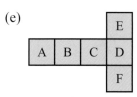

2 For the nets that *did* make cubes in question 1, state which of the faces B, C, D, E or F was opposite face A on the cube.

3 Ask your teacher for cardboard.

(a) Use a ruler and compasses to construct this triangle in the middle of the cardboard. All lengths are in cm.

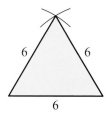

(b) 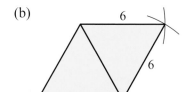 Use a ruler and compasses to construct this triangle joined to the first triangle.

(c) Use a ruler and compasses to draw 2 more triangles joined to your first triangle.

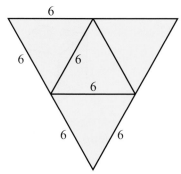

(d) Draw on some flaps like this:

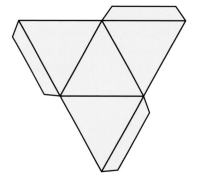

(e) *Score* all the lines then cut out the net. Fold and glue to make a triangular pyramid (called a *tetrahedron*).

4   Draw an accurate net for a closed cuboid measuring 5 cm × 3 cm × 2 cm.

5   Draw a net for any
    square-based pyramid.

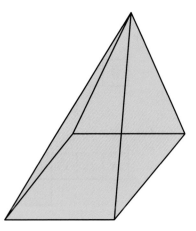

Need more practice with three dimensional objects?

1   Each diagram below shows *part* of the net of a cube. Each net needs one more square to
    complete the net.

    (a) 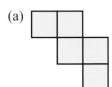   (b)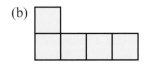

        Draw the four possible nets which would make a cube with each one.

2   Describe two different ways in which you could cut a cylinder into two identical pieces.
    Describe and/or sketch the solids you would obtain in each case.

3   Imagine a large cube which is cut in half along the dotted lines.
    Describe the two new solids formed.
    How many faces, edges and vertices does each solid have?

4   Suppose the same large cube is now cut in half along a different dotted line.
    Describe the two new solids formed.

    How many faces, edges and vertices does each solid have?

5   Use triangle dotty paper.
    Draw a net for a triangular based prism.

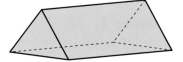

6   Here is an object made from four cubes.
    (a) Copy the drawing on isometric paper.
        (Make sure you have the paper the right
        way round.)
    (b) Make as many *different* objects as you can using
        four cubes. Draw each object on isometric paper.

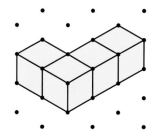

Extension questions with three dimensional objects

1

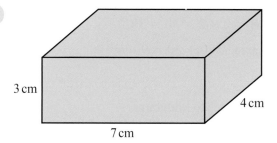

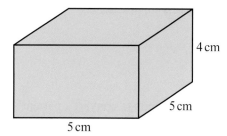

Draw a net for each cuboid above then work out the difference between the areas of each net.

2   Suppose you cut off one corner from a cube. How many faces, edges
    and vertices has the remaining shape? How about the piece cut off?

3   Draw a solid with 12 vertices, 8 faces and 18 edges.

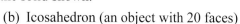

4   Use triangle dotty paper. Draw each net then make the solid shown.
    (a) Octahedron (octa: eight; hedron: faces)   (b) Icosahedron (an object with 20 faces)

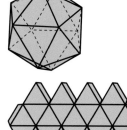

✖ Spot the mistakes 11 ✖

Units, angles, constructions and three dimensional objects

Work through each question below and *explain clearly* what mistakes have been made.
Beware – some questions are correctly done.

1   Find the area of the trapezium.

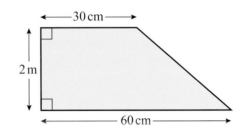

Solution: Cut the shape as shown below.

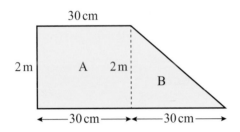

Area A = 2 × 30 = 60

Area B = $\frac{1}{2}$ × 2 × 30 = 30

Total area = 60 + 30 = 90 cm²

2   A nurse needs to convert a patient's weight from stones to kilograms.
What is the weight in kilograms if the patient weighs 213 pounds? (1 kg = 2.2 pounds)

Answer: 213 pounds = 213 ÷ 2.2 = 96.818
                              = 96.8 kg (to 1 decimal place)

3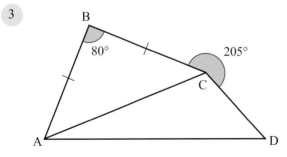

Triangle ABC is isosceles as shown.
Calculate AĈD, giving full reasons
for your answer.

Solution: BÂC = 80° (angles in an isosceles triangle)

BĈA = 180° − (80° + 80°) (angles in a triangle add up to 180°)
         = 20°

AĈD = 360° − (20° + 205°) (angles at a point add up to 360°)
         = 135°

4 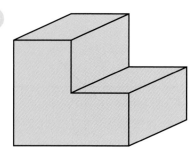 How many edges does this prism have?

Answer: 15

5 George has 0.8 kg butter. He uses 65 g butter.
How much butter does George now have?

Answer: 0.8 kg = 80 g

Remaining amount of butter = 80 − 65 = 15 g

6 Draw a net for the triangular prism opposite.

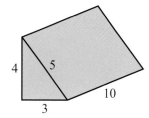

Answer:

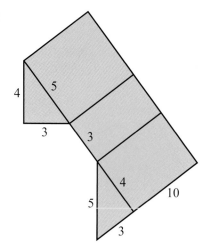

7 Callie has a multipack of 8 cans of lemonade and a 1.5 litre bottle of lemonade. Each can contains 330 ml. She wants to fill as many 120 ml cups as possible. What is the greatest number of cups she can fill with her lemonade?

Solution:
$$\begin{array}{r} 330 \\ \times \quad 8 \\ \hline 2640 \\ {}^{2} \end{array}$$

1.5 litres = 1500 ml

Total lemonade = 2640 + 1500
= 4140 ml

$$120\overline{)414^{64}0} \quad 3\ 5\ r.\ 40$$

so 35 cups can be filled.

8   Gemma does some constructions
as shown opposite. Without measuring,
what is the value of AB̂C?

Answer: 45°

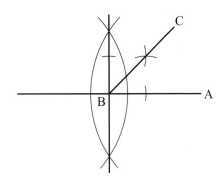

9

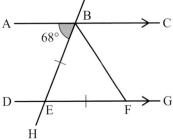

Find the value of BF̂E, giving full
reasons for your answer.

Solution: BÊF = 68° (alternate angles)
BF̂E = 68° (isosceles triangle)

10   Louis is asked to construct an angle of
30° with ruler and compasses only.

His diagram is shown opposite with
the 30° angle marked.
Is it drawn correctly?

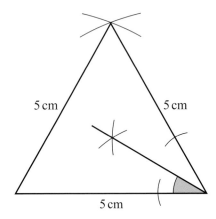

CHECK YOURSELF ON SECTION 6.3

1   Recognising common solid objects

Write down the names of these solids.

(a)   (b) 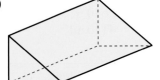   (c)

2   Counting faces, edges and vertices

For each solid below, write down how many faces, edges and vertices there are.

(a)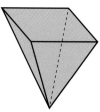

(b)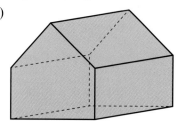

3   Making shapes with nets

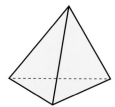   This is a tetrahedron (a triangular pyramid).

Which of these nets will make a tetrahedron?

(a)

(b)

(c)

(d) If time, copy these nets onto triangle dotty paper. Cut them out and see if you were right.

6.4 More equations

In section 6.4 you will:

- review equations covered in section 5.1
- solve equations with brackets

Remember with equations:

You may do the same thing to both sides.

Exercise 1M

1 Solve the equations below.

(a) $n - 7 = 9$ (b) $4x = 28$ (c) $19 + m = 27$

(d) $8y = 40$ (e) $w - 15 = 17$ (f) $6n = 42$

2 Now solve these equations.

(a) $3n + 4 = 19$ (b) $2w + 8 = 24$ (c) $7y - 5 = 9$

(d) $5m + 12 = 62$ (e) $6x - 8 = 16$ (f) $4m - 5 = 31$

3 I think of a number, multiply it by 9 and add 14. The answer is 68.
Write down an equation then solve it to find the number.

4 Solve these equations:

(a) $\dfrac{x}{5} = 8$ (b) $\dfrac{w}{3} = 12$ (c) $5 = \dfrac{n}{7}$

(d) $3 = \dfrac{m}{10}$ (e) $11 = \dfrac{n}{6}$ (f) $\dfrac{x}{9} = 9$

5 Solve

(a) $6x - 2 = 34$ (b) $10m + 17 = 47$ (c) $6w - 30 = 24$

(d) $9n + 8 = 71$ (e) $4x - 20 = 28$ (f) $6m - 15 = 33$

6 Solve these equations:

(a) $22 = 4n + 6$ (b) $47 = 12 + 5m$ (c) $43 = 19 + 3w$

(d) $49 = 6p - 11$ (e) $66 = 8n - 6$ (f) $34 = 7 + 9y$

7 Lois thinks of a number. She multiplies it
by 7 and subtracts 13. The answer is 50.
Write down an equation then solve it to
find the number.

8 Solve

(a) $3m + 7 = 22$ (b) $4x - 9 = 15$

(c) $4w + 80 = 200$ (d) $20n - 6 = 74$

(e) $3w + 20 = 95$ (f) $5y - 75 = 425$

Sometimes the answers are not whole numbers.

(a) Solve $5n - 3 = 1$

$$\overset{\textstyle +3}{} \quad \overset{\textstyle +3}{}$$

$$5n = 4$$

$$\overset{\textstyle \div 5}{} \quad \overset{\textstyle \div 5}{}$$

$$n = \frac{4}{5}$$

(b) Solve $9 = 6 + 2n$

$$\overset{\textstyle -6}{} \quad \overset{\textstyle -6}{}$$

$$3 = 2n$$

$$\overset{\textstyle \div 2}{} \quad \overset{\textstyle \div 2}{}$$

$$\frac{3}{2} = n$$

$$1\frac{1}{2} = n$$

Exercise 2M

1. Copy and complete the boxes:

   (a) $7n + 4 = 6$

   $$7n = \square$$

   $$n = \frac{\square}{\square}$$

   (b) $5 = 2 + 4n$

   $$\square = 4n$$

   $$\frac{\square}{\square} = n$$

2. Solve these equations:

   (a) $5n - 1 = 3$ (b) $7y - 2 = 2$ (c) $3m - 1 = 1$
   (d) $7x + 5 = 8$ (e) $13n + 10 = 12$ (f) $5w - 2 = 1$

3. Now solve these equations:

   (a) $5 = 6x + 4$ (b) $10 = 7 + 8m$ (c) $6 = 5 + 2w$
   (d) $13 = 10n + 6$ (e) $6 = 12m - 1$ (f) $2 = 8x - 5$

4. Abbie is 3 years older than her sister. The sum of their ages is 27. Let Abbie's age be x. Write down an equation involving x then solve it to find Abbie's age.

5.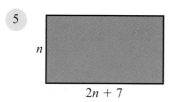

   n

   $2n + 7$

   The perimeter of this rectangle is 44 cm. Write down an equation involving n then solve it to find the actual length and width of this rectangle.

6. Solve

   (a) $5x + 4 = 7$ (b) $25 = 9 + 8m$ (c) $52 = 3 + 7p$
   (d) $4 = 9w - 3$ (e) $6a - 17 = 43$ (f) $2n + 6 = 11$
   (g) $21 = 12 + 2q$ (h) $13 = 5b - 3$ (i) $6d - 3 = 8$

Equations with brackets

Multiply out the brackets first.

(a) $3(2n + 1) = 27$

$6n + 3 = 27$

$\ominus 3 \quad \ominus 3$

$6n = 24$

$\ominus 6 \quad \ominus 6$

$n = 4$

(b) $2(5n - 3) = 8$

$10n - 6 = 8$

$\oplus 6 \quad \oplus 6$

$10n = 14$

$\ominus 10 \quad \ominus 10$

$n = 1.4$

Alternatively divide by 2 first:

$2(5n - 3) = 8$

$5n - 3 = 4$

$5n = 7$

$n = \dfrac{7}{5} = 1.4$

Exercise 2E

Solve the equations below to find x.

1   $4(2x + 3) = 52$

2   $3(3x - 2) = 30$

3   $5(4x - 2) = 110$

4   $8(x + 4) = 56$

5   $2(4x + 6) = 76$

6   $5(2x - 11) = 45$

7   $4(3x - 6) = 60$

8   $10(3x + 2) = 170$

9   $6(2x - 5) = 42$

10   $4(5x - 3) = 168$

In questions 11 to 19 find the value of the letter in each question.

11   $5(3m - 2) = 4$

12   $2(2p + 3) = 9$

13   $2(3y + 9) = 23$

14   $3(2x - 1) = 2$

15   $4(3c + 5) = 31$

16   $8(3w - 2) = 3$

17   $3(2f + 5) = 17$

18   $9(5a + 3) = 42$

19   $5(4n - 3) = 15$

20   Make up an equation with brackets which will give the answer $x = 4$.
Ask a friend to solve the equation to see if it works.

21   Make up any equation which gives the same x-value as the equation $4(3x - 2) = 76$.
Ask a friend to solve the equation to see if it works.

Need more practice with equations?

1. Solve the equations below.

    (a) $4n = 36$

    (b) $\dfrac{m}{4} = 8$

    (c) $2x + 5 = 35$

    (d) $\dfrac{w}{7} = 4$

    (e) $4p + 2 = 30$

    (f) $6x - 5 = 13$

    (g) $5y - 11 = 34$

    (h) $3w + 12 = 36$

    (i) $9m - 7 = 47$

2. Solve these equations.

    (a) $8 + 2m = 18$

    (b) $38 = 6n - 4$

    (c) $51 = 8w + 3$

    (d) $55 = 11 + 4p$

    (e) $35 = 17 + 3x$

3. Margo thinks of a number. When she trebles the number then subtracts 14, the answer is 10. Let the number be n. Form an equation using n then solve it to find the value of n.

4.

    $n + 20$

    $2n + 10$

    $2n$

    (a) Look at the triangle opposite and form an equation in terms of n.
    (Remember: the angles in a triangle add up to $180°$)

    (b) Solve the equation to find n.

    (c) Write down the actual value of each angle in the triangle.

5. Max solves the equation opposite. Identify clearly his mistake.

    $16 = 2x - 12$
    $4 = 2x$
    $x = \dfrac{4}{2} = 2$

Extension questions with equations

1. Solve

    (a) $4(2x + 3) = 60$

    (b) $3(5w - 2) = 54$

    (c) $5(3x - 1) = 100$

    (d) $6(2x + 5) = 66$

    (e) $9(3m - 2) = 63$

    (f) $7(2n + 7) = 77$

2   The two equal sides of an isosceles
     triangle are shown opposite.

     (a) Write down an equation involving x.

     (b) Solve the equation to find the value
         of x.

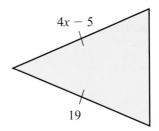

3   Alice, Ben and Charlotte have a total of £137. Ben has twice as much money as Alice.
     Charlotte has £12 more than Ben.

     (a) Copy and complete the table below to show an expression for how much money each
         person has.

Person	Alice	Ben	Charlotte
Amount	x		

     (b) Write down an equation in terms of x.

     (c) How much money does Alice have?

4   Solve these equations.

     (a) $5(2x + 3) = 24$ (b) $3(3x - 2) = 2$ (c) $5(3x - 2) = 11$
     (d) $6(2x - 5) = 15$ (e) $5(4x + 3) = 38$ (f) $2(5x - 4) = 23$

5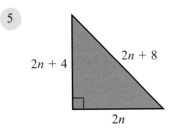

     (a) Write down an expression for the
         perimeter of this triangle.

     (b) Find the value of n if the perimeter
         equals 36 cm.

     (c) Work out the actual area of this triangle.

6.5 Sequences

In section 6.5 you will learn how to:

● find and use a rule for a sequence

Here is a sequence 3 7 11 15 19
● A number sequence is a set of numbers in a given order.
● Each number in a sequence is called a *term*.

Exercise 1M

1 Write down each sequence and find the next term.
   (a) 2, 5, 8, 11   (b) 2, 8, 14, 20   (c) −2, 0, 2, 4
   (d) 0.9, 1, 1.1, 1.2   (e) 22, 17, 12, 7   (f) 0.2, 0.5, 0.8

In questions 2 to 10 you may have to add, subtract, multiply or divide to find the next term.

2 21, 15, 9

3 0.2, 2, 20, 200

4 0.8, 1, 1.2

5 80, 40, 20, 10

6 11, 8, 5, 2

7 10 000, 1000, 100

8 3, 30, 300, 3000

9 200, 100, 50, 25

10 1, 2, 4, 7, 11

11 Write down the sequence and find the missing numbers.

   (a) | 3 | 6 | 12 | 24 | |

   (b) | 4 | | 10 | 13 | 16 |

   (c) | 32 | 16 | 8 | 4 | |

   (d) | | 6 | 3 | 0 | −3 |

12 Golf balls can be stacked in a 'solid' pyramid.
   The picture shows the view from above a pyramid
   with **1** ball at the top, **4** balls on the next layer
   and **9** balls on the next layer after that.
   How many balls will be on the next layer?

Sequence rules

- For the sequence 10, 13, 16, 19, 22, ... the first term is 10 and the
  term-to-term rule is 'add 3'.
- For the sequence 3, 6, 12, 24, 48, ... the term-to-term rule is
  'double' or 'multiply by 2'.

Exercise 2M

1 The first term of a sequence is 20 and the term-to-term rule is 'add 5'.
   Write down the first five terms of the sequence.

2   You are given the first term and the rule of several sequences.
Write down the first five terms of each sequence.

	First term	Rule
(a)	8	add 2
(b)	100	subtract 4
(c)	10	double
(d)	64	divide by 2

3   Write down the rule for each of these sequences.

(a) 3, 10, 17, 24   (b) 100, 89, 78, 67   (c) 0.7, 0.9, 1.1, 1.3   (d) 1, 2, 4, 8, 16

4   The rule for the number sequences below is

'double and add 1'

Find the missing numbers.

(a) $2 \rightarrow 5 \rightarrow 11 \rightarrow 23 \rightarrow \boxed{}$

(b) $\boxed{} \rightarrow 7 \rightarrow 15 \rightarrow 31$

(c) $\boxed{} \rightarrow 51 \rightarrow \boxed{} \rightarrow \boxed{}$

5   A sequence begins 2, 4, ...

(a) What is the next term? Give a reason for your answer.

(b) Could the next term be different to your part (a) answer? Give a reason for your answer.

6   The rule for the number sequence below is

'multiply by 3 and take away 2'

Find the missing numbers.

(a) $2 \rightarrow 4 \rightarrow 10 \rightarrow \boxed{}$ (b) $\boxed{} \rightarrow 7 \rightarrow 19 \rightarrow 55$ (c) $1 \rightarrow \boxed{} \rightarrow \boxed{} \rightarrow \boxed{}$

7   Write down the rule for each of these sequences.

(a) $2, 2\frac{1}{2}, 3, 3\frac{1}{2}, 4, ...$ (b) 5, 10, 20, 40, 80, ...

(c) 1.5, 1.6, 1.7, 1.8, ...   (d) 81, 27, 9, 3, 1, ...

8   Find the first five terms of each sequence.

(a)
> The 2nd term is 9
> The rule is 'add 5'

(b)
> The 4th term is 11
> The rule is 'take away 3'

(c)
> The 3rd term is 12
> The rule is 'multiply by 2'

(d)
> The 2nd term is 10
> The rule is 'multiply by 10'

9 (a) Copy this pattern and write down the next line.
$$1 + 9 \times \quad 0 = \quad 1$$
$$2 + 9 \times \quad 1 = \quad 11$$
$$3 + 9 \times \quad 12 = \quad 111$$
$$4 + 9 \times 123 = 1111$$

(b) Find the missing numbers

$$\boxed{} + 9 \times \boxed{} = 1\,111\,111$$

10 In this question the rule for several *different* sequences is 'add 5'.

(a) Find a sequence for which all the terms are divisible by 5.

(b) Find a sequence for which none of the terms is a whole number.

(c) Can you find a sequence with the 'add 5' rule in which all the terms are odd numbers?

Exercise 3M

1 Here is a sequence of triangles made from sticks.

 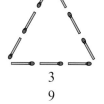

Shape number:	1	2	3
Number of sticks:	3	6	9

(a) Draw shape number 4 and count the number of sticks.

(b) Write down and complete the rule for the number of sticks in a shape:
'The number of sticks is _____ times the shape number'.

2 Louise makes a pattern of triangles from sticks.

Shape number:	1	2	3
Number of sticks:	3	5	7

(a) Draw shape number 4 and shape number 5.

(b) Make a table:

shape number	1	2	3	4	5
number of sticks	3	5	7		

(c) Write down the rule for the number of sticks in a shape.
'The number of sticks is _____ times the shape number and then add _____.'

An *arithmetic* (or linear) sequence is one where the gap between each pair of terms is always the same. This gap is known as the *difference*.

● Consider an arithmetic sequence of shapes made from sticks:

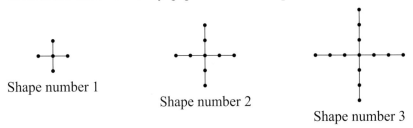

Shape number:	1	2	3
Number of sticks:	4	7	10

● There is a *rule* or *formula* which we can use to calculate the number of sticks for any shape number.

'*The number of sticks is three times the shape number add one*'.

Check that this rule works for all the shapes and also for shape number 4 which you can draw.

● We could also write the rule using symbols. Let n stand for the diagram number and let s stand for the number of sticks.

The rule (or formula) is '$s = 3n + 1$'.

3 Crosses are drawn on 'dotty' paper to make a sequence.

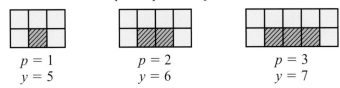

Shape number 1

Shape number 2

Shape number 3

(a) Draw shape number 4.

(b) Make a table:

shape number	1	2	3	4
number of dots	5	9	13	

(c) Write down the rule.
'The number of dots is _____ times the shape number and then add _____.'

4 In these diagrams pink shaded squares are surrounded on three sides by yellow squares. Let the number of pink squares be p and let the number of yellow squares be y.

$p = 1$
$y = 5$

$p = 2$
$y = 6$

$p = 3$
$y = 7$

(a) Draw the next diagram, which has 4 pink shaded squares.

(b) Write down the rule.
'The number of yellow squares is ......'

5   Look again at questions ①, ② and ③. Use n for the shape number and s for the number of sticks or dots. For each question write the rule connecting n and s without using words. In each question write '$s =$.'

- Here is a sequence 4, 8, 12, 16, …

The first term is	4×1
The second term is	4×2
The third term is	4×3
$\vdots$	$\vdots$
The 30th term is	4×30

Consider a term n. We call this the nth term.
The nth term is $4 \times n$ in this sequence.

$$n^{th} \text{ term} = 4n$$

This formula can be used to find any term in the sequence

eg. 15th term $= 4n = 4 \times 15 = 60$
       100th term $= 4n = 4 \times 100 = 400$

- In another sequence the nth term is $3n + 2$

1st term	$= 3 \times 1 + 2$	2nd term	$= 3 \times 2 + 2$	3rd term	$= 3 \times 3 + 2$
$(n = 1)$	$= 5$	$(n = 2)$	$= 8$	$(n = 3)$	$= 11$

Exercise 4M

1   The nth term of a sequence is $6n$. What is the value of:

     (a) the first term   (use $n = 1$)

     (b) the second term   (use $n = 2$)

     (c) the tenth term   (use $n = 10$)

2   The nth term of a sequence is $2n + 5$. What is the value of:

     (a) the first term   (use $n = 1$)

     (b) the fifth term   (use $n = 5$)

     (c) the one hundredth term   (use $n = 100$)

3   Write down the first four terms of each sequence using the nth term given.

     (a) $7n$ (b) $n + 3$ (c) $3n + 1$ (d) $25 - n$ (e) $4n + 7$

4   Match up each sequence and the correct formula for the nth term from the list given.

(a) 10, 20, 30, 40, ...

(b) 3, 6, 9, 12, ...

(c) 5, 9, 13, 17, ...

(d) 50, 100, 150, 200, ...

(e) $1^2, 2^2, 3^2, 4^2, ...$

(f) 8, 10, 12, 14, ...

(g) 11, 14, 17, 20, ...

(h) 12, 24, 36, 48, ...

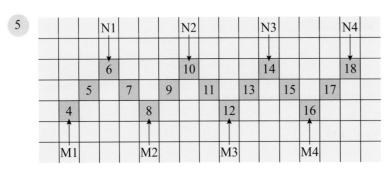

$3n$ $4n + 1$ $50n$ $10n$ $12n$ $2n + 6$ n^2 $3n + 8$

5

		N1			N2			N3			N4	
		6			10			14			18	
	5		7		9		11		13		15		17	
	4			8			12			16		
	M1			M2			M3			M4		

The numbers N1, N2, N3, N4 and M1, M2, M3, M4 form two sequences.

(a) Find M5, M6, N5, N6.

(b) Think of rules and use them to find M15 and N20.

6   Explain whether the number 12 belongs to the sequence with n^{th} term $= 5n - 3$ or not.

7   Explain whether the number 13 belongs to the sequence with n^{th} term $= 2n + 5$ or not.

8   Here is a sequence of touching triangles.
Find the coordinates of

(a) the top of triangle 5

(b) the top of triangle 50

(c) the bottom right corner of triangle 50

(d) the bottom right corner of triangle 100

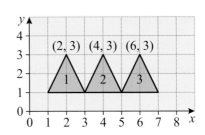

Need more practice with sequences?

In Questions ① to ⑥ write down the sequence and find the next term.

1   60, 54, 48, 42

2   1, 3, 9, 27

3   5, 7, 10, 14

4   7, 5, 3, 1, −1

5   1.7, 1.9, 2.1, 2.3

6   11, 10, 8, 5, 1

7   In the sequence of squares the number of matches is shown.

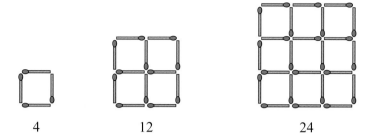

4   12   24

(a) Draw the next square in the sequence and write down the number of matches in the square.

(b) Copy and complete the number pattern below.

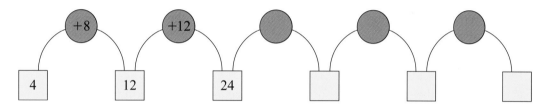

8   In an arithmetic sequence the terms go up or go down in equal steps.
For example 7, 10, 13, 16, … or 20, 18, 16, 14, …

Fill in the missing numbers in these arithmetic sequences.

(a) 2, ☐, 8, ☐, ☐, 17

(b) 10, ☐, 18, ☐, 26, 30, ☐

(c) ☐, 37, ☐, ☐, 28, 25

9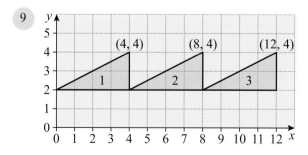

Find the coordinates of the top vertex of

(a) triangle 4

(b) triangle 20

(c) triangle 2000.

10 Here is a sequence of 'steps' made from sticks.

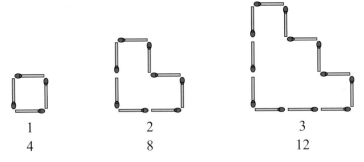

Shape number: 1   2   3
Number of sticks: 4   8   12

(a) Draw shape number 4 and count the number of sticks.

(b) Write down the rule for the number of sticks in a shape. 'The number of sticks is ____ times the shape number.'

(c) Write down a formula for s in terms of n where n is the shape number and s is the number of sticks.

(d) How many sticks are in shape number 50?

11 Write down the first four terms of each sequence using the nth term given.

(a) $n + 6$ (b) $3n - 2$ (c) $5n + 4$ (d) $16 - n$

12 A sequence made from a pattern of sticks has the formula $s = 5n + 3$ where n is the shape number and s is the number of sticks.
Anton says that one of the shapes contains 39 sticks.
Marie does not agree. Who is correct? Justify your answer fully.

Extension questions with sequences

1 The first term of an arithmetic sequence is 3.7 and the term-to-term rule is 'add 0.25'.
Write down the first five terms of the sequence.

2 The first number in a sequence is 5. Write down a possible rule so that all the terms in the sequence are odd numbers.

3 (a) Look at the pattern below and then continue it for a further three rows.

$2^2 + 2 + 3 = 9$
$3^2 + 3 + 4 = 16$
$4^2 + 4 + 5 = 25$
.   .   .   .
.   .   .   .
.   .   .   .

(b) Write down the line which starts
$12^2 + \dots$

4   Here is a sequence of hexagons made from sticks.

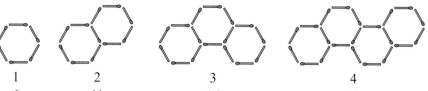

Shape number: 1   2   3   4
Number of sticks: 6   11   16   21

Let n be the shape number and s be the number of sticks.
(a) Write down a rule (or formula) for s in terms of n.
(b) How many sticks are in shape number 15?

5   Here is a sequence of touching squares.
Copy and complete the table.

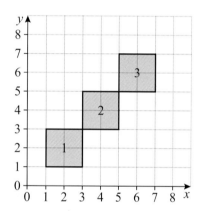

Square number	Coordinates of centre
1	(2, 2)
2	(4, 4)
3	
5	
40	
45	

6   Write down 4 terms of an arithmetic sequence by using four of the numbers from the list below.

35, 33, 41, 27, 32, 29, 39, 40, 31, 38

7   (a) Copy this pattern and write down the next line.

$3 \times 4 = 3 + 3 \times 3$
$4 \times 5 = 4 + 4 \times 4$
$5 \times 6 = 5 + 5 \times 5$

(b) Copy and complete

$10 \times 11 =$
$11 \times 12 =$

8   The odd numbers can be added in groups to give an interesting sequence.

$$1 \qquad\qquad\qquad = \quad 1 \;=\; 1^3 \;(1 \times 1 \times 1)$$
$$3 + 5 \qquad\qquad = \quad 8 \;=\; 2^3 \;(2 \times 2 \times 2)$$
$$7 + 9 + 11 \;=\; 27 \;=\; 3^3 \;(3 \times 3 \times 3)$$

The numbers 1, 8, 27 are called *cube* numbers. Another cube number is 5^3 (we say '5 cubed').

$5^3 = 5 \times 5 \times 5 = 125$

Write down the next three rows of the sequence to see if the sum of each row always gives a cube number.

394

9   Find the next term for each sequence below.

(a) 1, 2, 6, 24, 120
(b) $\dfrac{1}{3}, \dfrac{2}{5}, \dfrac{3}{7}, \dfrac{4}{9}$
(c) 2, 2, 4, 12, 48, 240

Investigation – count the crossovers

Two straight lines have a maximum of one crossover.

Three straight lines have a maximum of three crossovers.

Notice that you can have less than three crossovers if the lines all go through one point. Or the lines could be parallel.

In this work we are interested only in the *maximum* number of crossovers.

Four lines have a maximum of six crossovers.

Part A   Draw five lines and find the maximum number of crossovers.
Does there appear to be any sort of sequence in your results? If you can find a sequence, use it to *predict* the maximum number of crossovers with six lines.

Part B   Now draw six lines and count the crossovers to see if your prediction was correct (remember not to draw three lines through one point).

Part C   Predict the number of crossovers for seven lines and then check if your prediction is correct by drawing a diagram.

Part D   Write your results in a table:

Number of lines	Number of crossovers
2	1
3	3
4	6
5	
6	

Predict the number of crossovers for 20 lines.

✖ Spot the mistakes 12 ✖

Equations and sequences

Work through each question on the next page and *explain clearly* what mistakes have been made. Beware – some questions are correctly done.

1 Solve $5x + 3 = 17$

Solution: $5x + 3 = 17$

$$5x = 17 + 3$$
$$5x = 20$$
$$x = \frac{20}{5} = 4$$

2 Find the first 4 terms of the sequence with n^{th} term $= 2(n + 3)$

Solution: 1st term $= 2(1 + 3) = 24$

2nd term $= 2(2 + 3) = 25$

3rd term $= 2(3 + 3) = 26$

4th term $= 2(4 + 3) = 27$

3 Solve $4(n - 3) = 25$

Solution: $4(n - 3) = 25$

$$4n - 3 = 25$$
$$4n = 25 + 3$$
$$4n = 28$$
$$n = \frac{28}{4} = 7$$

4 Form an equation and work out the value of n for the square opposite.

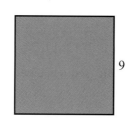

9

$8n + 2$

Solution: sides of a square are equal

so $8n + 2 = 9$

$$8n = 9 - 2$$
$$8n = 7$$
$$n = \frac{7}{8}$$

5 Is 49 a number in the sequence with n^{th} term $= 3n + 7$?

Answer: Try $3n + 7 = 49$

$$3n = 42$$
$$n = \frac{42}{3} = 14$$

so 49 is the 14th term of this sequence.

6   Here is a sequence made from sticks.

Shape number:	1	2	3	4
Number of sticks:	5	9	13	17

Let n be the shape number and s be the number of sticks.
Write down a formula for s in terms of n.

Answer: The number of sticks increases by 4 each time so $s = n + 4$

7   Find the 'term-to-term' rule for the sequence

$$\frac{1}{3}, \frac{1}{9}, \frac{1}{27}, \frac{1}{81}$$

Answer: Multiply by 3 each time to get the next term.

8   Asha is 4 years older than Ryan. The sum of their ages is 40. How old is Ryan?

Solution: Let Ryan's age $= x$

Asha's age $= 4x$

sum of ages $= x + 4x = 40$

$5x = 40$

$x = \dfrac{40}{5} = 8$

so Ryan is 8 years old.

9   What kind of sequence is 7, 12, 17, 22, …?

Answer: An 'arithmetic' sequence because 5 is added on to each term to get the next term.

10   Solve $10 = \dfrac{x}{5}$

Solution: $10 = \dfrac{x}{5}$

$x = \dfrac{10}{5} = 2$

CHECK YOURSELF ON SECTIONS 6.4 AND 6.5

1   Review of equations covered in section 5.1

Solve the equations below.

(a) $5n - 17 = 28$ (b) $\dfrac{m}{7} = 8$ (c) $34 = 3y + 10$

(d) $4 = 6w - 1$ (e) $9x + 16 = 34$ (f) $10 = 4p + 7$

2 Solving equations with brackets

Solve   (a) $2(4p + 3) = 54$ (b) $3(2x - 5) = 39$

3 Finding and using a rule for a sequence

Find the next term in each sequence.

(a) 61, 55, 49, 43

(b) $\frac{1}{2}$, 1, 2, 4

(c) $-14, -11, -8, -5$

(d) $\square \rightarrow 15 \rightarrow 33 \rightarrow \square$ The rule for this sequence is '*double and add 3*'. Find the missing numbers.

In the diagrams below, the blue (b) squares are surrounded by green (g) squares.

g	g	g
g	b	g
g	g	g

g	g	g	g
g	b	b	g
g	g	g	g

g	g	g	g	g
g	b	b	b	g
g	g	g	g	g

(e) Draw the next diagram, which has 4 blue squares.

(f) Make a table. Fill in the missing values.

number of blue squares	1	2	3	4
number of green squares	8	10		

(g) Complete the rule:

'The number of green squares is _____ times the number of blue squares and then add _____.'

(h) The nth term of a different sequence is $4n + 3$. What is the value of the tenth term of this sequence?

6.6 Applying mathematics 6

In section 6.6 you will apply maths in a variety of situations.

1 A baker is making cakes which need 1.65 kg of flour and biscuits which need 2350 g of flour. The baker has 2.4 kg of flour to begin with. How much more flour will the baker need to make the cakes and biscuits?

2 The tenth number in the sequence 1, 3, 9, 27, … is 19 683. What is the ninth number?

3 Write down these calculations and find the missing digits.

(a)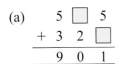

(b)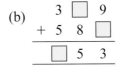

(c)
```
    □  1  □
+   5  □  4
─────────────
    7  5  0
```

4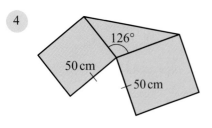

Martin has fitted together 3 patio slabs as shown opposite. Two of the slabs are rectangular and one is triangular.

He has one more triangular slab as shown here. Will it fit perfectly in the space between the two rectangular slabs? Justify your answer fully.

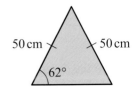

5 Sapphire wants to buy a T.V. She looks in two shops. The prices are shown below.

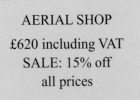

AERIAL SHOP

£620 including VAT
SALE: 15% off
all prices

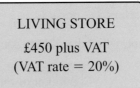

LIVING STORE

£450 plus VAT
(VAT rate = 20%)

Which shop has the lower price for the T.V. and by how much?

6 Maurice says that for any number n, the value of n^2 is always greater than the value of n.
Tamsin says that Maurice is not correct when $n = 0.2$.
Show clearly whether Maurice or Tamsin is correct.

7 A car uses 5 litres of petrol for every 80 km travelled. Petrol costs £1.50 per litre.
Calculate the cost in £'s of travelling 400 km.

8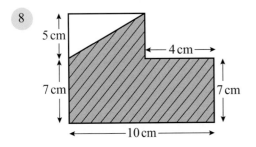

Work out the shaded area in the diagram opposite.

9 Look at the photo of the pile of matches.

(a) How many matches are there in each layer?

(b) Each match is 3 mm thick. How many matches are there in a tower of height 3 cm?

(c) How high a tower can you build with 14 boxes of matches if each box contains 48 matches?

10

| 1 | 2 | 2 | 2 | 2 | 2 | 3 | 4 | 5 | 5 | 5 |

Lucy removes five cards from above. She takes the cards shown below.

| 1 | 2 | 3 | 4 | 5 |

She works out the mean average *m* for these five cards. She now removes one more card from the original cards. Work out the probability that the new card will make the mean average of her six cards less than the mean average *m*.

UNIT 6   MIXED REVIEW

Part one

1 Write the missing number in this sequence:

5, 18, ☐, 44.

2 What is the reading in kilograms shown in this scale?

3 Name the 3D shape whose faces are all squares.

4 Solve the equations.

(a) $n - 8 = 13$ (b) $5n = 20$ (c) $2n + 4 = 12$

(d) $3n - 7 = 14$ (e) $\frac{n}{9} = 4$ (f) $8n - 15 = 33$

5 A metal rod is 14 cm long. A piece 2 cm 3 mm is cut off. What length of rod is left in centimetres.

6 What is the mathematical name for a snooker ball?

400

7   Here is the net for a cube.

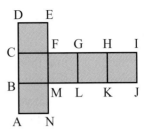

(a) When the net is folded up, which edge will be stuck to the edge JI?

(b) Which edge will be stuck to the edge AB?

(c) Which corner will meet corner D?

8   Sarah is 14 years old and her father is 35 years older than her.
Sarah's mother is 4 years younger than her father. How old is Sarah's mother?

9   Listed below are various items that can be measured.
Copy the list and insert next to each item the most suitable
unit of measurement.

Units

1. centimetres
2. millilitres
3. grams
4. kilometres
5. litres
6. metres

(a) The fuel tank of an aircraft.

(b) The mass of a packet of crisps.

(c) The height of your bedroom.

(d) The distance from London to Edinburgh.

(e) The amount of cough mixture on a teaspoon.

(f) The width of a postage stamp.

10

(a) Find the size of $A\hat{C}B$.

(b) Find the size of $C\hat{D}E$.

11   P ——————— 7 cm ——————— Q

Draw a line PQ of length 7 cm.
Construct the perpendicular bisector of PQ.

12   If 8 km is about 5 miles, how many miles is 56 km?

13   Answer true or false:

(a) $2n + n = 3n$

(b) $3n - 2 = 1$

(c) $n^2 = 2 \times n$

(d) $n \times 3 = 3n$

(e) $n \div 3 = \dfrac{n}{3}$

(f) $n \times 0 = n$

14 A 10p coin is 2 mm thick. Alex has a
pile of 10p coins which is 16.6 cm tall.
What is the value of the money in Alex's
pile of coins?

16.6 cm

2 mm

15 Unifix cubes can be joined together to make different sized cuboids.

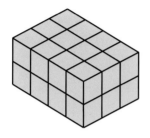

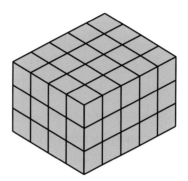

If the smaller cuboid weighs 96 g, how much does the large cuboid weigh?

Part two

1 Write each of the following in the units shown, using decimals when needed.

(a) 3 m 65 cm = ☐ m   (b) 850 g = ☐ kg   (c) 0.49 m = ☐ cm

(d) 4.2 kg = ☐ g   (e) 38 cm = ☐ m   (f) 46 mm = ☐ cm

2 What is the name of the shape which has one square face and four triangular faces?

3 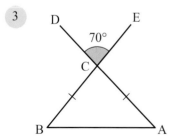 Find the size of AB̂C.

4 Draw a net for a cuboid 2 cm × 3 cm × 4 cm.

5 (a) How many 7 centimetre pieces of string can be cut from a piece of string which is
2 metres in length?

(b) How much string is left over?

6 A jar with 8 chocolates in it weighs 160 g. The same jar with 20 chocolates in it weighs 304 g. How much does the jar weigh on its own?

7 Here is a sequence of diagrams showing an arrangement of counters.

Diagram 1   Diagram 2   Diagram 3

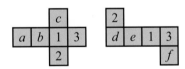

(a) Draw diagram number 4.

(b) Copy and complete this table for the diagrams so far.

Diagram Number	Counters used
1	7
2	
3	
4	

(c) Without drawing, how many counters will be needed for diagram number 5?

(d) Write in words how you found your answer without drawing.

8 Solve the equations

(a) $2(2n + 3) = 22$ (b) $5(4n - 7) = 65$ (c) $3(4n - 1) = 21$

9 These nets form cubical dice. Opposite faces of a dice always add up to 7.
Write down the value of a, b, c, d, e, and f so that opposite faces add up to 7.

c		
a	b	1	3
	2	

2		
d	e	1	3
	f	

10 The tenth number in the sequence 1, 4, 16, 64 …… is 262 144.

What is   (a) the ninth number

(b) the twelfth number?

11 *Construct* this triangle with a ruler and compasses only.
Use a protractor to measure the size of AB̂C.

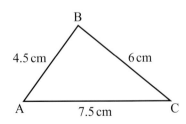

12 What is the name of the solids which have the same cross-section throughout their length?

13 The rule for a sequence is 'add 3'. The first three terms of the sequence are negative numbers. These are the only negative numbers in the sequence. Find what numbers the first term of the sequence could be.

14 A famous sequence in mathematics is Pascal's triangle.

(a) Look carefully at how the triangle is made. Write down the next row. It starts: 1 7 ...

(b) Look at the diagonal marked A. Predict the next three numbers in the sequence 1, 3, 6, 10, 15, ...

(c) Work out the *sum* of the numbers in each row of Pascal's triangle. What do you notice?

(d) Without writing down all the numbers, work out the sum of the numbers in the 10th row of the triangle.

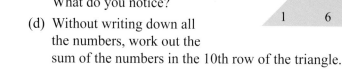

15 In a code the 25 letters from A to Y are obtained from the square using a 2 digit grid reference similar to coordinates. So letter 'U' is 42 and 'L' is 54. The missing letter 'Z' has code 10.

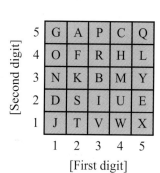

Decode the following messages:

(a) 41, 52
   13, 52, 52, 12
   43, 14, 34, 52
   22, 42, 43, 22

(b) 44, 25, 31, 52
   25
   13, 32, 45, 52
   12, 25, 53

(c) 22, 35, 42, 34, 22
   25, 34, 52
   34, 42, 33, 33, 32, 22, 44

In part (d) each pair of brackets gives one letter

(d) ($\frac{1}{4}$ of 140), ($7^2 + 5$), ($7 \times 8 - 4$), ($4^2 + 3^2$) ($\frac{1}{5}$ of 110), ($26 \div \frac{1}{2}$)

   ($3 \times 7 + 1$), ($83 - 31$), ($2 \times 2 \times 2 \times 2 + 5$).

   ($100 - 57$), ($4^2 - 2$), (17×2), ($151 - 99$)

   ($2 \times 2 \times 2 \times 5 + 1$), ($\frac{1}{4}$ of 56), ($2 \times 3 \times 2 \times 3 - 2$), ($5^2 - 2$)

(e) Write your own message in code and ask a friend to decode it.

ANSWERS TO CHECK YOURSELF SECTIONS

Page 31   ***Check yourself on sections 1.1 and 1.2***

1. (a) 2458   (b) 8425   **2.** (a) 903   (b) 369   (c) 3577   (d) 36   (e) 439

(f) 45   (g) 12   (h) 12   (i) 1488   **3.** (a) $\dfrac{7}{10}$ (b) $\dfrac{3}{100}$ (c) $\dfrac{15}{100}$

(d)

	3.2	0.54	0.9	1.8
2.7	5.9	3.24	3.6	4.5
8.6	11.8	9.14	9.5	10.4
0.04	3.24	0.58	0.94	1.84
8	11.2	8.54	8.9	9.8

4. RELATION

5. (a) 3.84   (b) 26.6

(c) 0.012   (d) £6.10

6. (a) 4.71   (b) 5.3

(c) 5.5   (d) 0.32 kg

Page 58   ***Check yourself on sections 1.3 and 1.4***

1. (a) 5   (b) 87   (c) 8   (d) 55   (e) 5   (f) 30

2. (a) 8.61   (b) 372   **3.** (a) 9   (b) 622.008

4. (a) $4x$ (b) $n - 6$ (c) $2w + 24$

5. (a) $2m + 9n$ (b) $7y$ (c) $4p + 6$ (d) $2a + 2b$ (e) $28mn$

(f) $24ab$ (g) $8pqr$ (h) $81n^2$ (i) A and C

6. (a) 645   (b) 33   (c) 6   **7.** (a) $\square = 8$ (b) $\square = 12, \bigcirc = 3$

Page 68   ***Check yourself on section 1.5***

1. (a) 2°C, 1°C, −3°C, −4°C, −8°C, −9°C   (b) −5

2. (a) −4   (b) −7   (c) −3   (d) −2   **3.** (a) −15   (b) 8   (c) −3   (d) 32

Page 99   ***Check Yourself on Sections 2.1 and 2.2***

1. (a) $\dfrac{7}{42}$ (b) $\dfrac{28}{36}$ (c) $\dfrac{2}{3}$ (d) $\dfrac{30}{42}$ (e) $\dfrac{49}{56}, \dfrac{63}{72}$

2. (a) 4   (b) 20   (c) 42   (d) 16

3. (a) $\dfrac{27}{70}$ (b) $\dfrac{21}{40}$ (c) $\dfrac{1}{10}$ (d) $\dfrac{8}{9}$ (e) $\dfrac{7}{15}$ cm^2

4. (a) $\dfrac{7}{9}$ (b) $\dfrac{29}{35}$ (c) $\dfrac{1}{12}$ (d) $\dfrac{13}{16}$

5. 40%, 0.4, $\dfrac{2}{5}$; 75%, 0.75 $\dfrac{3}{4}$; 5%, 0.05, $\dfrac{1}{20}$; 45%, 0.45, $\dfrac{9}{20}$

Page 114   ***Check Yourself on Sections 2.3 and 2.4***

1. (b) 2 (d) parallelogram **2.** (a) (5, 3) (b) (7, 5) (c) (4, 3)

3. (a) (1, 4) (b) $x = 1$ (c) $y = 2$ (d) (3, 3)

4. (a) (1, 4), (2, 5), (3, 6), (4, 7)

Page 144   ***Check Yourself on Sections 2.5 and 2.6***

1. (a) 62 cm (b) 7 m **2.** (a) 92 cm^2 (b) 7 m

3. (a) 28 m^2 (b) 36 cm^2 (c) 30 cm^2 (d) 132 cm^2 (e) 20 m

4. (a) 85° (b) 30° (c) 100° (d) 62° (e) 115°

5. (a) 65° (b) 125° (c) $X\widehat{W}Y = 100°$, $V\widehat{W}X = 80°$

6. (a) 28° (b) 102° (c) $P\widehat{R}Q = 64°$, $P\widehat{R}S = 116°$

7. (a) $B\widehat{E}F = 78°$, $F\widehat{E}H = 102°$ (b) 61°

Page 176   ***Check yourself on sections 3.1 and 3.2***

1. (a) 53, 59 (b) e.g. 23 and 7

2. (a) 1, 2, 3, 4, 6, 8, 12, 24 (b) 24 (c) 15 (d) $2 \times 3 \times 5 \times 5$

3. (a) 49 (b) 1 (c) 43 (d) 92 (e) 36, 49 (f) 9, 25 (g) 1, 100

4. (a) 432 (b) 16 226 (c) 144 (d) £24 (e) 0.056 (f) 16.82 (g) 3.76 (h) 53.6 cm^2

Page 185   ***Check Yourself on Section 3.3***

1. (a) 9 (b) 8.5 (c) 8 (d) 12 (e) 1, 5, 15

2. Warriors: mean = 23.8, range = 14 and Sabres: mean = 22.7, range = 12

Page 210   ***Check Yourself on Units 3.4 and 3.5***

1. (a) (i) 18 (ii) £6.50 (iii) Prawn

(b) (i) 10 (ii) 80 (iii) You cannot have, for example, $2\dfrac{1}{2}$ bedrooms.

2.

Stem	Leaf
3	1 3
4	4 5 5 8
5	2 2 5 7 7 7 9
6	3 4 4 5 8
7	3 6

Key: 5|7 means 57 years old

3. (a) Frequencies: 2, 5, 7, 4, 3

4. (a) $\dfrac{1}{3}$ (b) 30

6. (a) (i) true   (ii) true   (iii) false

(b) (i) white   (ii) $\dfrac{7}{11}$ (iii) $\dfrac{3}{11}$ (iv) 0   (v) $\dfrac{1}{11}$

Page 242   *Check Yourself on Sections 4.1 and 4.2*

1. (a) 0.4   (b) 50%

(c)	$\dfrac{2}{25}$	0.08	8%
(d)	$\dfrac{4}{5}$	0.8	80%
(e)	$\dfrac{9}{10}$	0.9	90%
(f)	$\dfrac{8}{25}$	0.32	32%
(g)	$\dfrac{18}{25}$	0.72	72%

2. (a) 75%   (b) 60%   (c) $33\frac{1}{3}$%

3. (a) £285   (b) £806.40

4. (a) $\dfrac{1}{3}$ (b) $\dfrac{9}{22}$ (c) £56

5. (a) 3:8   (b) 9   (c) £80

Page 255   *Check Yourself on Sections 4.3 and 4.4*

1. 5.3 cm or 5.4 cm   **2.** 43°

3. (a) AB or CD   (b) AB or CD   (c) AD or BC   (d) BC

4. (a) scalene   (b) two equal sides only and two equal angles only

(c) A trapezium, B square, C rhombus, D kite, E parallelogram

(d) Four equal sides, opposite sides are parallel, opposite angles are equal, two lines of symmetry, rotational symmetry order 2, diagonals perpendicular to each other, diagonals bisect each other.

(e) P, R (f) 10

Page 276   *Check yourself on sections 4.5, 4.6 and 4.7*

1. (a) (i) $\begin{pmatrix} 3 \\ 2 \end{pmatrix}$ (ii) $\begin{pmatrix} -2 \\ 1 \end{pmatrix}$ (iii) $\begin{pmatrix} 0 \\ 4 \end{pmatrix}$

2. (a), (b)

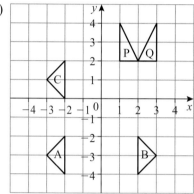

(c) $x = 2$

3. (a)

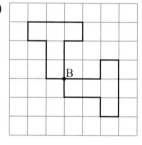

(b), (c), (d)

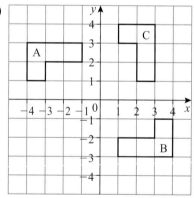

4. (a) 2   (b) 6   (c) 3   (d) 2   (e)

Page 309   *Check yourself on Sections 5.1 and 5.2*

1. (a) $4a + 7c$ (b) $2ab$ (c) $8m + 2n$ (d) x (e) $2c$

(f) $6a + ab$ (g) 9   (h) 28

2. (a) 26   (b) 30   (c) 10   (d) 7

3. (a) $5x + 35$ (b) $np - 3n$ (c) $x^2 + 8x$

4. (a) 15°C   (b) October   (c) April and November   (d) April, May   (e) 21°C

5. (a) 30 minutes   (b) 11.30   (c) (i) 50 km/h   (ii) 60 km/h

Page 328   **Check yourself on Sections 5.3 and 5.4**

1. (a) $2 \times 2 \times 3 \times 3 \times 5$ (b) 34   (c) $\dfrac{5}{12}$ (d) 56   (e) 0.15 m

     (f) $\dfrac{5}{\boxed{7}} \times \dfrac{3}{4} = \dfrac{15}{28}$ (g) $1\frac{1}{2}$ hours

2. (a) 5.7   (b) 0.18   (c) 0.8   (d) 17.84   (e) 0.193   (f) 5.4

3. (a) 150   (b) 40   (c) 10   (d) £60

Page 337   **Check yourself on Section 5.5**

1. (a) (i) $\dfrac{3}{7}$ (ii) $\dfrac{2}{7}$ (b) $\dfrac{3}{7}$

Page 368   **Check yourself on Sections 6.1 and 6.2**

1. (a) 7000 m   (b) 40 cm   (c) 7.5 litres   (d) 4800 g

2. (a) 6.6 pounds   (b) 36 litres   (c) 64 km   (d) 25 cm

3. (a) 2.5   (b) 0.25   (c) 1.6

4. (a) 6140 g   (b) P by 300 cm^2 (or 0.03 m^2)

5. (a) 79°   (b) 82°   (c) 122°   **6.** 83°/84°   **7.** 3.7 cm

Page 378   **Check yourself on Section 6.3**

1. (a) cone   (b) triangular prism   (c) cylinder

2. (a) 5 faces, 8 edges, 5 vertices   (b) 7 faces, 15 edges, 10 vertices

3. (a) and (c)

Page 396   **Check yourself on Sections 6.4 and 6.5**

1. (a) 9   (b) 56   (c) 8   (d) $\dfrac{5}{6}$ (e) 2   (f) $\dfrac{3}{4}$

2. (a) 6   (b) 9

3. (a) 37   (b) 8   (c) -2 (d) $6 \to 15 \to 33 \to 69$ (g) 2 times, add 6   (h) 43